Electric Power Generation, Transmission and Distribution

Second Edition

S.N. SINGH

Professor
Department of Electrical Engineering
Indian Institute of Technology Kanpur

PHI Learning Private Limited

New Delhi-110001

2011

Rs. 325.00

ELECTRIC POWER GENERATION, TRANSMISSION AND DISTRIBUTION, 2nd ed.
S.N. Singh

ISBN-978-81-203-3560-8

The export rights of this book are vested solely with the publisher.

Twelfth Printing (Second Edition) ... ... **August, 2011**

Published by Asoke K. Ghosh, PHI Learning Private Limited, M-97, Connaught Circus, New Delhi-110001 and Printed by Mudrak, 30-A, Patparganj, Delhi-110091.

To
my father, mother
and wife, (Late) Madhuri

Contents

Preface

The enthusiastic response to the first edition and several suggestions, feedback and comments received from the readers prompted me to come out with the second edition of the book. This edition includes two new chapters, viz. Diesel Engine Power Plant and Power System Restructuring. The chapter on diesel engine power plants gives an overview of diesel power engines, discussing advantages, problems and recent developments in the field. The chapter on power system restructuring deals with the fundamentals of the topic to make the students aware of the present changes in the electric power industry.

To make the basic concepts clearer, some more solved examples are added in various chapters, whereas to enhance the problem solving capability of the students, several unsolved problems are included at the end of each chapter.

I appreciate the effort made by the undergraduate and postgraduate students of Electrical Engineering at Indian Institute of Technology Kanpur (India), whose enthusiastic participation in classroom discussions helped me to present many ideas and concepts with greater clarity. I wish to thank Prof. S.C. Srivastava, Dean, Research and Development, IIT Kanpur, and Dr. K.G. Upadhayay, MMEC Gorakhpur for their encouragement. I appreciate the valuable help received from Ms. Deepti Shakya, Mr. Bharat Singh Rajpurohit, Mr. Jai Govind Singh, postgraduate students of IIT Kanpur, for typing the manuscript and drawing the diagrams. I express my gratitude to my father and mother for their encouragement and best wishes without which the present edition would not have been possible. Finally, my special thanks go to my wife Vandana and sons Prashant, Praveen and Prakhar for their support.

S.N. SINGH

Preface to the First Edition

The development of electric power systems has contributed to the phenomenal technological advances of humankind over the past century. Electric power provides clean and convenient energy to modern society.

The main purpose of this textbook is to provide single-source coverage of the full-spectrum of systems of electric power generation, transmission, and distribution. The book is an outcome of the author's experience of teaching power system courses at the Indian Institute of Technology Roorkee, and at the Asian Institute of Technology, Thailand. It is designed for undergraduate students of electrical engineering in accordance with the syllabi of Indian universities/institutions.

Beginning with a historical overview, Chapter 1 highlights the features and structure of modern power systems. Chapter 2 provides a brief review of various sources of electric energy. The basic principles and load characteristics are explained in Chapters 3 and 4, respectively. Chapters 5 through 8 are devoted to detailed systems descriptions of generation of electric power—steam, hydro, nuclear, and gas power plants.

Chapters 9–14 deal with calculations of transmission line constants, performance of transmission lines in terms of efficiency and regulation, corona and radio interference with communication lines, design of insulators for overhead transmission lines, mechanical design of overhead lines, and design of insulated cables. In Chapter 10 that describes the performance of transmission lines, various techniques of reactive power compensation are also discussed. Chapter 15 is a rigorous but clear treatment of converter–inverter circuits used in HVDC transmission. A detailed discussion of the advantages of HVDC transmission over HVAC transmission is also presented in this chapter.

Most of the undergraduate textbooks on power systems do not cover Flexible AC Transmission Systems (FACTS). Power electronics based FACTS technology can increase the power transfer capability of transmission systems and regulate power flow over designated routes. Chapter 15 also explains how the benefits of FACTS technology can be realized in practice.

The distribution systems are discussed in Chapter 16, whereas Chapter 17 is devoted to substation configurations and their equipment. Neutral grounding is explained in the final chapter.

Numerous solved examples are included within the text to illustrate the concepts discussed. Problems given at the end of chapters are aimed at furthering the students' understanding of the topics presented.

I gratefully acknowledge the support provided by several of my colleagues and friends who have contributed to the development of the text. Special mention must be made here of Prof. S.C. Srivastava, Head, Electrical Engineering Department, IIT Kanpur; Dr. K.N. Srivastava, ABB Sweden, Dr. G.K. Singh and Dr. Vinay Pant, IIT Roorkee; Mr. K.S. Verma, KNIT Sultanpur; Dr. K.G. Upadhayay, MMEC Gorakhpur; and Dr. Jovitha J., SIIT, Thailand. I am indebted to my many students who helped me immensely in typing the manuscript and making the diagrams. I also thank all my students whose enthusiastic participation in classroom discussions helped me to present many ideas and concepts, with greater clarity.

My thanks are also due to Prentice-Hall of India, especially its editorial and production teams for their utmost cooperation in bringing out the book on time.

Finally, no words are adequate to express my gratitude to my wife Madhuri and sons Prashant and Praveen for their loving support, patience, and understanding throughout the period of writing this book.

S.N. SINGH

Chapter 1

Introduction

This chapter provides a brief review of the development of electric power systems. Beginning with a historical sketch of their evolution, the basic structure of modern power systems is elaborated. A chapter-wise outline of the text has also been presented.

1.1 HISTORICAL DEVELOPMENTS OF ELECTRIC POWER SYSTEMS

The electricity was invented in very early age but its commercial usage began in the late 1870s when arc lamps were used for lighthouse illumination and street lighting. The credit for inventing electric power system goes to Thomas Edison. Edison had established an electric power station at the historic Pearl Station, New York in 1881, which began operation in September 1882. This station had capacity of four 25-hp boilers supplying steam to six engine-dynamo sets (dc generators) and supplied power to 59 consumers within area of roughly 1.5 km in radius at 110 V through underground cable system. There were similar developments in the other cities of the world within the next few years. DC motors load were added to such systems after its invention by Frank Sprague, in 1884.

The invention of transformers and ac system by L. Gaulard and J.D. Gibbs of Paris, France made ac electric power system possible. The first practical ac distribution system was installed for 150-lamps load in USA by William Stanley at Great Barrington, Massachusetts, in 1886 for Westinghouse; he also acquired the American rights to the transformers. The development of poly-phase system (three-phase) by N. Tesla increased the attraction of

1

ac systems. By 1888, Tesla held several patents on ac motors, generators, transformers and transmission systems. Westinghouse bought the patents of these early inventions. In 1889, the first ac transmission line at 4000 V, single-phase, 21 km was put into operation in Oregon, North America between Willamette Falls and Portland.

In the 1890s, there was great controversy over whether the power utilities should be standardized on ac or dc. Westinghouse advocated ac and Edison favoured dc. Finally, ac system won out over dc system due to its various advantages such as voltage transformation, possibility of long-distance transmission with high voltage, and simpler and economical utilization. In 1893, first three-phase line in southern California, North America came into operation at 2.3 kV, which was 12-km long. There was phenomenal growth of electric companies by 1895.

Operating voltages and frequencies were not same at the beginning. The used frequencies were 25, 50, 60, 66, 125 and 133 Hz, which created the difficulties in the interconnection, and therefore, the standardization of frequencies was felt necessary. North America adopted 60 Hz, however, many other countries use 50 Hz.

Up to 1921, the ac system voltage used were 12 kV, 44 kV and 60 kV (rms line-line), which rose to 165 kV in 1922, 220 kV in 1923, 287 kV in 1935, 330 kV in 1953, 500 kV in 1965, 735 kV in 1966, 765 kV in 1969 and 1100 kV in 1990. It was also felt necessary to standardize the voltage system. Every country has different standard ratings. In India, it is 132 kV, 220 kV for high voltage (HV), and 400 kV and 765 kV for extra high voltage (EHV). Although 765-kV line has been constructed in India but it is presently operating at 400 kV.

Early developments witnessed the different generating voltages and unit sizes. Generating unit sizes up to 1300 MW are in service, which was made operational in 1973 at Cumberland station of the Tennessee Valley Authority. The maximum generating voltage in advance countries are 33 kV. In India, it is 21 kV and the highest unit size is 500 MW. The growth of unit sizes was possible only after the interconnection and better cooling systems of generators.

The ac transmission systems was again challenged by high-voltage dc (HVDC) transmission system in 1954 when Swedish Power Board energized 60 mile, 100-kV dc submarine cable between Baltic island of Gotland and Swedish mainland. With the advent of mercury valves in early 1950s, HVDC transmission system became economical for long-distance transmission. The development of new solid-state technology, HVDC has become even more attractive. Today, numerous installations with voltages up to 800-kV dc have become operational in the world. The dc transmission may be advantageous to ac transmission for more than 500 km for overhead line and 50 km for underground cables. In India, ±500-kV HVDC transmission from Rihand to Dadri is operational.

In 1998, a high voltage synchronous machine, called powerformer that is suitable for direct connection to the high-voltage network without any step-up transformer, is launched. The rating of first powerformer was 45 kV, 42 MVA. One turbo machine rated at 136 kV, 42 MVA and one hydro machine rated at 155 kV, 75 MVA are installed in Sweden.

1.2 BASIC STRUCTURE OF THE POWER SYSTEM

Nowadays, power system is complex, interconnected and vary in sizes and configurations. A large amount of electrical energy is generated in thermal, hydroelectric, nuclear and gas-power stations, also called *conventional electric energy sources*. Some amount of electricity is generated through non-conventional sources of energy. This power is also called *green power* as it emits less pollution. Generated electric power is transmitted to the load centres through power supply network consisting of transmission lines, transformers and switchgears. Transmission networks are commonly classified into four parts: *transmission* system, *subtransmission* system, *primary distribution* system and *secondary distribution* system.

The main purpose of 'transmission' system is to connect all major generating stations and load centres in the system without supplying any consumers en route. The generating voltages are normally between 11 kV and 33 kV due to technical problems, such as heating and insulation problem and are stepped up with help of generating transformers to connect the generators and the transmission lines. The generating and transmission systems are often called *bulk supply system*. The interconnected transmission system of a state or a region is called the *grid* of state or region. State grids are interconnected with the help of tie lines and form the regional grid.

In India, power systems in most of the states are owned and operated by State Electricity Boards (SEBs) which generate, transmit and distribute power within the state territory. In addition to SEBs, which are controlled by respective state governments, a few private sector utilities operate in the metropolitan cities like Mumbai, Kolkata, Ahmedabad, etc. Five Regional Electricity Boards (REBs), namely Northern REB, Southern REB, Western REB, Eastern REB and North-Eastern REB exist to promote the integrated operation of the regional power systems. The responsibility of REBs are to review project progress, plan integrated operation among the utilities in the region, coordinate the maintenance schedules, determine the availability of power for inter-state utilities transfer, prescribe the generation schedule and determine a suitable tariff for the inter-utility exchange of power. The names of states in each REBs are given in Table 1.1 and Table 1.2 shows the installed capacity and energy generation of REBs.

Table 1.1 Organizational Structure of Regional Electricity Boards

NREB	WREB	SREB	EREB	NEREB
Chandigarh	Chhatisgarh	Andhra Pradesh	Andman &	Arunachal
Delhi	Dadar & Nagar	Karnataka	Nicobar	Pradesh
Haryana	Havelli	Kerala	Bihar	Assam
Himachal Pradesh	Daman & Diu	Lakshadweep	Jharkhand	Manipur
Jammu & Kashmir	Goa	Pondicherry	Orissa	Meghalaya
Punjab	Gujarat	Tamil Nadu	Sikkim	Mizoram
Rajasthan	Madhya Pradesh		West Bengal	Nagaland
Uttar Pradesh	Maharashtra			Tripura
Uttaranchal				

Table 1.2 Region-wise Installed Capacity MW as on 30-01-2008

Region	Hydro	Thermal			Nuclear	RES	Grand total
		Coal	Gas	Oil			
NREB	12899.15	18577.50	3543.19	14.99	1180.00	1271.28	37486.11
WREB	7198.50	23752.50	6600.72	17.48	1840.00	3010.74	42419.94
SREB	10646.18	16682.50	3586.30	939.32	1100.00	6220.69	39174.99
EREB	3348.93	15659.88	190.00	17.20	0.00	200.41	19416.42
NEREB	1116.00	330.00	771.50	142.74	0.00	146.01	2506.25
Islands	0.00	0.00	0.00	70.02	0.00	6.11	76.13
All India	**35,208.76**	**75,002.38**	**14,691.71**	**1,201.75**	**4120.00**	**10,855.24**	**1,41,079.84**
State sector	25896.76	42001.00	3869.72	604.61	0.00	2081.67	74,453.76
Private sector	1230.30	4491.38	4183.00	597.14	0.00	8773.57	19,275.09
Central sector	8082.00	28510.00	6638.99	0.0	4120.00	0.00	47,350.99

Source: Ministry of Power, India.

In addition to the electric organization described above, there are some Central Government Organization such as National Thermal Power Corporation (NTPC), National Hydro Power Corporation (NHPC), Nuclear Power Corporation (NPC), Damodar Valley Corporation (DVC), Bhakhara Beas Management Board (BBMB), etc., which operate large thermal, hydro and nuclear power plants and supply bulk power to the other electric utilities for transmission and distribution. Power Grid Corporation is responsible for bulk power transmission through Extra High Voltage (EHV) transmission lines besides the SEBs. Northern REB and Western REB have 60% share in the total installed capacity of India.

'Subtransmission' systems are used to transmit power to large consumers. It is very difficult to distinguish subtransmission system from the main transmission system. In India, we supply power to large consumers at 132 kV and 66 kV. Moreover, 132-kV systems come under transmission system. In early days when the transmission voltage was not high, lower voltages were used for transmission. Due to system expansion and increase in voltage level of transmission system, the lower voltage transmission systems are termed as subtransmission systems.

Energy is often converted into electrical form which is used in the form of heat, light and mechanical energy. Utilization of power is restricted to low voltage only. Before feeding the powers to consumers, the transmission voltages are stepped down and power is transmitted over distribution lines. Distribution systems are further divided into two parts, viz., primary and secondary distribution systems. Subtransmission systems form the link between the main receiving station and the secondary substation. At the secondary substations, the voltage is stepped down and power is fed into the primary distribution system, which feeds power to medium large consumers at distribution voltage higher than 400 V. It is normally 33 kV, 25 kV, 11 kV and 6.6 kV in India. The secondary distribution feeders supply residential and commercial customers at 400 V. Distribution systems have the largest share in power system network.

Figure 1.1 shows the basic elements of modern power system. Every power system network need not necessarily have all the components. In some cases, there is only one level of transmission, where a secondary transmission does not exist.

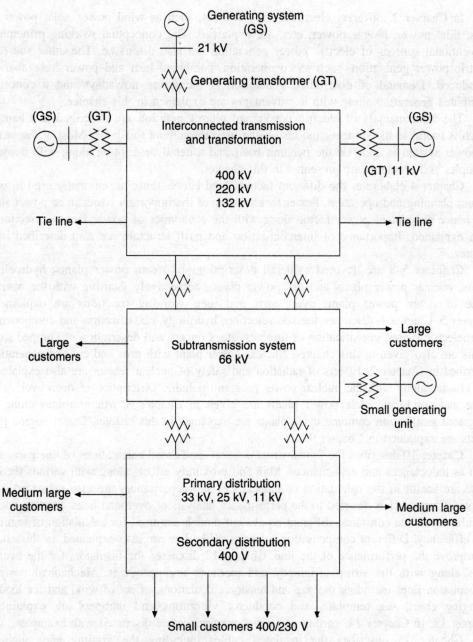

FIGURE 1.1 Structure of power system.

1.3 OUTLINE OF THE TEXT

Chapter 1 starts with a brief history of power systems' evolution and describes the structure of power system with emphasis on Indian power systems that includes the organizational structures, voltage levels, installed capacities, etc.

In Chapter 2, different electric energy sources, such as wind power, solar power, fuel cells, tidal power, biogas power, etc., are explained. The conceptual working principles of conventional sources of electric power generation are also discussed. The other sources of electric power generation, such as cogeneration, combined heat and power have also been introduced. Demand of distributed generation is increasing nowadays and a concept of distributed generation along with its advantages are explained in this chapter.

The fundamentals of electric power and phasor notation are described in Chapter 3, which is useful to the students and also being used throughout this book. Most of the analysis of power system is done on the per unit basis and a detail description along with numerical examples and problems are presented in this chapter.

Chapter 4 elaborates the different factors, load curves those are normally used in power system planning and operation. Power factor is one of the important issues in ac power supply and hence concept of power factor along with the economics of power factor correction has been explained. Importance of interconnection and tariff structure are also described in this chapter.

Chapters 5–8 are devoted to detail descriptions of steam power plants, hydroelectric plants, nuclear power plants and gas power plants, respectively. Starting with the operating cycle of steam power plant, main parts and their working functions are explained in Chapter 5. Chapter 6 discusses the site selection, hydrology, classification and components of hydroelectric plants, classification of turbines, etc. Concept and description of pumped storage plants are also given in this chapter. Nuclear power plant with pros and cons of generation is described in Chapter 7. Effects of radiation and safety of nuclear reactor are also explained in this chapter along with the nuclear power program in India. Description of open cycle, closed cycle and combined cycle power plants are given in Chapter 8. Microturbines along with integrated gasification combine cycle plants are explained in this chapter. Diesel engine power plants are explained in Chapter 9.

Chapter 10 describes the fundamental concepts and detail calculations of line parameters, such as inductances and capacitances. Skin and proximity effects along with various theorems those are useful in the calculation of inductances and capacitances are also presented in this chapter. Chapter 11 is devoted to the performance analysis of overhead lines. Starting with the calculation of line constants, different equivalent models are used for calculation of regulation and efficiency. Different compensation schemes of the line are also explained, in this chapter, to improve the performance of the line. Chapter 12 discusses the insulators for the overhead lines along with the string efficiency and methods to improve it. Mechanical design of transmission lines including the sag and tension calculations, effect of wind and ice loadings, stringing chart, sag template, and conductor vibrations and dampers are explained in Chapter 13. In Chapter 14, corona and radio interference are discussed with examples.

Chapter 15 describes the insulated cables including the grading and calculation of capacitances. Dielectric loss and faults in cables are also discussed in this chapter. HVDC transmission and flexible ac transmission systems (FACTS) have been explained, in detail, in Chapter 16. Starting with the comparison of HVDC to HVAC, the different HVDC links and analysis of converter/inverter systems have been presented in this chapter. Fundamental concepts of FACTS technology along with various devices are also explained in Chapter 16.

Comparisons of various transmission and distribution systems are done in Chapter 17. Calculation of suitable conductor size using the Kelvin's law is discussed with its shortcomings. Different types of distributors and submains are also explained in this chapter. Chapter 18 describes the different types of substations along with their merits and demerits. Different types of grounding systems are described in Chapter 19. Chapter 20 provides the concept of power system restructuring (deregulation).

Chapter 2

Sources of Electric Energy

2.1 INTRODUCTION

The consumption of electric energy in residential, commercial and industrial sector is increased in many folds, all over the world, due to its several advantageous features. Limited fossil fuels resources and their impact on environment, several countries have started to explore the alternative types of energy sources. Alternative energy is generally defined as any power source that is not based on fossil fuels or nuclear reactions, that includes electricity generated from wind, solar, geothermal, biomass or plant matter, and hydropower. Alternative fuels also can include ethanol from corn, bio-diesel made from vegetable crops and methane made from waste or other sources. Sources of electric energy are generally classified into two categories: *conventional* and *non-conventional* energy sources. Conventional energy sources include coal, diesel, gas and nuclear. On the other hand, non-conventional energy sources are water, wind, solar, fuel cells, tidal, biogas, etc., which are free of operating cost, pollution free and inexhaustible. These are also called *renewable* energy sources.

2.2 WIND POWER

Wind power is being used since very early days in different applications such as in ships, in agriculture purpose, etc. The exploitation of wind power, at present, is increasing due to high price of oil and fast depleting of oil, gas and coal deposits. The another concern is environmental problem that arises with the conventional source of energy. Wind energy is plentiful, inexhaustible and pollution free but great drawback on the utilization arises from both the intermittence and unreliability. Denmark was the first country to use wind for the generation of electricity.

The choice of windmills site depends on several factors such as windy area, scattered population, cheaper to grid electricity cost due to transmission, etc. It is more suitable near to coastal and remote areas. The great advantage of windmills is that they may be installed in any locality where the topographical and meteorological conditions are suitable and require no outside supplies for its operation except for a stand-by battery and lubricating oil.

The output power of windmill can be given by

$$\text{Developed power } P = 2.14 \times 10^{-3} A d v^3 \text{ kW} \tag{2.1}$$

where A = area swept by the windmill, d = wind density of air and, v = wind velocity in mile/hour.

Windmills or wind energy converters convert wind power to electrical power. Typical systems range from 30 kW for individual units to 5.0 MW for wind farms of multiple units. Hub heights are around 80 metre and rotor diameters are 65 metre. Rotor construction is either variable blade angle or non-variable, and conversion from mechanical to electrical energy is via either synchronous or induction generators. Synchronous generators are equipped with pulse width modulated converters and control for these converters are essential for regulating the behaviour of windmill on the electric grid. Windmills are often installed in groups, or wind farms, and are seldom used in isolation. A disadvantage of wind power is its irregularity; this further complicates the connection to power grids.

Most of wind turbines designed for production of electricity have consisted of a two- or three-bladed propeller rotating around a horizontal axis. Figure 2.1 shows a typical wind turbine. Efficiencies of different types of wind turbine are shown in Figure 2.2.

Wind direction

FIGURE 2.1 Wind-turbine system.

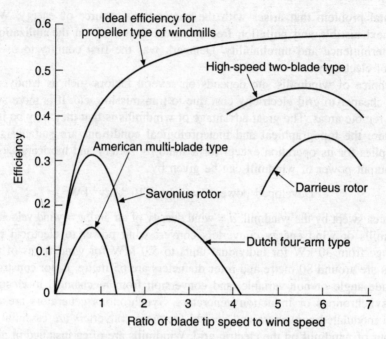

FIGURE 2.2   Typical performances of wind machine.

The cost of a wind turbine is around 1000 $/kW and electrical efficiency is around 25%. Footprint size is in the order of 0.01 kW/m^2 and operating cost is between 4 to 12 cents/kWh.

Following are disadvantages of windmills:

1. Blow down of towers due to hurricane or typhoon
2. High acoustic noise level
3. Electromagnetic interference with metal blades
4. Requires energy storage batteries
5. Low-energy density.

India ranks fifth in the world with a total wind power capacity of 7844.57 MW (till 31-12-2007).

2.3   SOLAR POWER

Conversion of solar power energy to electrical energy has been technically possible since the late 1930s. The main problem in solar power energy is its availability. The solar power, which falls upon the whole earth, is of the magnitude of 1.77×10^{14} kW. The rate at which solar energy reaches the earth's atmosphere (approximated to be 15 km from the earth's surface at sea level) is known as *solar constant*. Mathematically, solar constant is expressed as

$$\text{Solar constant} = 1200 \text{ kcal/(m}^2\text{-h)} = 1.39 \text{ kWh/(m}^2\text{-h)}$$

When the sun passes through the atmosphere, part of the sun's radiation is reflected, scattered and absorbed by heating air, dust and by evaporating water. The solar power densities at the surface of earth depend upon the sun's position and upon the clarity and humidity of the atmosphere. Following are several distinct applications of solar power:

- Space and water heating in domestic and commercial buildings, e.g. photovoltaic collectors as shown in Figure 2.3
- Large-scale heat collection for generation of electricity
- The chemical and biological conversion of organic materials to liquid, solid and gaseous fuel
- Domestic lighting
- Street lighting
- Village electrification
- Water pumping
- Desalination of salty water
- Powering of remote telecommunication repeater stations
- Railway signals.

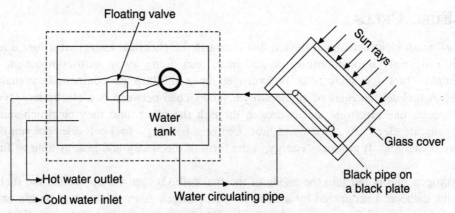

FIGURE 2.3 Solar water-heating arrangement.

India is among a few countries with long days and plenty of sunshine, especially in the Thar Desert region. This zone, having abundant solar energy available, is suitable for harnessing solar energy for a number of applications. In the areas with similar intensity of solar radiation, solar energy could be easily harnessed. Solar thermal energy is being used in India for heating water for both industrial and domestic purposes. A 140-MW integrated solar power plant is planned to set up in Jodhpur, but the initial expense incurred is still very high. Figure 2.4 shows schematic diagram of a solar power plant.

Solar energy can also be used to meet our electricity requirements. Through solar photovoltaic (SPV) cells, solar radiation gets converted into dc electricity directly. This electricity can either be used as it is or can be stored in the batteries. This stored electrical

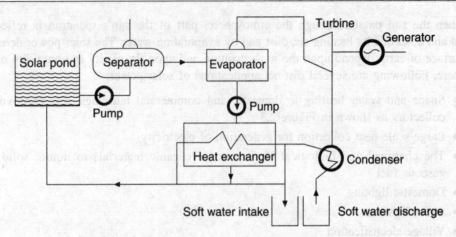

FIGURE 2.4   Schematic diagram of a solar power plant.

energy then can be used at night. SPV can be used for a number of applications. If the means to make efficient use of solar energy could be found, it would reduce our dependence on non-renewable sources of energy and make our environment cleaner.

2.4   FUEL CELLS

A *fuel cell* is an electrochemical device that converts the chemical energy of a fuel directly and very efficiently into electricity dc and heat, thus doing away with combustion. The most suitable fuel for such cells is hydrogen or a mixture of compounds containing hydrogen. A fuel cell consists of an electrolyte sandwiched between two electrodes. Oxygen passes through one electrode and hydrogen through the other, and they electrochemically react to generate electricity, water, and heat. Unlike a battery, a fuel cell does not run down or require recharging. It produces energy in the form of electricity and heat as long as fuel is supplied.

Hydrogen fuel is fed into the anode of the fuel cell. Oxygen (or air) enters the fuel cell through the cathode. Encouraged by a catalyst, the hydrogen atom splits into a proton and an electron, which take different path to cathode. Proton passes through the electrolyte. The electron creates a separate current that can be utilized before they return to the cathode, to be reunited with the hydrogen and oxygen in a molecule of water. A fuel cell system, which includes a fuel reformer, can utilize the hydrogen from any hydrocarbon fuel from natural gas to methanol, and even gasoline. Since the fuel cell relies on the chemistry and not on combustion, the emissions from this type of a system would still be much smaller than the emissions from the cleanest fuel combustion processes.

The type of electrolyte used characterizes fuel cells; examples include alkaline, proton exchange membrane, phosphoric acid, molten carbonate and solid oxide. Produced heat fuel-cell efficiency, when electrolytes are operated between 80 and 1000°C, can range between 35–65%. The heat produced by an electrolyte can be utilized to raise the efficiency of fuel cell to over 80%. Target capital cost (assuming large volume manufacturing) ranges from 800 to 1300 $/kW and footprint size ranges from 1 to 3 kW/m². Operating cost is estimated between 8 and 10 cents/kWh and emissions of NO_X gases are extremely low at 0.003–0.03 lb/BTU. Fuel cells are typically aimed at single-installation site that require between 50 and 1000 kW, e.g. high-rise office buildings, hospitals, schools, hotels, etc. However, new small fuel cells are available for residential purposes at about 5–10 kW. Figure 2.5 shows the typical operation of fuel cells.

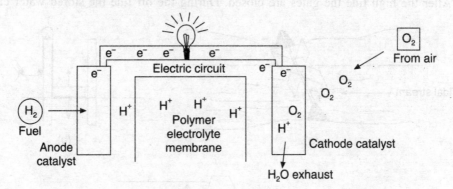

FIGURE 2.5   Fuel cell.

Though fuel cells have been used in space flights, and combined supplies of heat and power, electric vehicles are the best option available to dramatically reduce urban air pollution. Compared to vehicles powered by the internal combustion engine, fuel cell powered vehicles have very high-energy conversion efficiency, (almost double that of currently used engines) and near-zero pollution, CO_2 and water vapour being the only emissions. Fuel-cell-powered EVs (electric vehicles) score over battery operated EVs in terms of increased efficiency and easier and faster refuelling.

Fuel-cell systems are excellent candidates for small-scale decentralized power generation. Fuel cells can supply combined heat and power to commercial buildings, hospitals, airports and military installations at remote locations. Fuel cells have efficiency levels up to 55% as compared to 35% of conventional power plants. Fuel-cell systems are modular (i.e. additional capacity can be added whenever required with relative ease) and can be set up wherever power is required.

2.5 TIDAL POWER

The tides offer a source of energy because of the potential energy of raised tide water or the kinetic energy of tidal stream. The originating source of tidal energy is in kinetic energy of the orbiting and rotating earth, moon and sun. The water on earth rises and falls due to changing gravitation force. To date, there has been little development of tidal projects despite the fact that these schemes are quite attractive. There are at least three ways in which tidal energy might conceivably be harnessed (Figure 2.6).

The one way of harnessing the tidal energy is simply to place a water wheel in a tidal stream as shown in Figure 2.6(a). It is analogous to using a water wheel in the river and is not suitable for electric generation due to variability of the tidal stream flow. This scheme can be used for pumping water or milling grain.

In the second scheme, as shown in Figure 2.6(b), a large floating object such as a barge is raised by an incoming tide; it is constrained by pilings. It can be then held and dropped later or allowed to fall with the tide to drive the electric generator.

Third choice, as shown in Figure 2.6(c), is to build a low dam across the mouth of a bay or a tidal estuary. As the tide comes in, gates are opened and water flows into the bay or estuary. After the high tide the gates are closed. During the off tide the stored water can be

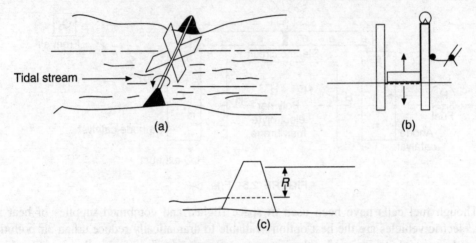

FIGURE 2.6   Tidal power.

used for electricity generation. The weight of water (W) stored behind the dam from high-tide level to low-tide level is $RS\rho$, where R is the tidal range in metre, S is the average surface area of storage reservoir and ρ is the density of water. As R changes with the discharge of water, the annual energy can be obtained by taking the average value. The available energy is

$$E = \frac{1}{2}RW = \frac{1}{2}R^2S\rho \qquad (2.2)$$

The average power can be obtained by dividing E by time (T). The basic problem with the development of tidal power projects is the requirement of huge capital cost. Following are criterions for selecting the site for tidal power projects:

- The tidal range R should be large
- The storage area should be large
- The site should allow the development of the necessary plant for reasonable cost
- It should be environmentally acceptable.

2.6   GEOTHERMAL POWER

The heat from the interior of the earth is a huge potential source of natural energy that can be used for the generation of electricity. The heat is tapped through wells drilled as much as two miles into the earth. The basic principle of geothermal generation is that steam is used to drive the turbine, as in thermal plant fuelled by Uranium or by fossil fuel. The first important generation of geothermal electric power came in Larderello, Italy in 1904 for lighting a few bulbs. Italy and Geysers area of San Francisco, USA are the largest geothermal producing regions in the world. Figure 2.7 shows the typical geothermal power plant at the Geysers.

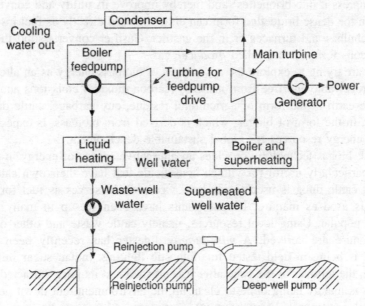

FIGURE 2.7 Typical geothermal power plant.

The main advantages of geothermal power are that it is environmentally clean and requires less space compared to hydro and solar power. The major potential problems are the possible destructive effect of contaminated wastewater and lad subsidence. It releases large amount of waste heat to the environment.

2.7 BIOMASS POWER

Biomass, a form of chemical energy, is a renewable energy resource derived from the carbonaceous waste of various human and natural activities. It is derived from numerous sources, including the by-products from the timber industry, agricultural crops, raw material from the forest, major parts of household waste and wood. Biomass does not add carbon dioxide to the atmosphere as it absorbs the same amount of carbon when consumed as a fuel. Its advantage is that it can be used to generate electricity with the same equipment or power plants that are now burning fossil fuels. Biomass is an important source of energy and the most important fuel worldwide after coal, oil and natural gas. This energy is being used for cooking, mechanical applications, pumping, power generation and transportation.

Traditional use of biomass is more than its use in modern application. In the developed world, biomass is again becoming important for applications such as combined heat and power generation. In addition, biomass energy is gaining significance as a source of clean heat for domestic heating and community heating applications. In fact, in the countries like Finland, USA and Sweden the per capita biomass energy used is higher than in India, China or in Asia.

Biomass fuels used in India account for about one third of the total fuel used in the country, being the most important fuel used in over 90% of the rural households and about 15% of the urban households. Instead of burning the loose biomass fuel directly, it is more practical to compress it into briquettes[1] and thereby improve its utility and convenience of use. Such biomass in the dense briquetted form can either be used directly as fuel instead of coal in the traditional chulhas and furnaces or in the gasifier. Gasifier converts solid fuel into a more convenient gaseous form of fuel called *producer gas*.

Scientists are trying to explore the advantages of biomass energy as an alternative energy source as it is renewable and free from net CO_2 (carbon dioxide) emissions and is abundantly available on the earth in the form of agricultural residue, city garbage, cattle dung, firewood, etc. Bio-energy, in the form of biogas, which is derived from biomass, is expected to become one of the key energy resources for global sustainable development.

At present, biogas technology provides an alternative source of energy in rural India for cooking. It is particularly useful for village households that have their own cattle. Through a simple process, cattle dung is used to produce a gas, which serves as fuel for cooking. The residual dung is used as manure. Biogas plants have been set up in many areas and are becoming very popular. Using local resources, namely cattle waste and other organic wastes, energy and manure are derived. A *mini-biogas* digester has recently been designed and developed, and is being in-field tested for domestic lighting. Indian sugar mills are rapidly turning bagasse, the leftover of the cane after it is crushed and its juice extracted, into generate electricity. This is mainly being done to clean up the environment, cut down power costs and earn additional revenue. From current estimates, it can be seen that about 3500 MW of power can be generated from bagasse in the existing 430 sugar mills in the country. Around 270 MW of power has already been commissioned and more is under construction. It is a fact that half a kilo of dry plant tissue can produce as much as 1890 kcal of heat that is equivalent to the heat available from a quarter of kilogram of coal.

2.8   Magneto-Hydrodynamic (MHD) Power

In magneto–hydrodynamic (MHD) generator, an ionized gas or plasma is passed through a strong magnetic field to produce an electric potential. It is a form of heat energy to electric energy converter. The ionized gas (positive and negative ions) is collected by metallic collecting plates. There are number of possible forms of working MHD generators. The MHD unit can be developed alone or combined with a gas turbine, or with a conventional steam generator. Figure 2.8 shows the basic physical action of the generator.

Figure 2.9 shows the MHD cycle with steam cycle. Fuel is introduced to the burner along with the seed material such as potassium which increases the conductivity of the gas to permit the practical operation of the device. The magnet deflects some of the ions to the plate, which get charged and produce a dc electric potential. The exhaust gas passes first through an air heater that heats out side air that has been compressed by the compressor attached to the steam turbine. The heated air is then used in the burner. The hot exhaust gas from MHD generator is then passed into the steam generator to drive the turbine. The steam turbine drives

---

1. A process of compressing something to form blocks of different shapes.

both the compressor and an electric generator. The exhaust gases continue on through a seed recovery stage where the seed is captured and fed back to burner. Since recovery is not perfect, some make-up seeds must be added. Next, the exhaust gas passes through a Nitrogen and Sulphur removal stage before being released by the stack.

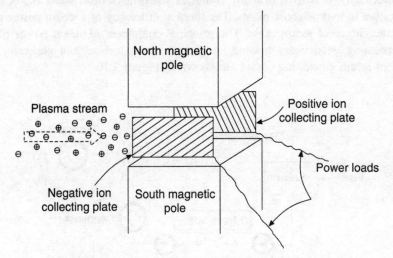

FIGURE 2.8 Magneto–hydrodynamic power generation.

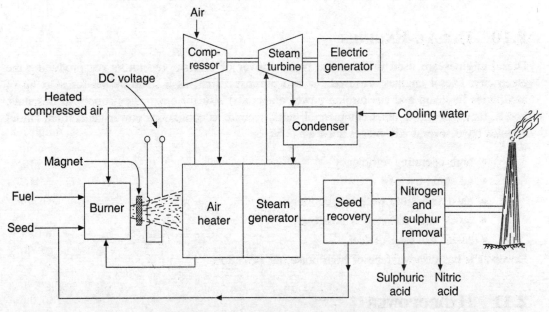

FIGURE 2.9 MHD cycle with steam.

2.9   Thermal Power

Coal is the main fuel used in thermal power plants. Coal is fired to generate heat that is used to produce steam. Steam is passed through a turbine that rotates the rotor of electric generator to produce electricity. It is used in many countries where high-head water is not available for power generation in hydroelectric plants. The thermal efficiency of a steam power plant mainly depends on the choice of steam cycle. The principal equipment of steam power plants are the boiler, superheating, feed water heating, steam reheating, turbine and generator. The major components of steam generating plants are shown in Figure 2.10.

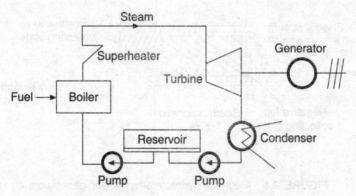

FIGURE 2.10   Major components of steam power plant.

2.10   Diesel Engines

Diesel engines are used to drive the prime mover of electric generators for producing the electricity. Diesel engines are used for two purposes: first, as a stand-by set for start up of auxiliaries in steam and gas turbine power plants and also for emergency supply to hospitals, hotels, factories and in other commercial units; second, as continuous power generation. Diesel engines have several advantages such as:

- high operating efficiency
- no stand-by loss
- need very little water for cooling
- quick start and stop is possible
- easier handling of fuel.

However it has disadvantage of high noise, air pollution.

2.11   Hydropower

Hydropower is one of the best, cheapest, and cleanest source of energy, although, with big dams, there are many environmental and social problems. The term *hydropower* refers to shaft power generated by converting potential and kinetic energy of water. Small hydroelectric plants are fairly common and are used in many countries. Hydroelectric plants are categorized into micro hydro (≤100 kW), mini hydro (from 101 kW to 1 MW), small hydro (from 1 MW to a few MW, i.e. normally 6 MW) and hydroelectric plants (more than 6 MW). Plants larger than 100 kW can use either induction generator or synchronous generator depending upon the design and cost analysis. Many of these smaller plants do not have dams but they run by flowing water of rivers. They are also called *run-of-river* plants.

Following are advantages of small-scale hydropower, particularly in developing countries:

- The infrastructure for manufacture of the components of a hydropower system, e.g. gates, valves, generators, etc., exists in most developing countries.
- Small-scale hydropower is regarded as more environmentally favourable than large plants, both hydro and fossil-powered.
- For electricity generation in remote or rural areas, small-scale hydro is competitive with alternative small-scale plants based on renewable energy or fossil fuels.
- It is proven technology and the plants are long lasting.

New environmental laws affected by the danger of global warming have made energy from small hydropower plants more relevant. These small hydropower plants can serve the energy needs of remote rural areas independently. The real challenge in a remote area lies in successful marketing of the energy and recovering the dues. Local industries should be encouraged to use this electricity for sustainable development. It is a technology with enormous potential, which could exploit the water resources to supply energy to remote rural areas with little access to conventional energy sources. It also eliminates most of the negative environmental effects associated with large hydro projects.

Large hydro plants are discussed in Chapter 6.

2.12　GAS POWER

When natural gas is used as fuel for running power plants, it is called as *gas power* plant. It has some advantages over steam plants:

- It is very simple. It does not contain the boiler or steam supply system, condenser and waste heat disposal system.
- It has ability to start and take load quickly. Its start up time is only 2–8 minutes.

Two types of gas turbines are available: *open* cycle and *combined* cycle. Figure 2.11 shows the typical open-cycle gas power plant. The detail description is given in Chapter 8. A comparison of steam and gas power plant efficiencies is shown in Figure 2.12.

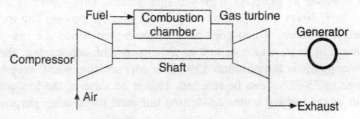

FIGURE 2.11　Steam-power plant.

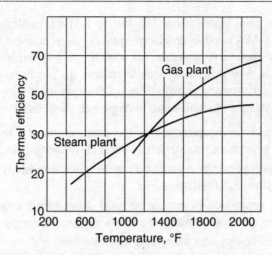

FIGURE 2.12   Thermal efficiencies of steam and gas plant.

2.13   Nuclear Power

In nuclear power plants, the heat is generated with the help of nuclear fission when a free neutron strikes the nucleus of a fissile material such as uranium, thorium, etc. The plant containing the radioactive material is called *reactor* or a *pile*. Reactor produces heat that is used for production of electric energy via heat exchanger, turbine and generator. There are different types of reactor with different coolants and moderators. A *moderator* is a substance that causes neutrons to slow down, hence increasing their probability of interacting with fissile nuclei. Detail description is given in Chapter 7.

2.14   Other Energy Sources

2.14.1   Cogeneration

Cogeneration is a process of capturing waste heat from manufacturing, industrial process or heating or cooling systems and using it to generate electric power that can be used to run one's own equipment and can be sold to the utility company. Cogeneration is the concept of producing two forms of energy from one fuel. One of the forms of energy must always be heat and the other may be electricity or mechanical energy. In a conventional power plant, fuel is burnt in a boiler to generate high-pressure steam. This steam is used to drive a turbine, which in turn drives an alternator to produce electric power. The exhaust steam is generally condensed to water, which goes back to the boiler. Since the low-pressure steam has a large quantum of heat, which is lost in the process of condensing, the efficiency of conventional power plants is only around 35%. In a cogeneration plant, very high efficiency levels, in the range of 75–90%, can be reached. This is because of the low-pressure exhaust steam coming out of the turbine is not condensed but used for heating purposes in factories or houses.

There are two types of cogeneration system arrangements discussed as follows:

Topping cycle. The input is first used to produce power and the exhaust heat from the power producing prime mover is used to generate steam or used directly in heating process.

Bottoming cycle. It is reverse of the topping cycle, utilizing waste heat from a heating process such as an industrial furnace, to produce electricity. Commonly waste heat is used to produce steam in heat recovery boiler and used in turbine to produce electricity.

As cogeneration can meet both power and heat needs, it has other advantages as well in the form of significant cost savings for the plant and reduction in emissions of pollutants due to reduced fuel consumption. Even at conservative estimates, the potential of power generation from cogeneration in India is more than 20,000 MW. Since India is the largest producer of sugar in the world, bagasse-based cogeneration is being promoted. The potential for cogeneration thus lies in facilities with joint requirement of heat and electricity, primarily sugar and rice mills, distilleries, petro-chemical sector and industries such as fertilizers, steel, chemical, cement, pulp and paper, and aluminium.

2.14.2 Combined Heat and Power (CHP)

How we produce energy and use them, nowadays, are concern of everybody. The concepts of liberalization, globalization and climate change are causing people to think differently. Internationally, the challenge is to cut greenhouse gas emissions; locally, the challenge is to meet customers' needs flexibly and effectively. Thinking differently is not just about policy but also about technology.

CHP is normally more common in cold countries where heat is more prominent in buildings. They produce power and waste heat is used for heating of the building by air or by water.

2.14.3 Distributed Generation

Distributed, or small generation units, typically less than 30 MW, strategically located near consumers and load centres, supports for the economic operation of the existing power distribution grid.

When Thomas Edison brought the Pearl Street Power Station online to service New York City in 1882, he was essentially following a strategy that today we would call distributed generation. But as technology advanced it led to larger, more efficiently generating facilities built farther and farther from the end user. Larger regional power transmission networks delivering power to local distribution systems and finally the end users were put into play. Over time the industry became regulated so that these changes could occur efficiently without wasteful duplication of facilities and slowly, the economic role of distributed generation became much more limited. Over the last thirty years, the cost of building and maintaining large centralized nuclear and coal fired generating facilities has become increasingly expensive and technology has improved their efficiency and cost of smaller modular power generating options. Restructuring of the industry paves the way for customers to select the optimum combinations of energy resources to fit their individual needs.

Lately, on-site distributed power generation is being practised that is reversing an almost 50-year trend towards centralized generation. As deregulation and restructuring sweeps through the world's energy corridors, utilities and other energy service providers will see distributed power generation as a threat or an opportunity, and will use a range of strategies and technologies to keep old customers find new ones and boost revenues. If wisely used, distributed power generation technologies can improve power quality, boost system reliability, reduce energy costs, and help delay or defray utility capital investments.

Proponents of distributed generation are quick to point out the untapped market that exists in the world with two billion people that currently have no access to electricity and several hundred million more that have to rely on a limited, unreliable, or impossibly expensive supply of electricity. Despite the tremendous social, economic, health and environmental benefits of widespread access to environmentally clean electricity, many nations are unable to maintain their current limited electrical grids and therefore afford the cost of extending electrical capacity to service the majority of their citizens. The combined influence of growing environmental concerns and the arrival of new distributed generation technologies are changing both the scale of power projects and the way utilities think about electricity. These trends give rise to important questions regarding the future providers of electricity and the form of service will they provide. It is becoming clear that any future electricity generating systems, on any scale, will include distributed generation services, concepts and technologies.

Distributed power generation in the form of turbine generators, internal combustion engine generators, microturbines, photovoltaic solar panels, wind turbines and fuel cells, provides electric power at a site closer to customers than the central station and can be connected either directly to the consumer or to a utility's transmission or distribution system. Systems in use today provide a multitude of services to utilities and consumers, including standby generation, peak shaving capability, base load generation or cogeneration. As technology advances, distributed power will provide economic and environmental benefits well into the 21st century.

New opportunities exist for electric utilities and their customers. The future of electric power lies in distributed generation—thousands of small power systems in industrial and commercial facilities, working together as 'virtual power plants'. In such applications, diesel and gas engine generator sets offer the benefits of low installed cost, high efficiency at full or partial load, reliability, fuel flexibility and heat recovery potential.

Applications

Following are the chief areas for distributed generation:

Standby power. For customers that cannot tolerate interruption of service, for either public health or safety reasons, or where outage costs are unacceptably high, standby generators installed at hospitals, water pumping stations and electronic dependent facilities such as server farms fill the bill.

Combined heat and power. Since all power generation technologies produce a great amount of heat locating a power generator near a customer's site will allow the use of combined heat and power (CHP) or cogeneration applications. This is significantly increasing system efficiency.

Peak shaving. Typically power costs fluctuate hour-by-hour depending upon demand and generation availability. Here, hourly variations are converted into seasonal and daily time-of-use rate categories such as on-peak, off-peak or shoulder rates. Customer's use of distributed generation during relatively high-cost on-peak is referred to as *peak shaving*. Peak shaving benefits energy providers when energy costs approach high prices.

Grid support. The *power grid* is a complex, integrated network of generation of high-voltage transmission. It functions as substations and local distribution networks. Strategic placement of distributed generation can provide system benefits and negates the need for expensive upgradation to the grid.

Stand-alone. *Stand-alone* distributed generation isolates the user, in remote locations, from the grid either by choice or by circumstance. Such applications include users requiring tight control on the quality of the electric power delivered, as in computer-chip manufacturing.

Technologies

Reciprocating engines. The most common form of distributed generation technology available today is reciprocating internal combustion (IC) engines fueled by natural gas. They offer low cost, easy start-up, proven reliability, high load following characteristics and heat recovery potential. Emissions from IC engines have been significantly reduced in the last few years.

Combustion turbines. Combustion turbines (CT) are an established technology available in sizes from several hundred kilowatts to hundreds of megawatts. They can be set to burn natural gas or dual-fuel. The combination of low maintenance cost and high-quality waste-heat make them an excellent choice for industrial and commercial applications larger than 5 MW.

Microturbines. Microturbines with outputs of 30–200 kW are nowadays catching the eyes of technology-driven marketers. Recent developments of microturbines have focussed on the hybrid electric vehicle market, but is quickly becoming a technology of interest as a stationary power source for commercial buildings or light industrial markets for cogeneration or power-only markets.

Fuel cells. Fuel cells producing electrochemical power similar to a battery are also becoming popular in the distributed-generation (DG) market. Several different liquid and solid media can be used to create the fuel cell's electrochemical reaction. Fuel cells are inherently quiet and extremely clean source of energy. At the moment the high costs of fuel cells make them best suited to environmentally sensitive areas with power quality concerns. They are being aimed at small commercial and residential markets as well as in industrial cogeneration applications.

Photovoltaics. Photovoltaic power cells use solar energy to produce power and can be sited anywhere the sunshines, making them suitable in sensitive environment areas and for remote applications. High costs make them a niche technology, but a lot of development work is being done in this area, so costs are expected to decrease in the future.

Opportunities

With the worldwide electricity consumption expected to reach 22 trillion kilowatt hours, by 2020, largely due to growth in developing countries without nationwide power grids, there is no doubt about the importance of the distributed generation market. The projected distribution generation capacity associated with the global market is conservatively estimated at 20 gigawatts per year over the next decade. As utility restructuring sets in, the financial burden of new capital investments will shift from consumers to energy suppliers along with capacity additions.

This favours less capital-intensive projects and shorter construction schedules. The opening up of new energy marketplaces has increased pressure on energy suppliers to multiply the capacity to meet growing demand of consumers during outages. Customer concerns over reliability have escalated, particularly in the manufacturing sector. With the increased use of sensitive electronic components, the need for high-quality power supplies is of paramount importance.

3

Basic Principles

3.1 INTRODUCTION

Normally, during steady state, power system voltages and currents are balanced three-phase sinusoidal in nature. If the supply is balanced, single-phase analysis is suitable. In dc supply power, the calculation of power is simple as it has only real-power component, however, in ac supply it has both real and reactive powers.

3.2 ELECTRICAL POWER

Consider a single-phase circuit as shown in Figure 3.1. The instantaneous voltage and current can be written as

$$v = V_{\max} \sin(\omega t) \tag{3.1}$$

and

$$i = I_{\max} \sin(\omega t - \phi) \tag{3.2}$$

where $\omega(=2\pi f)$ is in radian/second, ϕ is the phase angle or power factor angle with respect to voltage reference which is positive when voltage leads current, and $V_{\max}$ and $I_{\max}$ are the real numbers called the *amplitudes* or *peak values* of voltage and current respectively.

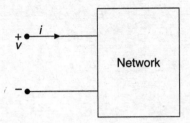

FIGURE 3.1 Power into one-port network.

The transmitted instanteneous power (p), to one-port network, which is defined as the rate change of energy, can be written as

$$p = vi = V_{max} I_{max} \sin(\omega t) \sin(\omega t - \phi) = \frac{V_{max} I_{max}}{2} [\cos \phi - \cos(2\omega t - \phi)] \qquad (3.3)$$

From Equation (3.3), it is seen that p has two parts: a constant (average) component and a sinusoidal component of frequency 2ω. Figure 3.2 shows the relationship among p, v and i. From this figure it is observed that the average power is positive; but it can be positive, negative or zero. The power consumed in resistive element is positive, however, it is zero in pure inductance or pure capacitance. In active network, power may be negative. The average power P over one period, $T = 2\pi/\omega$, can be defined as

$$P = \frac{1}{T} \int_0^T p \, dt = \frac{V_{max} I_{max}}{2} \cos \phi \qquad (3.4)$$

In all applications, generally, P is used rather than p. Cosine of phase angle is known as *power factor*. In ac power, leading and lagging power factors terminology are used. In a description, "a load draws 100 watts at a power factor of 0.707 lagging", means current lags voltage by angle $\tan^{-1}(0.707)$. The angle ϕ is equal to 45°.

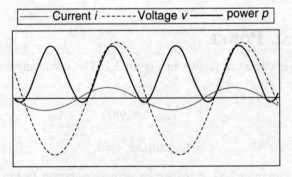

FIGURE 3.2 Instantaneous power.

3.3 PHASOR NOTATION

Using following Euler's formula of complex numbers

$$e^{j(\omega t + \phi)} = \cos(\omega t + \phi) + j \sin(\omega t + \phi) \qquad (3.5)$$

the current-time function i can be written in following form

$$i = \text{Im}\left[I_{\max} e^{j(\omega t + \phi)}\right] = \sqrt{2}\, \text{Im}\left(\frac{I_{\max}}{\sqrt{2}} e^{j\phi} e^{j\omega t}\right) \tag{3.6}$$

The current phasor I can be defined as the complex number

$$\overline{I} = \frac{I_{\max}}{\sqrt{2}} e^{j\phi}$$

In abbreviated form, the phasor is generally written as

$$\overline{I} = \frac{I_{\max}}{\sqrt{2}} \angle\phi = \left|\overline{I}\right| \angle\phi \tag{3.7}$$

The rms (root mean square) or effective value of phasor I will be equal to $I_{\max}/\sqrt{2}$ and phase will be ϕ. Phasors are always denoted by capital letters and modulus is always the rms value, however in instantaneous values, the peak values are used. The phase value is normally represented in degrees, otherwise stated.

3.4 REAL AND REACTIVE POWER

From Equation (3.4), the average power, which is also known as *active* or *real* power, is the useful power and greatly depends on the power factor. It can be written in terms of rms values of current and voltage, as

$$P = \left|\overline{V}\right|\left|\overline{I}\right| \cos\phi \tag{3.8}$$

Equation (3.3) can also be written as

$$\begin{aligned}
p &= \left|\overline{V}\right|\left|\overline{I}\right|\left[\cos\phi - \cos(2\omega t - \phi)\right] \\
&= \left|\overline{V}\right|\left|\overline{I}\right|\cos\phi - \left|\overline{V}\right|\left|\overline{I}\right|\left[\cos(2\omega t)\cos\phi + \sin(2\omega t)\sin\phi\right] \\
&= \underbrace{\left|\overline{V}\right|\left|\overline{I}\right|\cos\phi[1 - \cos(2\omega t)]}_{a} - \underbrace{\left|\overline{V}\right|\left|\overline{I}\right|\sin\phi \sin(2\omega t)}_{b}
\end{aligned} \tag{3.9}$$

The instantaneous power p has been decomposed into two components. First component, marked as 'a' in Equation (3.9), pulsates around the same average value as before but never goes negative. The second term, as marked 'b' in Equation (3.9), has a zero average value. This can be seen in Figure 3.3.

Reactive power (Q) is defined as

$$Q = \left|\overline{V}\right|\left|\overline{I}\right| \sin\phi \tag{3.10}$$

Equation (3.9) can be written in terms of real and reactive powers as

$$p = P[1 - \cos(2\omega t)] - Q \sin(2\omega t) \tag{3.11}$$

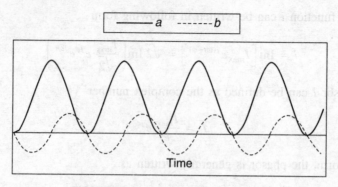

FIGURE 3.3 Components *a* and *b*.

From Equation (3.11), the reactive power Q is equal to the peak value of that power components, which travels back and forth on the line, resulting in zero average and therefore capable of no useful work. The physical dimension of both P and Q is watt. But the symbolized unit of P is 'watt' (W) and of Q is 'var' (VAr). More practical and bigger units of real power are kW, MW and for Q it is kVAr and MvAr.

Using Equation (3.8), the real power (P) can also be written as

$$P = \mathrm{Re}\left(\left|\overline{V}\right|\left|\overline{I}\right| \angle -\phi\right) = \mathrm{Re}(\overline{V}\,\overline{I}^*) \tag{3.12}$$

Real power is the real term of the product of voltage phasor and conjugate of current phasor.

3.5 APPARENT POWER

Apparent power or *volt ampere* is defined as the product of rms values of current and voltage across the circuit. It is very useful in defining the apparatus of a unit. Mathematically

$$\text{Volt ampere} = \left|\overline{S}\right| = \left|\overline{V}\right|\left|\overline{I}\right| = \sqrt{P^2 + Q^2} \tag{3.13}$$

kVA and MVA are the practical units of apparent power.

3.6 COMPLEX POWER

Phasor notations are very useful in calculating the complex power (S). Let voltage (V) and current phasors (I) be

$$\overline{V} = \left|\overline{V}\right|\exp(j\phi_1) = \left|\overline{V}\right| \angle \phi_1 \tag{3.14}$$

and

$$\overline{I} = \left|\overline{I}\right|\exp(j\phi_2) = \left|\overline{I}\right| \angle \phi_2 \tag{3.15}$$

The conjugate of current phasor can be written as

$$\overline{I}^* = \left|\overline{I}\right|\exp(-j\phi_2) = \left|\overline{I}\right| \angle -\phi_2 \tag{3.16}$$

The *complex power* is defined as the product

$$\bar{S} = \bar{V}\bar{I}^* = |\bar{V}|\exp(j\phi_1)|\bar{I}|\exp(-j\phi_2) = |\bar{V}||\bar{I}|\exp[j(\phi_1 - \phi_2)] \tag{3.17}$$

The difference of ϕ_1 and ϕ_2 is known as *phase* angle or *power factor* angle (ϕ) and thus we get

$$\bar{S} = |\bar{V}||\bar{I}|e^{j\phi} = |\bar{V}||\bar{I}|\cos\phi + j|\bar{V}||\bar{I}|\sin\phi = P + jQ \tag{3.18}$$

From Equation (3.18), the reactive power Q can also be defined as

$$Q = \mathrm{Im}\,(\bar{V}\bar{I}^*) \tag{3.19}$$

Vector representation of complex power (inductive circuit) is shown in Figure 3.4.

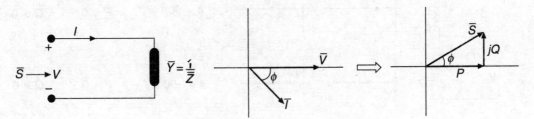

FIGURE 3.4 Complex power.

The real, reactive and apparent powers are equal in magnitude to the three sides of a right triangle known as *power triangle*. If V leads I, which is same as I lags V, both P and Q will be positive. For V lags I or I leads V, the reactive power Q will be negative. Complex power can also be written in terms of voltage and current. Table 3.1 shows the phasor relationship for different loads. Different terminology and units of power are presented in Table 3.2.

Considering the circuit as in Figure 3.4, the following relationship can be written:

$$\bar{V} = \bar{Z}\bar{I} \quad \text{and} \quad \bar{I} = \bar{Y}\bar{V}$$

From Equation (3.17), we can write

$$\bar{S} = \bar{V}\bar{I}^* = \bar{V}(\bar{Y}\bar{V})^* = \bar{V}\bar{V}^*\bar{Y}^* = \bar{Y}^*|\bar{V}|^2$$

or

$$\bar{S} = \bar{V}^* = \bar{Z}\bar{I}\bar{I}^* = \bar{Z}|\bar{I}|^2 \tag{3.20}$$

For a network supplied by several independent sources, all at same frequency, the sum of the complex power supplied by the independent sources equals to the sum of the complex power received by all the other branches of the network. This is known as the *theorem of conservation of complex power*. Mathematically, for n sources, it can be written as

$$S_{\text{total}} = \sum_{i=1}^{n} |\bar{S}_i| \tag{3.21}$$

Table 3.1 Phasor Relationship for Different Load

Type of load	Phasor diagram		Phase angle	Power absorbed by load	
	Taking current as reference	Taking voltage as reference		Real power	Reactive power
R load			$\phi = 0$	$P > 0$	$Q = 0$
L load			$\phi = 90°$	$P = 0$	$Q > 0$
C load			$\phi = -90°$	$P = 0$	$Q < 0$
R, L load			$0 < \phi < 90°$	$P > 0$	$Q > 0$
C, R load			$-90° < \phi < 0$	$P > 0$	$Q < 0$

Table 3.2 Notations and Units of Power

Notation	Terminology	Descriptive units
p	Instantaneous power	Watts: W, kW, MW
S	Complex power	Voltamperes: VA, kVA, MVA
$\lvert S \rvert$	Apparent power	Voltamperes: VA, kVA, MVA
P	Real or active or average power	Watts: W, kW, MW
Q	Reactive power	Voltamperes reactive: VAr, kVAr, MVAr

Using the concept of complex numbers, it can also be written as

$$\left| S_{\text{total}} \right| \leq \sum_{i=1}^{n} \overline{S}_i \tag{3.22}$$

Example 3.1 For $\overline{Z} = R + j\omega L$ and the current $i = \sqrt{2}\left|\overline{I}\right| \sin(\omega t + \phi)$,

(a) Calculate P and Q

(b) Calculate the instantaneous power.

Solution   (a) We have

$$\overline{S} = \overline{V}\,\overline{I}^{*} = \overline{Z}\left|\overline{I}\right|^{2} = (R + j\omega L)\left|\overline{I}\right|^{2}$$

Therefore, the real power $P = R\left|\overline{I}\right|^{2}$ and reactive power $Q = \omega L\left|\overline{I}\right|^{2}$.

(b) Instantaneous voltage v can be written as

$$v = Ri + L\frac{di}{dt} = R\sqrt{2}\left|\overline{I}\right|\sin(\omega t + \phi) + L\sqrt{2}\left|\overline{I}\right|\omega\cos(\omega t + \phi)$$

Instantaneous power can be calculated as

$$p = vi = 2R\left|\overline{I}\right|^{2}\sin^{2}(\omega t + \phi) + 2\omega L\left|\overline{I}\right|^{2}\sin(\omega t + \phi)\cos(\omega t + \phi)$$

$$= 2P\sin^{2}(\omega t + \phi) + Q\sin 2(\omega t + \phi)$$

$$= P[1 - \cos 2(\omega t + \phi)] + Q\sin 2(\omega t + \phi)$$

Example 3.2   Compute the powers in each elements of the circuit shown in Figure 3.5. Take supply voltage of 220 volt.

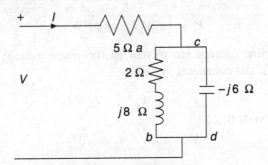

FIGURE 3.5   Example 3.2.

Solution   Let us find the equivalent impedance of parallel branches.

$$\overline{Z}_{eq} = \frac{(2 + j8)(-j6)}{(2 + j8) + (-j6)} = 9.0 - j15.0 = 17.50 \angle -59.04° \text{ ohm}$$

The current $\overline{I}$ will be

$$\overline{I} = \frac{220\angle 0}{5\angle 0° + 17.5\angle -59.04°} = (7.31 + j7.84)\,\text{A}$$

and the power in 5-ohm resister = $I^{2}R = 574.39$ W

If current in branch ab is $\overline{I}_{1}$ and current in branch cd is $\overline{I}_{2}$, these can be calculated as

$$\overline{I}_{1} = \frac{\overline{I}\,\overline{Z}_{cd}}{\overline{Z}_{ab} + \overline{Z}_{cd}} = \frac{(7.31 + j7.84)(-j6)}{(2 + j8) + (-j6)} = 22.81 \angle -88.03°\,\text{A}$$

and

$$\overline{I}_2 = \frac{\overline{I}\,\overline{Z}_{ab}}{\overline{Z}_{ab} + \overline{Z}_{cd}} = \frac{(7.31 + j7.84)(2 + j8)}{(2 + j8) + (-j6)} = 31.26 \angle 77.94° \, \text{A}$$

Hence the power loss in resister of branch $ab = I_1^2 R = 1040.59$ watts, power loss in inductor $(= I_1^2 X_1) = 4162.37$ VAR and power loss in capacitor $(= I_2^2 X_c) = -5863.13$ VAR.

3.7 THREE-PHASE SYSTEMS

The electric-supply system nowadays in use is of three-phase. However, in low-power applications such as lighting and other domestic use, it may also be of single phase. Earlier, 2-phase systems were used. But, now such systems have been made up to six phases for special purposes. Now the industry has generally standardized on the three-phase system, which can be either star- (wye-) or delta-connected.

In a balance system, the power in circuit will be equal to the √3 times the line voltage and line current times the power factor. It can be mathematically written as

$$P = \left(\sqrt{3} V_L I_L \cos\phi\right) \, \text{W} \tag{3.23}$$

The line voltage and line current are related to the phase voltage and phase current for different connections. In star-connected system

$$V_L = \sqrt{3} V_P; \qquad I_L = I_P$$

and in delta-connected system

$$V_L = V_P; \qquad I_L = \sqrt{3} I_P$$

where

    V_L = Line-to-line voltage

    V_P = Phase or line-to-ground voltage

    I_L = Line current

    I_P = Phase current

3.8 PER-UNIT REPRESENTATION

Sometime, it is convenient to use per unit (or percentage) quantity rather than the actual quantity for the analysis of power system. In power system, the different operating voltage are used due to presence of transformers, different rating of generators, etc., and therefore calculation becomes difficult. Moreover, system data is generally available in per-unit value on its own base. Per-unit value is a dimensionless quantity and is represented as 'pu'.

Per-unit value of a quantity is the ratio of the actual value in any unit to the base or reference value of that quantity in the same unit. Thus

$$\text{Quantity in per unit (pu)} = \frac{\text{Actual quantity in any unit}}{\text{Base or reference value of quantity in the same unit}}$$

A well-chosen per-unit system can reduce the computational effort, simplify evaluation and facilitate the understanding of system characteristics. The selections of base quantities are also very important. Some of the base quantities are chosen independently and arbitrarily while others automatically follow depending upon the fundamental relationships between system variables. Out of the four power system quantities, viz., power (VA), voltage (V), current (A) and impedance (Ω), only two are independent. The universal practice is to use machine rating, power and voltage as base values and base values of current and impedance are calculated.

Consider a single-phase system with base voltamperes (VA_b) and base voltage (V_b), the base current and base impedance will be calculated as

$$\text{Base current } I_b = \frac{VA_b}{V_b} \text{ A} \tag{3.24}$$

and

$$\text{Base impedance } Z_b = \frac{V_b}{I_b} = \frac{V_b^2}{VA_b} \text{ ohm} \tag{3.25}$$

The per unit impedance, then, can be given by

$$Z_{pu} = \frac{\text{Actual impedance } (Z)}{\text{Base impedance } (Z_b)} = \frac{Z \times VA_b}{V_b^2} \tag{3.26}$$

The practical choice of base power is kVA_b or MVA_b, however, base voltage is selected in kV_b. With these, base current and base impedance can be derived as

$$\text{Base current } I_b = \frac{kVA_b}{kV_b} = \frac{1000 \times MVA_b}{kV_b} \text{ A} \tag{3.27}$$

and

$$\text{Base impedance } \overline{Z}_b = \frac{1000 \times kV_b}{I_b} = \frac{kV_b^2}{MVA_b} = \frac{1000 \times kV_b^2}{kVA_b} \text{ ohm} \tag{3.28}$$

Similarly, per-unit impedance can be derived as

$$Z_{pu} = \frac{\overline{Z} \times MVA_b}{kV_b^2} = \frac{Z \times kVA_b}{kV_b^2 \times 1000} \tag{3.29}$$

In 3-phase systems, the base values usually chosen are 3-phase kVA_b or MVA_b and line-to-line voltage (kV_b). The base current, base impedance and per-unit impedance can be found as

$$\text{Base current } I_b = \frac{kVA_b}{\sqrt{3}kV_b} = \frac{1000 \times MVA_b}{\sqrt{3}kV_b} \text{ A} \tag{3.30}$$

$$\text{Base impedance } Z_b = \frac{1000 \times kV_b}{\sqrt{3}I_b} = \frac{kV_b^2}{MVA_b} = \frac{1000 \times kV_b^2}{kVA_b} \text{ ohm} \tag{3.31}$$

$$\text{Per-unit impedance } Z_{pu} = \frac{Z \times MVA_b}{kV_b^2} = \frac{Z \times kVA_b}{kV_b^2 \times 1000} \tag{3.32}$$

It is necessary to change per unit impedance from one set of base values to the new set of base values. When base *MVA* is changed from $MVA_{b,old}$ to $MVA_{b,new}$ and base voltage from $kV_{b,old}$ to $kV_{b,new}$, per-unit impedance can be calculated from following equation as

$$\left(\begin{array}{c} \text{Per-unit impedance} \\ \text{referred to new base } Z_{pu,new} \end{array} \right) = \left(\begin{array}{c} \text{Per-unit impedance} \\ \text{referred to old base } Z_{pu,old} \end{array} \right) \left(\frac{MVA_{b,new}}{MVA_{b,old}} \right) \left(\frac{kV_{b,old}}{kV_{b,new}} \right)^2 \quad (3.33)$$

3.8.1 Per-unit Representation of Transformers

A three-phase transformer can be represented by a single-phase transformer in getting the per-phase solution of the system. The delta-winding transformer is replaced by an equivalent star so that the transformation ratio of equivalent single-phase transformer is always line-to-line voltage ratio of a three-phase transformer. Figure 3.6 represents the single-phase equivalent transformer with primary winding impedance Z_P and secondary winding impedance Z_S. The turn ratio is $N : 1$.

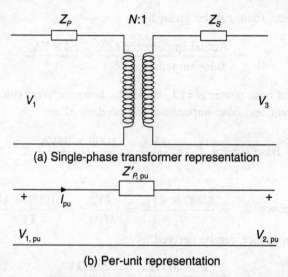

(a) Single-phase transformer representation

(b) Per-unit representation

FIGURE 3.6 Single-phase equivalent transformer representation.

If primary winding voltage base is V_{1B} and the secondary side-base voltage is V_{2B}, these can be written in the following form:

$$\frac{V_{1B}}{V_{2B}} = N = \frac{I_{2B}}{I_{1B}} \quad (3.34)$$

where I_{1B} and I_{2B} are the current bases of primary and secondary sides, respectively.

Base impedances can be calculated as

$$Z_{1B} = \frac{V_{1B}}{I_{1B}}; \qquad Z_{2B} = \frac{V_{2B}}{I_{2B}}$$

and their ratio can be defined as

$$\frac{Z_{1B}}{Z_{2B}} = \frac{V_{1B}}{I_{1B}} \frac{I_{2B}}{V_{2B}} = \frac{V_{1B}}{V_{2B}} \frac{I_{2B}}{I_{1B}} = N \times N = N^2 \tag{3.35}$$

Impedance referred to primary side (Z'_P) and secondary side (Z'_S) will be

$$Z'_P = Z_P + N^2 Z_S; \qquad Z'_S = Z_S + \frac{Z_P}{N^2}$$

and per-unit impedance on primary side ($Z'_{P,pu}$) will be

$$Z'_{P,pu} = \frac{Z_P + N^2 Z_S}{Z_{1B}} = \frac{Z_P}{Z_{1B}} + N^2 \frac{Z_S}{Z_{1B}} = Z_{P,pu} + N^2 Z_{S,pu} \frac{Z_{2B}}{Z_{1B}} = Z_{P,pu} + Z_{S,pu} \tag{3.36}$$

On secondary side

$$Z'_{S,pu} = \frac{Z_S + (Z_P/N^2)}{Z_{2B}} = \frac{Z_S}{Z_{2B}} + \frac{1}{N^2} \frac{Z_P}{Z_{2B}} = Z_{S,pu} + \frac{1}{N^2} Z_{P,pu} \frac{Z_{1B}}{Z_{2B}} = Z_{P,pu} + Z_{S,pu} \tag{3.37}$$

From Equations (3.36) and (3.37), we have

$$Z'_{P,pu} = Z'_{S,pu} \tag{3.38}$$

This shows that per-unit impedance referred to the primary side will be equal to per-unit impedance referred to the secondary side.

3.8.2 Advantages of Per-unit System

Per-unit representation has several advantages, such as:

1. In large electric power systems, the capacity and rating of equipment are different and the use of per-unit quantities simplifies the calculations.
2. Per-unit representation of the impedance of any equipment is more meaningful than its absolute value.
3. Using per-unit system, the chances of making mistakes in phase and line voltages, single- or three-phase quantities are minimized.
4. In case of transformers, the per-unit impedance referred to primary side or secondary side will be the same which further simplifies the calculations.

3.8.3 Per-unit Impedance Diagram

Single-line diagram of a power system can be represented by the per-unit impedance diagram, as shown in Figure 3.7.

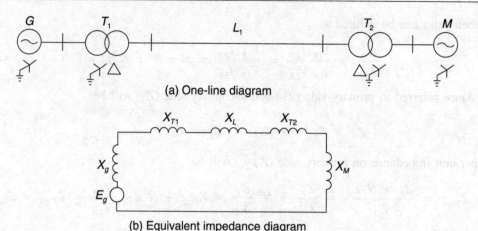

(a) One-line diagram

(b) Equivalent impedance diagram

FIGURE 3.7   Per-unit impedance diagram.

Following procedure is normally used for calculating the per-unit impedances, which are used in drawing the impedance diagram.

(a) Choose an appropriate MVA or kVA base for the system. (Generally, 100 MVA is used in power system.)
(b) Choose the voltage base and calculate the appropriate base voltages for other sections according to the transformation ratio.
(c) Calculate the per-unit impedance of each equipment and connect them as per topology of the single-line diagram.

Example 3.3   Find complex power S_2 in terms of S_1, L and V for the circuit shown in Figure 3.8

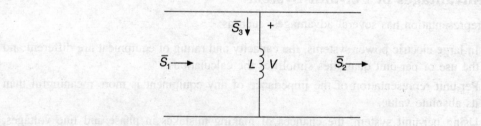

FIGURE 3.8   Example 3.3.

Solution   Complex power S_3 can be written as

$$\bar{S}_3 = \bar{V}\bar{I}^* = \bar{Y}^*\left|\bar{V}\right|^2 = \frac{\left|\bar{V}\right|^2}{Z^*} = \frac{\left|\bar{V}\right|^2}{-j\omega L} = j\frac{\left|\bar{V}\right|^2}{\omega L}$$

Using conservation of complex power theorem, we get $S_2 = S_1 - S_3$. Thus, we obtain

$$\bar{S}_2 = \bar{S}_1 - j\frac{\left|\bar{V}\right|^2}{\omega L}; \qquad P_2 = P_1; \qquad Q_2 = Q_1 - \frac{\left|\bar{V}\right|^2}{\omega L}$$

This shows ($Q_2 < Q_1$) that inductor is source of consuming reactive power.

Example 3.4 A three-generator system is shown in Figure 3.9. Find the impedances in per unit on the 100-MVA and 11-kV base. Also draw the impedance diagram for the same. Given that

$$G_1 \rightarrow 100 \text{ MVA, } 11 \text{ kV, } x = 25\%$$

$$G_2 \rightarrow 150 \text{ MVA, } 16 \text{ kV, } x = 10\%$$

$$G_3 \rightarrow 200 \text{ MVA, } 21 \text{ kV, } x = 15\%$$

$$T_1 \rightarrow 150 \text{ MVA, } 11/132 \text{ kV, } x = 5\%$$

$$T_2 \rightarrow 200 \text{ MVA, } 16/132 \text{ kV, } x = 10\%$$

$$T_3 \rightarrow 250 \text{ MVA, } 21/132 \text{ kV, } x = 5\%$$

Line $L_1 \rightarrow 100$ ohm

Line $L_2 \rightarrow 50$ ohm

Line $L_3 \rightarrow 80$ ohm

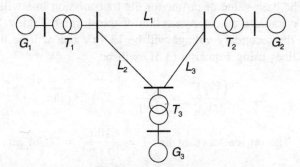

FIGURE 3.9 Example 3.4.

Solution Taking the base of 100 MVA and 11 kV, the following pu values can be calculated as

(a) *Generators pu reactances:* Since the reactance of the generators are given on their own bases, the reactance of the generator-1 on the 100-MVA and 11-kV bases will be

$$X_1 = 0.25 \text{ pu}$$

Reactance of generator-2 (G_2) is given on 150-MVA and 16-kV base and the pu reactance on 100-MVA and 11-kV base can be calculated using Equation (3.33) as

$$X_2 = 0.1 \times \left(\frac{100}{150}\right)\left(\frac{16}{11}\right)^2 = 0.141 \text{ pu}$$

Similarly, the pu reactance of generator-3 (G_3) on new bases will be

$$X_3 = 0.15 \times \left(\frac{100}{200}\right)\left(\frac{21}{11}\right)^2 = 0.273 \text{ pu}$$

(b) *Transformers pu reactances:* The per-unit reactances of transformers on the new base values will be

$$\text{Per-unit reactance of transformer-1 } (T_1) = 0.05 \times \left(\frac{100}{150}\right)\left(\frac{11}{11}\right)^2 = 0.033 \text{ pu}$$

Since the generator-1 is connected with T_1 on the primary side, the base voltage will be 11 kV for this transformer. Normally, pu values are calculated starting from one end and reaching the another end of the system.

$$\text{Per-unit reactance of transformer-2 } (T_2) = 0.10 \times \left(\frac{100}{200}\right)\left(\frac{16}{11}\right)^2 = 0.106 \text{ pu}$$

$$\text{Per-unit reactance of transformer-3 } (T_3) = 0.05 \times \left(\frac{100}{250}\right)\left(\frac{21}{11}\right)^2 = 0.073 \text{ pu}$$

(c) *Transmission line pu reactances:* Since the line reactances are given in the actual values, therefore it is required to calculate the base values for the lines to calculate the base value of reactance. The base value of power for the transmission line will be the same but the voltage base will be calculated as per connection of transformer. Taking 11 kV at the primary of the transformer-1, the secondary voltage will be 132 kV that will be the base for the lines. Therefore Z_b for the lines using Equation (3.31) will be

$$Z_b = \frac{(kV_b)^2}{MVA_b} = \frac{132^2}{100} = 174.24 \text{ ohm}$$

$$\text{The pu reactance of line-1} = \frac{100}{174.24} = 0.574 \text{ pu}$$

$$\text{The pu reactance of line-2} = \frac{50}{174.24} = 0.287 \text{ pu}$$

$$\text{The pu reactance of line-3} = \frac{80}{174.24} = 0.459 \text{ pu}$$

The reactance diagram can be drawn as Figure 3.10.

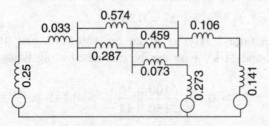

FIGURE 3.10 Impedance diagram.

Example 3.5   A 220 kV/400 kV, 240 MVA, transformer has primary winding impedance $3 + j8$ ohm and secondary winding impedance of $5 + j10$ ohm. Find the pu impedance on its own base referred to HV side and LV side.

Solution   Impedance referred to LV side

$$\left(\bar{Z}_{LV}'\right) = (3 + j8) + (5 + j10) \times \left(\frac{220}{400}\right)^2$$

$$= 4.5125 + j11.025$$

$$\left(\bar{Z}_{LV}'\right)_{pu} = \left(\bar{Z}_{LV}'\right) \times \frac{(MVA_b)}{(kV_{b_{LV}})^2}$$

$$= (4.5125 + j11.025) \times \frac{240}{(220)^2} = 0.022376 + j0.0546694$$

Impedance referred to HV side

$$(\bar{Z}_{HV}') = (5 + j10) + (3 + j8) \times \left(\frac{400}{220}\right)^2$$

$$= (14.917355 + 36.446281) \times \left(\frac{240}{(400)^2}\right)$$

$$= 0.0223756 + j0.0546694$$

thus $$(\bar{Z}_{LV}')_{pu} = (\bar{Z}_{HV}')_{pu}$$

Example 3.6   A wye connected load is supplied from 3-phase 240 V mains. Each branch of the load is a resistor of 20 ohms. Using 240V and 10 kVA bases, calculate the pu values of the current and power taken by the load.

Solution

Let V_{base} = 240 V

$VA_{base} = 10 \times 10^3$

So, $Z_{base} = 240 \times 240/10^4 = 5.76\Omega$

So, load impedance in pu/phase = 20/5.76 = 3.472 pu.

$I_{base} = 10 * 10^3/(\sqrt{3} * 240) = 24.057$ A.

So current drawn in pu (I_{pu}) = 1/3.472 = 0.288 pu.

Current drawn in amps = 0.288 * 24.057 = 6.93 A

Power drawn in = $V_{pu} * I_{pu}$ = 0.288 pu.

The power drawn = 0.288 * 10 * 10^3W = 2.88 kW.

PROBLEMS

3.1   Calculate the power consumed in different elements of circuit shown in Figure 3.11. Draw the phasor diagram taking voltage as reference. Take supply voltage of 220 volt.

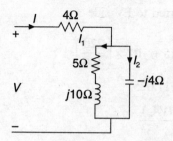

FIGURE 3.11   Problem 3.1.

3.2   Find $\bar{S}_2$ in terms of $\bar{S}_1$, L, C and voltage for the circuit shown in Figure 3.12.

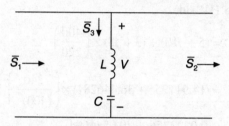

FIGURE 3.12   Problem 3.2.

3.3   Voltage magnitudes at both the ends of the circuit shown in Figure 3.13 are maintained to same value. Show that $\bar{S}_2 = -\bar{S}_1^*$.

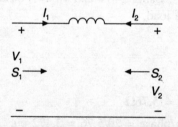

FIGURE 3.13   Problem 3.3.

3.4   Find the load power at Bus-1 and Bus-2 in Figure 3.14.

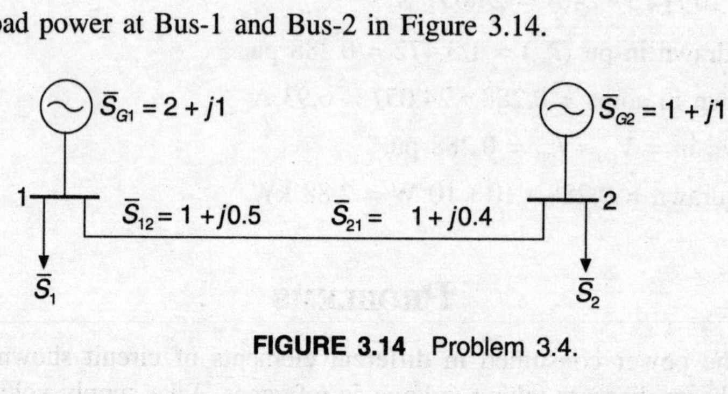

$\bar{S}_{G1} = 2 + j1$ $\bar{S}_{G2} = 1 + j1$

1

$\bar{S}_{12} = 1 + j0.5$ $\bar{S}_{21} = 1 + j0.4$ 2

$\bar{S}_1$ $\bar{S}_2$

FIGURE 3.14   Problem 3.4.

3.5 A 100-MVA 33-kV, 3-phase generator has a subtransient reactance of 15%. The generator is connected to the motors through a transmission line and transformers as shown in Figure 3.15. The motors have rated inputs of 30 MVA, 20 MVA and 50 MVA at 30 kV with 20% subtransient reactance. The 3-phase transformers are rated at 110 MVA, 32 kVΔ/110 kV Y with leakage reactance 8%. The line has reactance of 50 ohm. Selecting the generator rating as the base quantities in the circuit, determine the base quantities in the other part of the system and evaluate the corresponding pu values. Also, draw the reactance diagram.

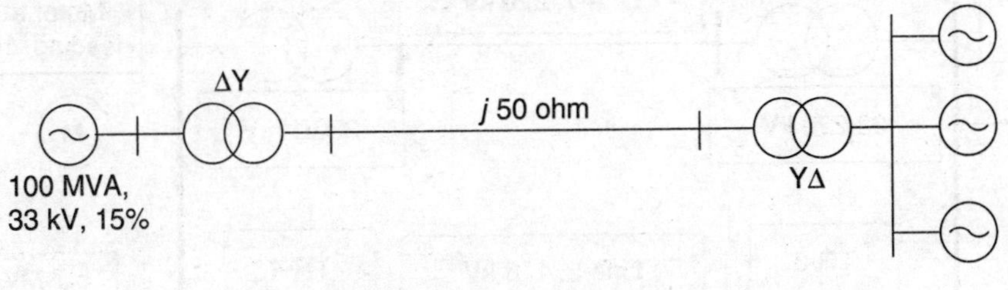

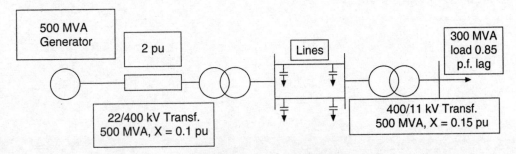

FIGURE 3.15 Problem 3.5.

3.6 Two generators rated at 10 MVA, 13.2 kV and 15 MVA, 13.2 kV are connected in parallel to a busbar. They feed supply to two motors of inputs 8 MVA and 12 MVA respectively. The operating voltage of motors is 12.5 kV. Assuming the base quantities as 50 MVA and 13.8 kV draw the reactance diagram. The percentage reactance of generators is 15% and that for motors is 20%.

3.7 A 11 kV/132 kV 50 MVA, 3-phase transformer has an inductive reactance of j 0.005 ohms referred to the primay (11 kV). Calculate the pu value of reactance based on the rating. Neglect resistance.

3.8 Express in pu all the quantities shown in the line diagram of the 3-phase transmission system in Figure 3.16. Construct the single phase equivalent circuit. Use a base of 100 MVA. The line is 80-km long with resistance and reactance of 0.1 and 0.5 ohms, respectively. It has a capacitive susceptance of 10 uS per km (split equally between two ends).

FIGURE 3.16 Problem 3.8.

3.9 The one line diagram of a 3-phase system is shown in Figure 3.17. Transformers TR-2, TR-3 and TR-4 are rated at 40 MVA each and their reactances are 6.0%, 6.4% and 8.0%, respectively. TR-1 is rated at 50 MVA and its reactance is 10%. The generator and motor reactances are 18% and 18.5%, respectively. Series res. and shunts neglected). Select a common power base of 100 MVA and voltage base of 22 kV on generator side, and

(a) Compute pu impedance values and load values, and draw the impedance diagram.

(b) For the given loads, compute the generator terminal and its internal voltages in kV.

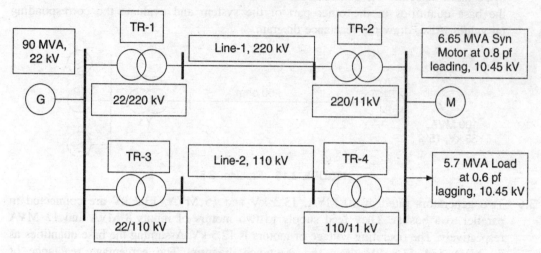

FIGURE 3.17 One-line diagram.

4

Load Characteristics and Economic Aspects

4.1 INTRODUCTION

A correct idea of the load characteristic of a particular area is very much important to meet the power requirement. The major portion of power generation comes from thermal, hydroelectric, nuclear and gas-operated power plants. Presently, combined cycle gas operated plants are becoming more popular due to high efficiency, minimum erection time, easily available to produce power, etc. The location and size of different plants are decided based on requirements of loads and their locations. The other factors affecting the sitting and sizing are availability of fuel (input energy), space, etc. The evacuation of power is also one concern.

The load demand in a power system is always varying during the whole day. Figure 4.1 shows a typical demand at a station during the day. The minimum capacity of generator should be such that it should meet the maximum demand. But use of single unit to supply the whole load will not be practical due to economic, reliability and efficiency reasons. Therefore, large numbers of units are used to fit the load curve, which is a curve of demand vs time during the day. Having the lower size of units, the maintenance cost, operational cost and capital cost increase. Hence, a compromise between selection of size and number of generating units is made. Its selection also depends upon the cost of power, fix and operating, depreciation, interest payment, etc. The electricity utilities derive their income from the customers through the electricity bills. Different methods of charging consumers are known as *tariffs*.

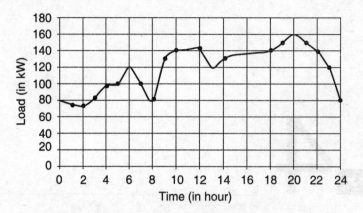

FIGURE 4.1 Demand at a station during the day.

4.2 COMMONLY USED TERMS

The load can be categorized in terms of domestic, agricultural, industrial and commercial loads. Present-day power stations invariably feed power to grid and consumers draw power from the grid. The estimate of power and increase in generation capacity depend on maximum demand, distribution and variation of demand, and energy requirement. Following factors are normally used in electricity system planning, operation and management.

Connected load

Each device at consumers' terminal has its rated capacity. The *connected load* is the sum of the continuous rating of the entire load consuming apparatus and outlets connected to the system.

Maximum demand

The *maximum demand* of a consumer means the maximum power that the circuit is likely to draw at any time. In other words, the maximum demand of an installation or system is the greatest of all demands that have occurred during the specified period of time, which may be daily, monthly, or yearly. If all apparatus and outlets are used simultaneously to full extent, the maximum demand will be equal to the connected load. But consumers do not use all the devices and outlets at full load simultaneously and therefore the maximum demand is always less than the connected load.

Demand factor

The *demand factor* is the ratio of maximum demand to the connected load. Mathematically, it can be written as

$$\text{Demand factor} = \frac{\text{Maximum demand}}{\text{Connected load}} \qquad (4.1)$$

Demand factor, generally lies between 0.5 and 0.8.

Diversity factor

The maximum demand of all consumers of a group does not occur simultaneously. When considering the rated capacity of any equipment, it is seldom necessary to choose rating equal to the sum of maximum loads. A term commonly used in this connection is *diversity factor* (DF) being defined as

$$\text{Diversity factor} = \frac{\text{Sum of individual maximum demands}}{\text{Maximum demand of whole}} \qquad (4.2)$$

In other words, it is the ratio of the sum of the maximum demands of all subdivisions or groups or consumers to the maximum demand of the whole of subdivisions or groups or consumers. It is also known as *group diversity factor* and is always greater than unity. This factor gives idea about the demand at distribution transformers.

Diversity will exist in the time of maximum demand of transformers on the feeders and also as regards the feeders to the substations and substations to the generating stations. The diversity factor between transformers, between feeders and between substations can be combined into a single term commonly referred to as *peak diversity factor* and is defined as

$$\text{Peak diversity factor} = \frac{\text{Maximum demand of a consumer group}}{\substack{\text{Demand of consumer group at the time} \\ \text{of system peak demand}}} \qquad (4.3)$$

It gives an indication of the effective demand of consumer group at the time of system peak. When the demand factors and the diversity factors are known, the system demand can be calculated as follows:

Let L_1, L'_1, L''_1, $\cdots$ and L_2, L'_2, L''_2, ... be individual connected loads of group-1 and group-2, respectively. d_1 and d_2 be demand factors of group-1 and group-2, G_1 and G_2 be group diversity factors for group-1 and group-2, p_1 and p_2 are peak diversity factors for group-1 and group-2, respectively.

The maximum demand and demand at the system peak can be calculated as

$$\text{Maximum demand of group-1} = \frac{\Sigma L_1 \times d_1}{G_1}$$

$$\text{Maximum demand of group-2} = \frac{\Sigma L_2 \times d_2}{G_2}$$

$$\text{Demand of group-1 at the system peak} = \frac{\Sigma L_1 \times d_1}{G_1 \times p_1}$$

$$\text{Demand of group-2 at the system peak} = \frac{\Sigma L_2 \times d_2}{G_2 \times p_2}$$

$$\text{The system peak demand will be} = \frac{\Sigma L_1 \times d_1}{G_1 \times p_1} + \frac{\Sigma L_2 \times d_2}{G_2 \times p_2}$$

Peak diversity factor will be multiplication of DF between transformers, DF between feeders and DF between substations. High diversity factor is always beneficial for economic operation of the system, which can be achieved by

- Giving incentives to users to use power in light load period
- Using day-light saving
- Staggering office time
- Using two parts tariffs both for maximum demand and energy consumption.

Coincidence factor

It is the ratio of the maximum coincident of total demand of a group of consumers to the sum of the maximum power demands of individual consumers comprising the group both taken at the same point of supply for the same time. Thus, it is reciprocal of diversity factor.

$$\text{Coincidence factor} = \frac{\text{Maximum demand}}{\text{Sum of individual maximum demand}} \qquad (4.4)$$

Load diversity

It is the difference between the sum of the peaks of two or more individual loads and the peak of the combined load. Mathematically, it is defined as

Load diversity = Sum of all individual loads − Peak of the combined load

Contribution factor

It is the contribution of a particular load, in per unit of the individual maximum demand, to the group maximum demand. If c_i is the contribution factor of ith load in a group of n loads and D_i is its maximum demand. Therefore

$$\text{Group maximum demand } (D_g) = \sum_{i=1}^{n} c_i \times D_i \qquad (4.5)$$

and

$$\text{Coincidence factor} = \frac{\sum_{i=1}^{n} c_i \times D_i}{\sum_{i=1}^{n} D_i} \qquad (4.6)$$

If the maximum demands of the load are the same, the coincidence factor will be equal to the average of contribution factor and if contribution factors of each load are the same, the coincidence factor will be equal to the contribution factor itself.

Loss factor

The ratio of the average power loss to the peak load power loss during a specified period of time is known as *loss factor*. Mathematically

$$\text{Loss factor} = \frac{\text{Average power loss}}{\text{Power loss at peak load}} \qquad (4.7)$$

This is applicable for only copper losses of the system and not for iron losses.

Load factor

Load factor of a plant or system is the ratio of the average load to the peak load for a certain period of time. If period considered is a day, the load factor is the daily load factor and for month, it is monthly load factor and so on. Therefore

$$\text{Load factor} = \frac{\text{Average demand}}{\text{Maximum demand}}$$

$$= \frac{\text{Energy generated in a given period of time}}{\text{Maximum demand} \times \text{Hours of operation in the given period}} \quad (4.8)$$

Load factor is always less than unity. However, diversity factor is greater or equal to unity. For better performance, the load factors should be as high as possible. The effect of diversity factor is to reduce the simultaneous maximum demand on the station for the same individual demands. The effect of diversity factor is to reduce the capital cost for the station and consequently a lower overall rate for generation of electricity. Load factor depicts the variation of load during certain period but does not give any indication of the shape of the load curve.

Plant capacity factor

The *plant capacity factor* (also known as *plant factor*) is the ratio of the average annual load to the power plant capacity (also called *installed capacity*) during given period. Therefore

$$\text{Plant capacity factor} = \frac{\text{Average annual load}}{\text{Plant rated capacity}}$$

$$= \frac{\text{Energy produced in a year}}{\text{Plant rated capacity} \times 8760} \quad (4.9)$$

The maximum value of plant capacity factor can be unity when the plant is operating at its rated capacity throughout the year. Plant capacity is also defined in terms of monthly plant load factor. It is also known as *plant load factor* (PLF).

The *capacity factor* indicates the extent of use of the generating station. It is different from load factor because of reason that the rated capacity of each plant is always greater than expected maximum load due to some reserve capacity. Thus

$$\text{Capacity factor} = \frac{\text{Maximum load}}{\text{Plant capacity}} \times \text{Load factor} \quad (4.10)$$

Plant use factor

It is the ratio of actual energy produced to the multiplication of plant capacity and time (hours) of the plant operation.

$$\text{Plant use factor} = \frac{\text{Actual energy produced}}{(\text{Plant capacity}) \times (\text{Plant operation time in hours})} \quad (4.11)$$

The two important observations can be made saying that ideal condition for cheap electric supply exists when,

(a) The installed capacity and hence the corresponding capital cost of the generating plant is kept low (this can be obtained by good diversity factor) and

(b) The daily output of each generator unit is large (which means good load factor for the station). The reduction in costs with good load factor is due to the fact that overall working cost/unit become low, the fixed charges have been distributed over more units generated.

Utilization factor

It is defined as the ratio of maximum demand to the rated capacity of plant. Thus

$$\text{Utilization factor} = \frac{\text{Maximum load}}{\text{Rated capacity}} \qquad (4.12)$$

Utilization factors of efficient generators are kept high. The value of utilization factor can be more than unity due to overloading of the plant. It is evident that

$$\text{Plant capacity factor} = \text{Load factor} \times \text{Utilization factor} \qquad (4.13)$$

Reserves

(a) *Spinning reserve* is that generating capacity which is connected to the bus and ready to take load.

(b) *Cold reserve* is that reserve-generating capacity which is available for service but not in operation.

(c) *Hot reserve* is that reserve-generating capacity which is in operation but not in service.

(d) *Firm power* is power intended to be always available (even under emergency conditions).

(e) *Reserve margin* is the difference between rated capacity minus actual loading on the generator.

Example 4.1 Loads on a feeder during 24 hours of a day are given below:

Time	Load (kW)	Time	Load (kW)	Time	Load (kW)
12 am	400	8 am	900	16 pm	1400
1 am	380	9 am	1200	17 pm	1300
2 am	350	10 am	1350	18 pm	1500
3 am	300	11 am	1200	19 pm	1800
4 am	350	12 pm	1000	20 pm	2000
5 am	500	13 pm	950	21 pm	1950
6 am	700	14 pm	1250	22 pm	1000
7 am	750	15 pm	1300	23 pm	800

Calculate the maximum demand, average demand and load factor of the feeder. If the feeder has the peak loss of 108 kW at peak load and annual loss factor of 0.14, find the following:

(a) The average power loss of the feeder

(b) The total annual loss of the feeder

Also calculate the demand factor of the feeder if the connected demand is 2500 kW.

Solution From the table, it can be seen that the maximum demand is 2000 kW at 20 pm. Assuming the linear variations of load between the intervals, the energy during the day will be

$(400 \times 1) + (380 \times 1) + (350 \times 1) + (300 \times 1) + (350 \times 1) + (500 \times 1) + (700 \times 1)$

$+ (750 \times 1) + (900 \times 1) + (1200 \times 1) + (1350 \times 1) + (1200 \times 1) + (1000 \times 1) + (950 \times 1)$

$+ (1250 \times 1) + (1300 \times 1) + (1400 \times 1) + (1300 \times 1) + (1500 \times 1) + (1800 \times 1)$

$+ (2000 \times 1) + (1950 \times 1) + (1000 \times 1) + (800 \times 1)$

$= 24630$ kWh

$$\text{Average demand} = \frac{\text{Total energy produced}}{\text{Time}} = \frac{24630}{24} = 1026.25 \text{ kW}$$

and

$$\text{Load factor} = \frac{\text{Average demand}}{\text{Maximum demand}} = \frac{1026.25}{2000} = 0.513125$$

(a) Using Equation (4.7),

$$\text{Average power loss} = \text{Loss factor} \times \text{Power loss at peak load}$$

$$= 0.14 \times 108$$

$$= 15.12 \text{ kW}$$

(b) Annual power loss $= 15.12 \times 365 = 5518.8$ kW

Using Equation (4.1),

$$\text{Demand factor} = \frac{\text{Maximum demand}}{\text{Connected demand}} = \frac{2000}{2500} = 0.80$$

Example 4.2 Maximum demand of a generating station is 100 MW, a load factor is 65%. The plant capacity factor and plant use factor are 50% and 80%, respectively. Determine (a) the daily energy produced, (b) installed capacity of plant, (c) the reserve capacity of plant, (d) the maximum energy that could be produced daily if the plant is running all the time, (e) the maximum energy that could be produced daily if the plant is running at full load (according to the operating schedule) and (f) utilization factor.

Solution We have

$$\text{Average demand} = (\text{Maximum demand}) \times (\text{Load factor})$$

$$= 100 \times 0.65$$

$$= 65 \text{ MW}$$

(a) Daily energy produced = (Average demand) × 24 = 65 × 24 = 1560 MWh

(b) Using Equation (4.9),

$$\text{Plant-rated capacity} = \frac{\text{Average load}}{\text{Plant capacity factor}} = \frac{65}{0.5} = 130 \text{ MW}$$

(c) Reserve capacity = (Installed capacity) – (Maximum demand)

$$= 130 - 100$$
$$= 30 \text{ MW}$$

(d) Maximum energy that could be produced if plant is running all the time will be

Installed capacity × 24 = 130 × 24 = 3120 MWh

(e) Maximum energy that could be produced if plant is running at full load (according to the operating schedule) will be

$$\frac{\text{Actual energy produced}}{\text{Plant use factor}} = \frac{1560}{0.80} = 1950 \text{ MWh}$$

(f) Utilization factor = $\dfrac{\text{Maximum load}}{\text{Rated capacity}} = \dfrac{100}{130} = 0.769$

Example 4.3 Using the data given in Example 4.1 where the street lighting loads of 200 kW included in the total load is only during 6 pm to 6 am (12 hours), determine the following:

(a) The class contribution factor for street lighting and the remaining load

(b) The diversity factor of the feeder

(c) The coincidence factor of the load group.

Solution (a) The class contribution factor (c_i) is defined as

$$c_i = \frac{\text{Class demand at time of system peak}}{\text{Class non-coincidence maximum demand}}$$

For street lighting and rest of the load

$$c_{\text{street}} = \frac{200 \text{ kW}}{200 \text{ kW}} = 1.0 \quad \text{and} \quad c_{\text{rest}} = \frac{1800 \text{ kW}}{1800 \text{ kW}} = 1.0$$

(b) Diversity factor is defined as

$$\text{Diversity factor} = \frac{\text{Sum of the class maximum demand}}{\text{Group maximum demand}}$$

$$= \frac{\sum\limits_{1}^{n} D_i}{\sum\limits_{1}^{n} c_i \times D_i}$$

$$= \frac{200 + 1800}{1.0 \times 200 + 1 \times 1800}$$

$$= 1.0$$

(c) Coincidence factor $= \dfrac{1}{\text{Diversity factor}} = 1.0$

4.3 CURVE USEFUL IN SYSTEM OPERATION AND PLANNING

4.3.1 Load Curve

Load on a station always changes and thus the generation. Load curve is a graphical representation of variation of load with respect to time in chronological order. Load curve is called *daily load curve* if the graph is for whole day. If the time is one month, it is called *monthly load curve* and so on.

The daily load curve for a station is not the same for all the days. It differs from day-to-day and season-to-season. Typically two load curves—one for winter and other for summer—are used to calculate the base annual load curve. Figure 4.1 shows a daily load curve. The load curves are very useful in providing information such as

1. Area under the curve gives the actual unit generated required during the period.
2. The ratio of area under the curve to the total area under the rectangle in which it is contained gives the load factor for the period.
3. The peak of the curve gives the maximum demand on the station during that period.
4. Area under the curve divided by number of hours gives the average demand.

4.3.2 Load Duration Curve

Load duration curve is a rearrangement of all the load elements of load curve in descending order with the greatest load on the left hand. Some time load is also represented in terms of percentage of peak demand. Abscissa corresponds to the time duration in the hours but the actual time. The load curve can be daily, monthly or annual. It shows the hourly load during the time, but not in the order that they occurred. Figure 4.2 shows the load duration curve.

4.3.3 Energy Load Curve

For hydro plants it is necessary to know the amount of energy between different demand levels. This is obtained by plotting energy curve which can be derived from chronological curve or load duration curve. The energy load curve plots the cumulative integration of area under load curve starting at zero load to particular load. It is also called *integrated duration curve*. If energy and demand are plotted in terms of percentage, it is called *peak percentage curve*. Figure 4.3 shows the energy load curve.

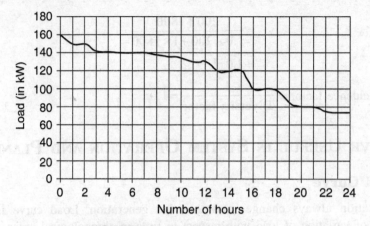

FIGURE 4.2 Load duration curve.

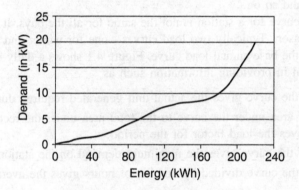

FIGURE 4.3 Energy load curve.

4.4 POWER FACTOR

Power factor is normally used in the case of alternating current where the phase of voltage wave is not necessarily same as current wave. However in the case of dc, it is always same and therefore power factor, which is cosine of phase difference of voltage and current, is unity. For efficient operation of system the power factor should be as high as possible. The main disadvantages of having poor power factors are

    (a) High cost of station and distribution equipment

    (b) Poor voltage regulation

    (c) High energy loss in conductor.

The main causes of low power factors are following:

    (a) Transformers draw magnetizing current that causes total current to lag with respect to induced electromotive force. At normal load its effect is less but at light load, it reduces power factor.

(b) Excessive use of induction motors.

(c) Arc lamps and arc furnaces operate at low power factor due to vary nature and characteristics of the arc.

(d) Overloading of distribution feeders.

There are several measures by which low power factor can be avoided which are given below:

1. It is preferable to use synchronous motors compared to induction motors.

2. Use of high-speed induction motors compared to low-speed induction motors.

3. Operate induction machine at rated output.

4. Switch induction motor delta winding to star winding at less than half load.

5. Used dc motors instead of ac motors, if possible.

Static capacitors, synchronous condensers or phase modifier and phase advancers[1] are normally used to improve the power factors. The effect of series capacitor on power factor improvement is very less however shunt capacitor is used for power factor improvement. It can be easily understood by phasor diagram. Power factor is a local phenomenon and power correction equipment is installed near to the load where it is responsible for low power factor.

4.5 ECONOMICS OF POWER FACTOR CORRECTION

Power factor of the system should be equal or close to the unity. Low power factor means larger rating of equipment such as generators, transformers, etc. Power factor can be improved in two ways:

(a) keeping the real power (kW) demand same and varying the apparent power (kVA)

(b) keeping the apparent power (kVA) same and varying real power (kW) demand.

For the same kW demand, if power factor is improved, the kVA demand will be reduced and consumer will pay less for his kVA demand, if electric utility is charging some money for kVA consumption. On the other hand consumer will have to pay some amount for power factor improvement equipment. If power factor is improved by keeping kVA same, the consumer has to consume more kW and has to pay the charges for equipment and the extra consumption of the energy.

Constant kW demand

Figure 4.4 shows the power factor improvement when real power demand (kW) is constant. For improving the power factor a reactive power generating device such as shunt capacitor, synchronous condenser, static condensers, etc., must be installed.

---

1. A machine which may be connected in the rotor circuit of induction machine to improve power factor.

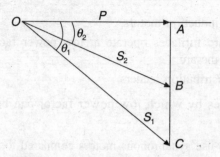

FIGURE 4.4 Constant kW demand.

Let a load is consuming the real power P at lagging power factor $\cos \theta_1$ represented by OA. The kVA demand S_1 will be

$$S_1 = \frac{P}{\cos \theta_1} \qquad (4.14)$$

After power factor improvement, let the power factor is $\cos \theta_2$, the kVA demand S_2 will be

$$S_2 = \frac{P}{\cos \theta_2} \qquad (4.15)$$

and

The reduction in the kVA demand $\Delta S = S_1 - S_2$

$$= OC - OB$$

$$= \frac{P}{\cos \theta_1} - \frac{P}{\cos \theta_2}$$

If a is the rate of charge per kVA, the saving in the kVA demand charge (C_1) would be $a\,\Delta S$. The required reactive power kVAR to reduce the demand will be BC ($=AC - AB$). If b is the annual working cost (i.e. interest and depreciation etc. on the capital investment) per kVAR, the total cost (C_2) on this account will be

$$b \times BC = b(P \tan \theta_1 - P \tan \theta_2) \qquad (4.16)$$

The net saving (R) will be $C_1 - C_2$. Maximum saving for a particular power factor improvement can be calculated as

$$\frac{dR}{d\theta_2} = 0 = -aP \sec \theta_2 \tan \theta_2 + bP \sec^2 \theta_2 \qquad (4.17)$$

After simplifying, we get

$$\sin \theta_2 = \frac{b}{a}$$

This indicates that for getting maximum saving, the sine of power factor improvement angle should be equal to the ratio of the annual cost of the reactive power device to the rate of the kVA charge.

Constant kVA demand

To improve the power factor with keeping kVA consumption same, the load must absorb some extra power and that can be generated through new plant. Figure 4.5 shows an arrangement, where

OA = the original kW output

OD = the kW output after the installation of new plant

OC = original kVA (S)

OB = final kVA.

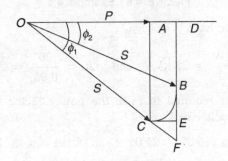

FIGURE 4.5 Constant kVA demand.

CF represents the additional kVA generated by this plant which can be written as

$$CF = \frac{AD}{\cos \phi_1} = \frac{S(\cos \phi_2 - \cos \phi_1)}{\cos \phi_1} \qquad (4.18)$$

kVA can be reduced by installing phase advancing plant rating equal to FB ($=FD - BD$). Mathematically, FB can be written as

$$FB = OD \tan \phi_1 - S \sin \phi_2$$
$$= S \cos \phi_2 \tan \phi_1 - S \sin \phi_2$$
$$= S (\cos \phi_2 \tan \phi_1 - \sin \phi_2)$$

The cost of both options must be compared and cheap option should be used which depends on the cost.

Example 4.4 A consumer is taking load of 20 kW at power factor of 0.8 lagging.

(a) Find the rating of capacitor to raise the power factor to 0.95 lagging.

(b) If a phase advancing device is used which takes current at leading power factor of 0.1, find the rating of the device.

Solution Original power factor angle $\phi_1 = \cos^{-1}(0.80) = 36.87°$. Power factor angle after improvement (ϕ_2) $= \cos^{-1}(0.95) = 18.19°$. From the phasor diagram as shown in Figure 4.6, kVA loading before and after power factor improvement are OC and OB.

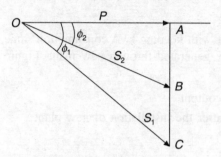

FIGURE 4.6 Example 4.4.

(a) From the figure, we have

$$OB = \frac{20 \text{ kW}}{0.80} = 25 \text{ kVA} \quad \text{and} \quad OC = \frac{20}{0.95} = 21.05 \text{ kVA}$$

The rating of the capacitor required to raise the power factor will be BC $(=CA - AB)$. Therefore, the rating of capacitor will be

$$25 \times \sin (36.87) - 21.05 \times \sin(18.19) = 8.43 \quad \text{kVAR}$$

(b) The phase advancing device works at leading power factor of 0.1

$$\phi_3 = \cos^{-1}(0.1) = 84.26°$$

From Figure 4.7, we have following relations, $\angle AOB = \phi_2$, $\angle AOC = \phi_1$, $\angle DOA = \phi_3$. Let $\angle BOC = \alpha$, $\angle OCB = \beta$, $\angle OBC = \delta$. These angles can be calculated as

$$\alpha = 36.87 - 18.19 = 18.68°, \ \beta = 58.87° \ \delta = 102.45°$$

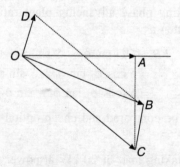

FIGURE 4.7 Example 4.4.

Using trigonometric relation, we get

$$\frac{OC}{\sin \delta} = \frac{BC}{\sin \alpha}$$

Therefore

$$BC = OC \times \frac{\sin \alpha}{\sin \delta} = 25 \times \frac{\sin 18.68}{\sin 102.45} = 8.20 \text{ kVA}$$

4.6 INTERCONNECTION OF POWER STATIONS

In early days generating power stations were close to load centres and there was less need to connect several generating stations together. The advantage of interconnection forces the regulators to connect the power system. The interconnection of stations has the main advantages as under:

1. With an interconnected system, the total reserve capacity can be reduced considerably.
2. The capital cost per kilo watt of larger-capacity generator is less than the small-capacity generator. In an interconnected system, it is possible to have larger generator rating and thus reduce capital cost of the system.
3. It is possible to run most effective units at higher load factor and inefficient station can be used at peak hours only.
4. Interconnection reduces the requirement of high installed capacity. The load curves of two different stations are seldom identical. The maximum demand is less than the sum of maximum demand of the individual stations.
5. It also increases the reliability of the system.

The main drawbacks of interconnections are:

(a) Fault in one system gets transferred to other part of the system.
(b) High switchgear rating is to be employed at different point of the system.
(c) Proper management is required to dispatch them.

Base load and peak load power stations

Since load is changing throughout the year and generators must cope up the varying demand. Some generators must be on/off depending upon the requirement. Peak load on station is relatively for small duration. If some generator is used to peak load, its energy will be expensive, as load factor will be low. In a coordinated operation hydro, steam, gas and nuclear power stations are used to meet the load demand. Some power plants are used as base load plants and some of them are used as peak load plants. Base load plants are the plants, which operate most of the time and have high plant load factor. However, peak load plants are operated during peak demand hours. The operation of the power plants depends on the following criteria:

- Cheaper electricity generating unit should be used as a base load power plant.
- Highest starting time generating plant is also used as base load plants.
- Size on plants is also a decisive factor.

Table 4.1 shows the generating plants, generally, used as base load and peak load plants.

Table 4.1   Base Load and Peak Load Power Stations

Type of generating plant	Normal nature of operation
Run-of-river	Base load plant
Nuclear	Base load plant
Pondage (high reservoir)	Base load plant
Steam	Both peak and base load plants
Pondage with small storage	Peak load plant
Pump storage	Peak load plant
Diesel	Peak load plant
Gas*	Peak load plant

*Nowadays gas stations are also used as both peak and base load plants depending upon the size.

4.7 TARIFFS

For the proper management of any electricity utility, it is important to have a source of income to meet its expenses. It is also important that electricity industry should have some income for future expansion work. There are two different types of charges: *Fix* charges and *running* charges. Fixed charges include (a) capacity related: interests and depreciation, cost of plant, buildings, transmission and distribution network, part of salaries of staff and (b) consumer related: cost of meter, billing, collection, service, etc. Running charges, also called *variable cost*, include fuel cost, operation and maintenance cost and some wages.

The total cost of supply is to be shared by consumers and should pay a sum according to use. The main objectives in framing a tariff are:

(a) The consumers must readily understand the tariffs.

(b) The tariff must be equitable as amongst different consumers.

(c) The tariff should also be such as to encourage consumers to improve the power factor.

(d) The tariff should also be such as to encourage consumers to improve load factor or to transfer their demand from peak to off-peak hours.

(e) Tariffs can be modified from time to time.

(f) Use of electricity is encouraged so that the economy of utilities is improved.

There are different types of consumers who consume electricity for different purposes. They can be classified into four subgroups:

1. *Domestic* consumers use electricity for domestic purposes.

2. *Agricultural* consumers use electricity of agricultural purposes such as irrigation, thrashing, etc.

3. *Industrial* consumers use electricity for industrial production such as heavy industries, manufacturing companies, etc.

4. *Commercial* consumers use electricity for commercial purposes such as municipalities, hospitals, etc.

The general form of tariff is

$$a \text{ kWh (or hp)} + b \text{ kW} + c$$

where a, b, c are the constants. Different types of tariffs are discussed below:

Flat rate tariff. In this rate, b and c are zero. The electricity charge is directly multiplication of energy consumption and the factor a. It is simple to understand and is independent on the contracted maximum demand.

Two-part tariff. The total charge under this kind of tariff is split into two components: a fixed charge based on the maximum demand (irrespective of energy consumption) and variable charge on the basis of actual energy consumption. The main objection of this tariff scheme is that consumer has to pay even if his consumption is nil.

Block rate tariff. Under this tariff scheme, different blocks of energy consumption are charged at different rates. The problem of two-part tariff is eliminated by this tariff. For example,

First 50 units	Rs 4.00/unit
Next 50 units	Rs 3.00/unit

And for additional unit @ Rs 2.00 per unit. This is for a particular month.

Maximum demand tariff. In this scheme of tariff, the charges are calculated based on the maximum demand only. The coefficient a and c are zero.

Power factor tariff. In ac system, the size of plant not only depends on the kW but also on power factor. Power factor tariffs are devised to differentiate between good power factor users and poor power factor users. The three main classes are:

1. *kVA maximum demand tariff:* Instead of charging the maximum real power (kW) demand, maximum kVA demand is charged in addition to the charge corresponding to the energy.

2. *kWh and kVArh tariff:* Under this scheme, both kWh (real power energy) and kVArh (reactive power consumption) are charged separately.

3. *Sliding scale or average power factor tariff:* There is some extra charge if the power factor is worsening from the set value. In this scheme, if consumers improve the power factor, an incentive will be given to those consumers. Let power factor is set to 0.8 lagging. If the power factor is 0.9, some discount will be offered and if power factor is 0.7, some extra charges are taken.

Example 4.5 Load factor of a consumer is 35% and the monthly consumption is 504 kWh. If the rate of electricity is Rs 180 per kW of maximum demand plus Rs 2.00 per kWh, find

(a) the monthly bill and the average cost per kWh

(b) the overall cost per kWh if the consumption is increased by 20% with the same load factor

(c) the overall cost per kWh if the consumption remains same but load factor is increased to 40%.

Solution

$$\text{Maximum demand} = \frac{\text{Average monthly consumption}}{\text{Load factor} \times 24 \times 30} = \frac{504}{0.35 \times 720} = 2.0 \text{ kW}$$

(a) Monthly bill (Rs) = $(2 \times 180) + (2 \times 504) = 1368$

$$\text{Overall cost per kWh} = \frac{1368}{504} = \text{Rs } 2.71$$

(b) New consumption = $504 \times 1.20 = 604.8$ kWh

Since the load factor is same, the maximum demand = $\dfrac{604.8}{0.35 \times 720} = 2.4$ kW

Monthly bill (Rs) = $(2.4 \times 180) + (2 \times 604.8) = 1641.6$

$$\text{Overall cost per kWh} = \frac{1641.6}{604.8} = \text{Rs } 2.71$$

(c) Since the load factor is 40%, the maximum demand = $\dfrac{504}{0.40 \times 720} = 1.75$ kW

Monthly bill (Rs) = $(1.75 \times 180) + (2 \times 504) = 1323$

$$\text{Overall cost per kWh} = \frac{1323}{504} = \text{Rs } 2.63$$

Example 4.6 The load variation at a power supply station is given as:

$$P = 30 - 8 * \sin(kt) + 0.325t \text{ MW}.$$

where t is time in hours of a day and $k = 0.6$ red/sec. There are three generators of 15 MW each. It is advantageous to fully load a machine before connecting the others. Determine:

(a) Maximum demand on the system.

(b) Load factor of the system.

(c) The total installed load, if density factor is 3.

(d) The minimum no. hours of each generator is in operation.

Solution   Maximum demand can be obtained by $\delta P / \delta t = 0$

Thus $-4.8 \times \cos(0.6t) + 0.325 = 0.$

$\cos(0.6t) = 0.325/4.8 = 0.0677083 = \cos(1.0503032 + 2n\pi)$ $n = 0, 1, 2...$

$0.6t = 2n\pi + 1.503032$ or $2n\pi - 1.503032, n = 0, 1, 2...$

t = 2.5051, 7.9669, 12.977, 18.4389, 23.449.

During t = 0 to 24 hrs, the load curve has 5 maxima and minimas.

The corresponding load at these times will be

P = 22.8325, 40.5709, 26.2359, 43.974, 29.639 MW.

Thus

(a) Maximum demand = 43.974 MW.

(b) Average load = $(1/24) \times \int_{0}^{24} (30 - 8 \times \sin(0.6t) + 0.325t) \, dt$

$$= (1/24) \times [30 \times 24 + (8/0.6) \times \cos(0.6t)|_{0}^{24} + 0.325 \times 24^2/2] = 33.20 \text{ MW.}$$

Load factor = 33.20/43.974 = 0.755

(c) Total installed load = peak demand × Diversity factor = 43.974 × 3 = 131.922 MW.

(d) Since min. load is 22.8325 MW, two units will run for whole day, 3rd unit will run when P > 30MW. Hence finding the t when P > 30

$30 - 8 \times \sin(kt) + 0.3250 = 30$

$\sin(kt) = 0.040625t$

Using hit and trial methods (or using graph),

t = 4.904, 11.265, 14.65, 22.94

Unit-3 will be in operation for = (11.265 − 4.904) + (22.94 − 14.65) hrs.

$$= 14.651 \text{ hrs.}$$

PROBLEMS

4.1 A generating station has a maximum demand of 80 MW, a load factor of 65%, a plant capacity factor of 40% and a plant use factor of 85%. Find (a) daily energy produced, (b) reserve capacity of plant, (c) maximum energy that could be produced daily if the plant was running all the time and (d) maximum energy that could be produced daily if the plant was running as per operating schedule.

4.2 The load on the mains of a supply system is 1000 kW at p.f. of 0.8 lagging. What must be the kVA rating of the phase advancing plant which takes leading current at a power factor 0.15 in order to raise the power factor of whole system to 1.0.

4.3 A residential consumer has a connected load of 6 lamps each of 100 W and 4 fans of 60 W at his premises. His demand is as follows:

From midnight to 5 a.m.	120 W	From 7 p.m. to 9 p.m.	680 W
From 5 a.m. to 6 p.m.	No load	From 9 p.m. to midnight	420 W
From 6 p.m. to 7 p.m.	380 W		

(a) Plot the load curve.

(b) Find the energy consumption during 24 hours.

(c) Calculate the demand factor, average load, maximum load and load factor.

4.4 A factory having a load of 5 MW at 0.8 lagging for 2000 hours per annum buys energy on tariff of Rs 500 per kVA plus Rs 2.5 per kWh consumed. If the power factor is improved to 0.95 lagging by means of capacitors costing Rs 1350 per kVA and having a power loss of 200 watts per kVA, calculate the annual charge for electrical energy (a) before (b) after the installation of capacitors and (c) the saving effected by their use. Allow 8% per annum for interest and depreciation on the capacitors.

4.5 The load (kW) on a substation is as follows:

Time	Street lighting	Domestic	Commercial	Time	Street lighting	Domestic	Commercial
12 a.m.	400	600	400	12 p.m.	0	500	1100
1 a.m.	400	500	400	1 p.m.	0	600	900
2 a.m.	400	450	400	2 p.m.	0	600	1100
3 a.m.	400	450	400	3 p.m.	0	600	1000
4 a.m.	400	500	400	4 p.m.	0	600	900
5 a.m.	400	700	500	5 p.m.	0	700	600
6 a.m.	400	1000	400	6 p.m.	400	800	500
7 a.m.	0	800	700	7 p.m.	400	1050	500
8 a.m.	0	700	900	8 p.m.	400	1200	500
9 a.m.	0	600	1200	9 p.m.	400	1100	500
10 a.m.	0	500	1300	10 p.m.	400	900	400
11 a.m.	0	500	1200	11 p.m.	400	700	400

(a) Find the maximum demand, average demand and load factor of the feeder.

(b) The class contribution factor for street lighting and the remaining load.

(c) The diversity factor of the feeder.

(d) The coincidence factor of the load group.

(e) If the feeder has the average loss of 14 kW and annual loss factor of 0.14, find the following:

   (i) The peak power loss of the feeder at peak load,

   (ii) The total annual loss of the feeder,

   (iii) The demand factor of the feeder if the connected demand is 2500 kW.

4.6 Installed capacity of a generating station is 200 MW and (daily) plant capacity factor is 40%. If the daily maximum demand is 160 MW and plant use factor is 75%, find

(a) Daily average load,

(b) Daily load factor,

(c) Daily energy produced,

(d) Reserve capacity,

(e) Maximum energy that could be generated daily if the plant was running all the time,

(f) The maximum energy that could be produced daily if the plant was running as per the operating schedule,

(g) Utilization factor.

4.7 The variation of load (P) with time (t) in a power supply system is given by the expression

$$P(\text{kW}) = 4000 + 8t - 0.00091t^2$$

where t is in hours over a total period of 1 year.

This load is supplied by three 10 MW generators and it is advantageous to fully load a machine before connecting the others. Determine:

(a) The load factor on the system as a whole.

(b) The total magnitude of installed load if the diversity factor is equal to 3.

(c) The minimum no. of hours each machine is in operation.

(d) The approximate peak magnitude of installed load capacity to be cut off to enable only two generators to be used.

Chapter 5

Steam Power Plants

5.1 INTRODUCTION

The use of steam power started when it was first used in locomotives invented by James Watt. Thereafter, steam power is used to rotate the prime mover of electric generator and it is known as steam power plant. In this process heat energy is converted into mechanical energy and then to electrical energy through turbine–generator system. Heat energy may be obtained by the proper combustion of a commercial fuel such as coal, gas, oil etc. Since abundant availability with reasonably no cost, water is used to generate steam, which readily conveyed through pipes, in a boiler by burning fuel in furnace. Steam power plants are also called *thermal power plants*. The prime movers of steam power plant may be operated either in noncondensing or condensing.

In the noncondensing operation, the steam is exhausted from the prime movers and is discharged at atmospheric pressure or at greater than atmospheric pressure. Whereas in condensing plant, the prime movers exhaust discharge steam into a condenser in which the pressure is less than atmospheric and steam is converted to water. This is most commonly used in modern age power plants.

5.2 SELECTION OF SITE FOR STEAM POWER PLANTS

Following are the factors to be considered for the site selection of thermal power plant and installation of its equipments:

(a) Availability of land on reasonably cheap for its equipment and for future expansion;

(b) Availability of sufficient and suitable amounts of good boiler feed water and cooling or circulating water for condensers;

(c) Availability of fuel and its cost delivered to the boiler furnaces;

(d) Probable necessity for future expansion of the plant;

(e) The availability of other power services;

(f) Away from the urban areas due to pollution etc.;

(g) The initial cost of plant;

(h) The magnitude and nature of load to be handled.

These plants can be either near to the coalmines or the load centres. The choice of this is made on the basis of transportation cost of the fuel and electrical energy. If the quality of coal is poor, the cost of transportation of coal near to the load centres will be high and therefore power plants are normally installed near to coal pits. In India, the modern thermal power stations are located near to coalmines due to the poor quality of coal. In those countries the coal is imported, the thermal power stations are installed near to the harbours. In India, steam power stations are categorized as thermal power plants and super thermal power plants. Those stations having generating units (not the total capacity) of 500 MW or more are called *super thermal power stations.*

5.3 THERMODYNAMIC CYCLE OF STEAM FLOW

First law of thermodynamics. This law relates the energy equation in its various forms and states that when a system executes a cyclic process, the algebraic sum of the work transfer is proportional to the algebraic sum of the heat transfer. *Or,* energy can neither created nor destroyed.

Second law of thermodynamics. This law is used in dealing with entropy and loss relations. It has been enunciated in a number of ways:

1. Heat cannot, on its own, flow from a body at lower temperature to a body at higher temperature. (*Clausius*)

2. It is impossible to construct a heat engine which performs one complete cycle and delivers work exchanging heat from a single source. (*Kelvin–Planck*)

When heat is transferred to water, its enthalpy and physical state change. As heating takes place the temperature of water rises and generally its density decreases. The vapour formed in this process is known as *steam*, which is a gaseous state but does not entirely follow the laws of a perfect gas. The temperature at which boiling or vaporization occurs is dependent upon the purity of water and the absolute pressure exerted upon it. The Carnot cycle cannot be applied to the steam turbines as compression phase does not exist in steam plants. A steam power plant basically works on the Rankine cycle with small deviations from ideal Rankine cycle.

5.3.1 Rankine Cycle

Figure 5.1 shows the pressure–volume diagram, and enthalpy–entropy diagram of an ideal Rankine cycle. Water can be assumed as incompressible during the pumping process. The process 1–2 shows the reversible adiabatic pumping of feed water from the condenser to the boiler pressure. The work done in this process is given by

$$w_{1\text{-}2} = -\int_{p_1}^{p_2} v\, dp = -\int_{h_1}^{h_2} dh = -(h_2 - h_1) \tag{5.1}$$

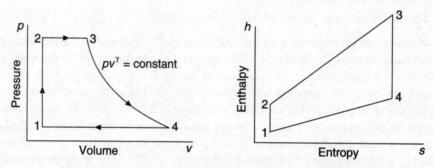

FIGURE 5.1   *p–v* and *h–s* diagrams of ideal Rankine cycle.

The negative sign indicates that the work done on feed pump is from outside. The process 2–3 shows the heating of feed water up to its saturation temperature, its evaporation and super heating at constant pressure. Let heat supplied during this process is Q_s. Thus,

$$Q_s = h_3 - h_2 \tag{5.2}$$

Process 3–4 is reversible adiabatic (isentropic) expansion of steam in turbine and work done by the steam in the turbine is given by

$$w_{3\text{-}4} = -\int_{p_3}^{p_4} v\, dp = -\int_{h_3}^{h_4} dh = \frac{\gamma}{\gamma - 1}(p_3 v_3 - p_4 v_4) = h_3 - h_4 \tag{5.3}$$

The condensation of steam at constant pressure is represented by the process 4–1 and heat rejected during this process is Q_r (say). Using first law of thermodynamics, we get

$$w_{1\text{-}2} + Q_s = w_{3\text{-}4} + Q_r$$

Therefore, the net work output of the plant will be

$$W = w_{3\text{-}4} - w_{1\text{-}2} = Q_s - Q_r \tag{5.4}$$

Thus efficiency of cycle is given by

$$\eta = \frac{W}{Q_s}$$

Using Equations (5.1)–(5.4), the efficiency of an ideal Rankine cycle will be given by

$$\eta = \frac{(h_3 - h_4) - (h_2 - h_1)}{h_3 - h_2} = \frac{(h_3 - h_4) - (h_2 - h_1)}{(h_3 - h_1) - (h_2 - h_1)} \tag{5.5}$$

Normally, the $(h_2 - h_1)$ which is feed pump work, is negligible compared to other quantities in Equation (5.5), therefore, it can be written as

$$\eta = \frac{h_3 - h_4}{h_3 - h_1} \tag{5.6}$$

The efficiency of ideal Rankine cycle is never achieved which is a reference value of an ideal steam power plant. Figure 5.2 shows the temperature–entropy (*T-s*) diagram of an ideal Rankine cycle.

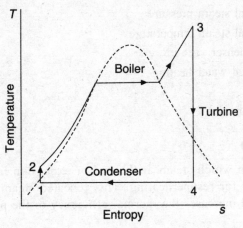

FIGURE 5.2   *T-s* diagrams of an ideal Rankine cycle.

5.3.2   Actual Rankine Cycle

Due to the pressure drops in the steam passages and irreversibilities in various components, the ideal Rankine cycle deviates from the actual Rankine cycle. Figure 5.3 shows the actual Rankine cycle where 1–2′ is due to irreversible process in feed pump and 3–4′ is due to the turbine irreversibility.

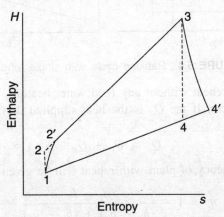

FIGURE 5.3   *H-s* diagrams of an actual Rankine cycle.

The actual efficiency of steam power plant, by replacing the enthalpies h_2 and h_4 by $h_{2'}$ and $h_{4'}$, will be

$$\eta_{ac} = \frac{(h_3 - h_{4'}) - (h_{2'} - h_1)}{h_3 - h_{2'}} = \frac{(h_3 - h_{4'}) - (h_{2'} - h_1)}{(h_3 - h_1) - (h_{2'} - h_1)} \tag{5.7}$$

The aim of power plant engineer or designer is to achieve the actual thermal efficiency as close as possible to ideal thermal efficiency. The thermal efficiency of a steam plant can be increased by following ways:

(a) Increase in initial steam pressure
(b) Increase in initial steam temperature
(c) Increase in condenser vacuum
(d) Regenerative feed water heating
(e) By reheating
(f) By use of economizer.

5.3.3   Reheat Cycle

Reheating is a process in which steam at the end of expansion in turbine stages is taken out to boiler or reheater for resuperheating. This reheated steam does more work in the next stage of turbine and increases the thermal efficiency of the plant. Figure 5.4 shows a

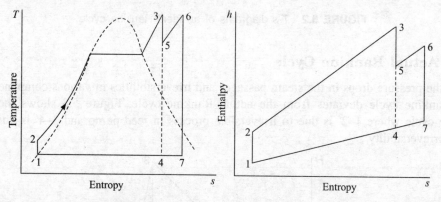

FIGURE 5.4   Rankine cycle with single reheat.

Rankine cycle with single reheat without any feed water heating. The constant pressure line 5–6 shows the reheat process. If the Q_R is the heat supplied during the reheating, the total heat supplies will be

$$Q'_s = Q_s + Q_R \tag{5.8}$$

Therefore, the thermal efficiency of plant with reheat will be given by

$$\eta_r = 1 - \frac{h_7 - h_1}{(h_3 - h_2) + (h_6 - h_5)} \tag{5.9}$$

The efficiency of the cycle depends on the reheat pressure. There is an optimum value of reheat pressure. At first reheat, it is 0.2 to 0.25 times the initial pressure of steam whereas for next reheat it is 0.2 to 0.25 times the first reheat pressure of steam and so on.

5.3.4 Regenerative Cycle

The heating of feed water by steam extracted at various points while sending it to the boiler is termed as *regenerative heating*. The extracted heat is used, otherwise it would be lost in the condenser, to raise feed water temperature above saturated liquid condition. By doing so the thermal efficiency can be increased by 10% and therefore it is universally used in all steam power plants. The large number of heaters makes the complication in design and leads to considerable loss of pressure. It is found that for maximum efficiency in a non-reheat cycle, the enthalpy rise is approximately the same in all the heaters and the economizer. However the cycle efficiency does not seem to be sensitive to the distribution of the total enthalpy rise in the heaters. The number of heaters employed in large steam plants is 6 to 10 with a final feed water temperature of about 285°C.

5.3.5 Heat Rate

Heat rate is a measure of the performance of the power plant in converting heat to useful output. It is defined as the number of heat units required to develop unit power output in an hour. The heat rate decreases with the increase in thermal efficiency.

5.4 GENERAL LAYOUT OF STEAM POWER STATION

Schematic layout of a typical modern coal fired power plant is shown in Figure 5.5. The main power plant can be subdivided into several small units, namely

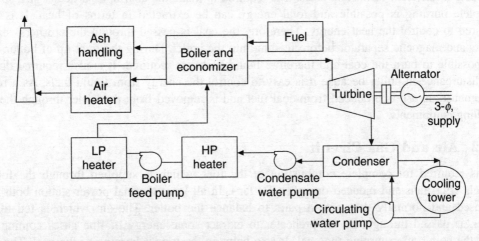

FIGURE 5.5 Layout of a typical steam power plant.

(a) Fuel handling unit

(b) Ash handling unit

(c) Boiler unit

(d) Feed water unit

(e) Cooling water unit

(f) Generator unit

(g) Turbine unit.

5.5   MAIN FLOW CIRCUITS

The flow circuit of a thermal power plant can be divided into four main circuits, such as

1. Fuel and ash circuit
2. Air and gas circuit
3. Feed water and steam circuit
4. Cooling water circuit.

They are discussed in the following sections.

5.5.1   Fuel and Ash Circuit

In a steam power plant, different types of fuels are required and are stored in the storage. Steam can be generated from coal, gas or nuclear as main fuel. Here, it is assumed that coal is main fuel for operating the steam power plant and other types of power plant, such as nuclear and gas, discussed in other chapters.

Fuel is stored in the storage and fed to the boiler through conveyor belt. Since coal is available in different forms and sizes, it is required to make the coal in a particular size so that complete burning is possible and total energy can be extracted in terms of heat. It is also required to control the heat energy. Therefore, the coal is passed through the crushers, sizers, dryers and magnetic separator before feeding into the boiler. During the light up of boiler, it is not possible to burn the coal and therefore liquid fuels are required. It is also required during the disturbance in boiler because it is easy to control the energy from liquid fuels. As a result of combustion, ash is produced from coal fuel and is removed from the boiler through the ash handling equipments.

5.5.2   Air and Gas Circuit

Air is required for complete combustion of the fuel, which is supplied through the forced draught (FD) fans and induced draught (ID) fans. In all large thermal power station both fans are used and normally they are in pairs to balance the boiler. The air, which is fed to the boiler, is passed through the air preheater to extract some energy of flue gases coming out from the boiler after burning the coal. It also helps in the proper burning of the coal. The flue gases consist of several gases and ash, which are passed through the precipitator (or dust collector) and then finally go to atmosphere through chimney.

5.5.3 Feed Water and Steam Circuit

Since most of the steam power plants are condensing type, the steam is converted to water by condenser. Due to the safety of turbine, the water used is demineralized (DM) and therefore it is not wasted to have better economic operation of plant. Some part of steam and water is lost while passing through the different components of the system due to leakages. Adding the make-up water in feed water system compensates it. The boiler feed pump (BFP) feeds the water into the boiler drum where it is heated to form the steam. The wet steam from the drum is again heated in superheater before it passed to the turbine. The superheated steam is expanded in the turbine to run it. Depending upon the size of power plant unit, there are different stages of the prime mover such as high-pressure (HP) turbine, intermediate-pressure (IP) turbine and low-pressure (LP) turbine. The steam after the expansion in HP turbine is sent back to boiler for reheating to increase the temperature and pressure. After coming out from LP turbine, steam is passed through the condenser into the hot well and finally to boiler through the BFP. Figure 5.6 shows the steam and water flow of the steam power plant.

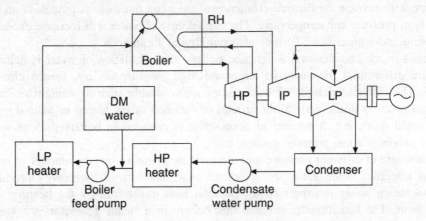

FIGURE 5.6 Feed water and steam flow circuit.

5.5.4 Cooling Water Circuit

To condensate the steam in condenser and maintaining low pressure in it, a large quantity of cooling water is required which is taken from the river or pondage. After passing it through the condenser, it is fed back to the river or pondage. When there is not enough water, the cooling tower or cooling ponds are used. Sometimes due to fear of water pollution, this scheme is normally preferred. However there is an excessive loss of water during this process and is taken from the pondage or river.

5.6 Main Parts of Steam Power Plant

Different elements of steam power plants are discussed in the following subsections:

5.6.1 Boiler

Boiler, which is the second tallest part after the chimney in a power plant, is used for producing the steam and reheating it. Steam boilers are of two types: water-tube boilers and fire-tube boilers. Generally, water-tube boilers are used for electric power production. As the name, in water-tube boilers, the water flows in tubes and fire is outside whereas in fire-tube boilers, it is opposite. Fire-tube boilers are cheap but are more likely to explode. Furthermore, the volume of water is more and therefore it is difficult to control the steam production quickly.

The outer shell of a fire-tube boiler is more than that of water-tube boiler for the same output. The water-tube boiler has advantages in respect of low stresses from pressure and temperature differential and therefore small drum size can be achieved. The area of heating in straight water-tube boiler is varied by (a) varying the length of tubes, (b) having high tube numbers and (c) varying the sections of tubes wide. Water-tube boilers have less weight of metal for a given size and are less liable to explode, produce high pressure and quickly controlled steam in demand. It has been mentioned in Section 5.3.2 that high pressure and temperature will increase the thermal efficiency of the plant but there is limitation on the boiler to go for high pressure and temperature. The capital cost of boiler will increase excessively for high pressure and temperature. Turbine also put similar limitations.

In most of the conventional water-tube boilers, the circulation of water is natural due to temperature differential. However in large and high pressure boilers, forced circulation is employed. The different designs of water tubes are available such as straight or bent tubes, longitudinal or cross drum, vertical, horizontal or inclined tubes, forced or natural circulation, single or multi drum, etc. A number of accessories is required in boilers such as water level indicators, valves, alarms, pressure gauges, etc.

Since steam at different pressure and temperature contains varying amount of energy, the number of kilogram steam generated is not an exact measure of the energy produced. The capacity of steam boiler is expressed as the total heat transferred by the heating surface in BTU per hour. The heat transfer process that occurs in a steam generator is a steady flow process for which the transferred heat is equal to the change in enthalpy of the fluid. The boiler output, as measured by the heat absorbed by water and steam, is given by

$$Q = m_s (h_s - h_f) \text{ BTU per hour} \tag{5.10}$$

where

m_s = Weight of steam delivered by boiler (or superheater, if used), kg/hr

h_s = Enthalpy of steam at observed pressure and quality or temperature, BTU/kg

h_f = Enthalpy of the fluid of feed water at observed condition as water reaches the boiler (or economizer, if used), BTU/kg.

The overall boiler efficiency of a steam generating unit at any operating condition is the ratio of the transferred heat to the energy supplied at by fuel, i.e. output divided by input, or

$$\eta_b = \frac{m_s(h_s - h_f)}{m_f F} \tag{5.11}$$

where m_f is the total weight of fuel fired per hour (in kg) and F is the high heat value of fuel as fired (in BTU/kg).

5.6.2 Coal Mills

The use of pulverized fuel in power plant is common nowadays. The pulverized coal mills are used for drying of coal, grinding, separation of particles of desired size, forming proper fuel–air ratio and suitable control of all these operations. The two systems of preparing and burning pulverized fuels are (a) the central or storage system where one independent plant prepares and transport to all unit and (b) the unit or direct fire system in which one or more units connected to it. Preheated forced air passed through pulverizer eliminates the necessity of separate driers. The fuel is first crushed to a general size (approximately 1 cm) and then passed over the magnetic separator to remove the tramp iron such as nuts, volts and rivets. This crushed coal goes to the pulverizers and then directly to furnace.

Pulverizers may be divided into four types based on the method of fuel size reduction, namely, ball race, bowl mill, impact mill and ball mill. The advantages of pulverized fuel include complete combustion, simpler ash disposal, absence of smoke, use of cheap fuel, equipment adoptable to other fuels (oil and gas), easy control of fuel and air supply, absence of all moving parts in the furnace, no stand-by losses, lower labour cost, increase of capacity per unit furnace volume and higher efficiency. Some of the disadvantages are high capital cost, high cost of fuel preparation, furnace depreciation and possibility of fly ash discharge through the chimney.

Grate and stokers. A *grate* is a sectional metallic structure designed to support the fuel in a furnace and to permit passage of primary combustion air through openings to the fuel. A *stoker* is a power-operated fuel feeding mechanism. It is used for supplying solid fuel to a furnace and admitting air to the fuel for proper combustion. By use of stokers, a cheaper grade of fuel can be burned with higher efficiency, greater operational flexibility, better maintenance of furnace and production of less smoke compared to the usual hand firing. Automatic stokers are classified as travelling grate, overfeed, spreader and underfeed stokers.

5.6.3 Boiler Feed Pump

A high-capacity induction motor is used to feed the water to the boiler. Due to high power rating of this motor a special consideration is taken for cooling of the bearings. In thermal power station approximately 10% of generated power is consumed by its auxiliaries and boiler feed pump is the highest power consuming auxiliaries in the steam power plants.

Feed water. Natural water cannot be used as such for steam generation as it contains solid, liquid and gaseous impurities, which damage the blades of the turbine. Although the steam is converted to water in condenser and fed to the boiler by BFP but still some make-up water is required due to the loss in steam and water.

5.6.4 Air Preheater

Air preheaters are used to extract heat from flue gases to combustion air. The advantages of air preheaters are improved combustion, successful burning of low-grade fuel, increased efficiency and increased capacity of plant. Air preheaters apply either convection or the regeneration principle of heat transmission.

5.6.5   Draught System

The main purpose of draught system is to supply air to the furnace and to take the flue gases from the boiler through chimney. The pressure difference known as *draft* is usually measured in centimetres (cm) of water gauge. The resistances to flow air and flue gases which make draught system necessary, are ducts, stacks, chimney, fuel beds, dampers, air preheaters, economizers, accumulation of sooth and ashes in gas passages, etc. If the pressure difference is by chimney or stack, it is known as *natural* draft. In *forced* draught scheme, fans are used to create pressure difference. In most of modern, big steam power plants two types of fans are used, namely forced draught (FD) and induced draught (ID) fans.

5.6.6   Economizers

The *economizers* are used to extract heat from the flue gases for the heating of feed water. It recovers some part of energy of flue gases, which are disposed in the air. Their placements may be in the last flue gas pass within the boiler setting or in casing between the boiler setting and the chimney or stack. Economizers increase the resistance to the flow of flue gases and also reduce their temperature and therefore induced draft is required.

5.6.7   Superheaters and Reheaters

The steam that exists at the vaporization temperature corresponding to its absolute pressure is defined as *saturated steam*, which may or may not carries water with it. The temperature and the total enthalpy of saturated steam, at any pressure, can be increased by the application of additional heat, i.e. superheating.

Advantages of superheating of steam are: (a) the additional heat imparted to vapour causes it to behave more likely to perfect gas, (b) steam condensation can be avoided, (c) increase in efficiency and (d) elimination of moisture.

Superheaters are simple heat exchangers for imparting additional energy to steam for a given pressure. A reheater is essentially a superheater as it is designed to bring the partially expanded steam back to superheat temperature by passing it through the tubes.

5.6.8   Turbines

Turbine, used to rotate the synchronous alternator, is a device, which converts steam energy to rotational kinetic energy. The turbines can be classified on the basis of steam flow direction, expansion process, number of stages, speed, etc., as given in Table 5.1.

The potential energy in steam due to pressure and internal energy is converted to kinetic energy when passing through the nozzles. In steam turbine the steam expands in the stationary nozzles and attains a higher velocity. There are several stationary blades and moving blades. In reaction turbines, there are no nozzles but they have also fixed and moving blades. The steam pressure is gradually reduced in the blades as the steam passes through them. The rating of generating unit depends on the rating of turbines. Commercial turbines use series combination of impulse and reaction type because steam can be used more efficiently by using impulse and reaction blades on the same shaft.

To increase the shaft output, several stages are used such as HP, IP and LP turbines. For low rating of alternator, only one stage is used. In large steam power units, all HP, IP and LP turbines are used.

Table 5.1 Classification of Turbines

Basis of classification	Types of turbine
Expansion process	(a) Impulse turbine
	(b) Reaction turbine
	(c) Combination of impulse and reaction turbine
Steam flow direction	(a) Axial turbine
	(b) Radial turbine
	(c) Tangential turbine
Number of stages	(a) Single-stage turbine
	(b) Multi-stage turbine
	• Velocity compounded impulse (Curtis stage)
	• Pressure compounded impulse (Rateau stage)
	• Pressure–velocity compounded impulse (Curtis–Rateau stage)
	• Pressure compounded reaction (Parson's)
Number of flows	(a) Single flow
	(b) Double flow
	(c) Divided flow
	(d) Tandem or cross-compounded
Relative motion of rotor	(a) Single rotation
	(b) Double rotation
Rotational speed	(a) $N = 3000$ rpm, $f = 50$ Hz
	(b) $N = 3600$ rpm, $f = 60$ Hz
	(c) $N = 1500$ rpm, $f = 50$ Hz
	(d) Geared units
Applications	(a) Electric power generation
	(b) Industrial
	(c) Marine
Steam conditions	(a) High-pressure non-condensing
	(b) High-pressure condensing
	(c) Back pressure
	(d) Regenerative
	(e) Reheating
	(f) Extraction
	(g) Mixed pressure
	(h) Exhaust turbine

5.6.9 Condenser

Steam condenser is a device in which the exhaust steam from engines and turbines is condensed and air and other noncondensable gases are removed in a continuous process. The two basic advantages of condenser are (a) to increase the efficiency of plant and (b) recovery of condensate for re-use as boiler water. The condensation in a closed vessel produces a partial vacuum by reduction in the volume of the low-pressure vapour. There are two types of condensers, namely, surface and jet.

Cooling of the surface of condenser by passing air over its surface is not adequate and water is used as a cooling medium. Huge amount of water is needed for this purpose which is taken from the river etc. The warm water is disposed off to the river. When an ample supply of water is not available at a low cost or from natural source, some means of cooling circulating water must be used. The oldest means of cooling and storing condenser water is to discharge the hot water into a spray pond with nozzles, which increase the cooling of the water at a faster rate.

5.6.10   Cooling Tower

The circulating water or the cooling water system forms the major section of the condensing system and represents the second largest single power consumer of the power generated by a set. In closed cooling system, involving the cooling towers, the cooling water follows a closed cycle through the cooling tower. There are some losses of water due to droplets evaporation. Cooling towers are either natural or mechanical draught type.

5.6.11   Alternators

In steam power plants, several generating units are used to increase the total capacity of the plant. For generating the electricity, high-speed synchronous generators are used because the efficiency of steam turbines is high at high speed. Whereas the efficiency of hydro turbines is larger at low speed and therefore low speed alternators are used. Since the frequency of the grid is one, the speed of the generator is decided by its number of poles. If P is the number of poles and f is the frequency of the system, the speed (N) in round per minute (rpm) is given by

$$N = \frac{120f}{P} \text{ rpm} \tag{5.12}$$

Since the poles must be in even numbers ($P = 2$), the highest possible speed for 50-Hz supply system will be 3000 rpm. However for 60-Hz supply system it is 3600 rpm. With two numbers of poles, the cylindrical construction is advantageous in terms of cost and performance. Field winding is placed at the rotor of the alternator and armature winding is in stator. Since the speed of turbo-alternator is high, the diameters of the machine is kept minimum so that the centrifugal force acting on the rotor is minimized. To keep the same electrical loading (proportional to area × length) the length of the turbo-alternator is increased.

Normally, concentric type (or involute) and diamond type windings are used for alternators. In concentric type windings, the straight bars are placed in series enclosed slots and separate-end connectors are concentrically disposed. Yoke is extended at either end to protect the end-windings. Both ends of each phase are brought out for differential protection. Involute and diamond windings consist of half coils made up of straight bars in one piece with two half-end connectors and are placed in open slots. Core conductors are placed in semi-enclosed slots, so that internal reactance of the machine is high. There may be three or more coils per slot with graded insulation. Concentric windings are preferred in high- voltage machines due to several advantages.

To minimize the current flow in the armature, which reduces the copper loss, the voltage rating of the alternators is increased but it is also limited due to the cost and insulation loss of the material. In India, the maximum rating of the alternators are 21 kV, 500 MW. The ratings of other Indian thermal generator units are: 11 kV, 50 MW; 11 kV, 100/110 MW; 15.56 kV, 200/210 MW.

5.7 COOLING OF ALTERNATORS

Cooling of alternators is very important due to damage of insulation at high temperature. The heat generated due to the losses in rotor and stator of the generators is to be taken away. Based on the circulation of cooling medium, it can be classified as open circuit where air is drawn by fans etc. and discharged to the atmosphere, and closed circuit where fixed volume of air or hydrogen is re-circulated. Closed circuit cooling is widely used in modern alternators having hydrogen as cooling medium, which is passed between rotor and stator. There are numerous radial and axial ducts in the stator and rotor cores. Main advantages of hydrogen cooling are as follows:

1. The heat transfer is more than that of air and its thermal conductivity is 7 times more than air.
2. Ventilation losses (fan power absorbed) are lower by 10% since the density of hydrogen is lower (1/10th).
3. There is no oxidation of insulating material and therefore the life of insulation is more in hydrogen cooling.
4. Since hydrogen is not supporting medium of consumption, the chances of fire hazards are minimized.
5. Less noise due to the lower density of hydrogen.
6. Due to hydrogen cooling, the size of frame can be reduced.

Hydrogen cooling has some disadvantages, too, such as:

1. There are chances of formation of explosive mixture of hydrogen and air.
2. Problem of ensuring the complete tightness of hydrogen.
3. Expensive than air.
4. Special oil seals are required where the generator shaft is coming out.

Water is a superior cooling medium since it is cheap and it can absorb a large quantity of heat for a given weight. Furthermore, power required for circulating the water is less compared to hydrogen. The use of condensate water for conductor cooling is not only readily available of high purity water but also enable to utilization of the heat produced by stator losses. The water-cooling of the rotor is more complex than in case of stator cooling due to rotation of core and conductor.

5.8 PROTECTION OF TURBO-ALTERNATORS

Being one of the expensive devices in the power plant, alternator must be protected from faults, which may be either in stator or rotor and other abnormal conditions. Different faults and their protections on stator side are given in Table 5.2.

Table 5.2   Types of Faults and Their Protection

Type of fault	Relay used
External phase fault	Over current relay with inverse time delay
Faults between phases	Differential protection
Phase to earth fault	Earth fault relay
Faults between turns	Differential protection
Open circuit fault	No special protection (almost impossible fault)
Overheating	Some thermal relays for alarm etc.

If generator field is not earthed, single earth fault will not cause any problem but due to another earth fault there will be unbalance voltage induced by rotor, which is severe. Therefore, an earth fault relay is used. Fault between turns of rotor coils may also occurs and there will be vibration due to magnetic unbalance. Due to open circuit, there is a failure of excitation and synchronous machine will run as induction generator, which is normally not allowed due to several reasons.

Abnormal condition will arise in the generator due to high voltage, over-speed or unbalance loading which generate the negative sequence current. Whenever there is over-voltage in generator and persists, it is not safe to operate the generator. The generator main circuit breaker and generator field breaker must be tripped. Over-speeding is also not desirable due to mechanical consideration. There is an over-frequency relay which trip the generator whenever the frequency exceeds the set value for a particular time period. Negative sequence current relay is used to protect from unbalance loading.

5.9   EXCITATION SYSTEM

Alternators control both power and voltage with two different control loops. The control of turbine input (steam, water, gas) are called *MW-frequency* (P-f) control loop. It is also known as *load frequency control* (LFC) or *automatic load frequency control* (ALFC) or *automatic generation control* (AGC). Second control loop is MVAR-voltage (Q-V) control loop or excitation control loop. Figure 5.7 shows both the control loops.

The basic function of excitation system is to provide direct current to the field winding of synchronous machine along with the control and protective functions for satisfactory operation of the system. Excitation system controls the terminal voltage of generator and reactive power generation. It also responds to the system disturbances. For satisfactory operation of the system it must fulfill following requirements such as meeting specified response criteria, provide limiting and protective function, flexible operation and to meet desired reliability and availability. The functional block diagram of typical excitation control system is shown in Figure 5.8.

The excitation system can be categorized based on the excitation power source as dc excitation, ac excitation and *satic* excitation systems. DC excitation system was used in early days but now ac excitation systems are widely used. AC excitation system utilizes as main sources of the main generator excitation power with the help of rectifiers. There are two arrangements possible such as stationary rectifier system and rotating rectifier system. With stationary rectifier system, dc output is fed to the field winding through slip rings.

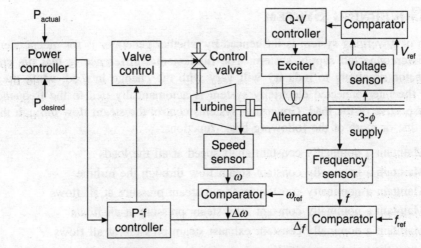

FIGURE 5.7 Generator control loops.

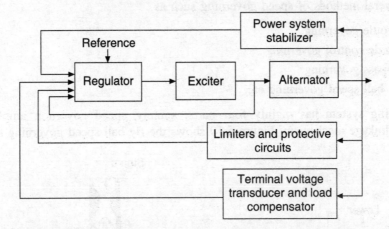

FIGURE 5.8 Functional diagram of excitation control system.

With rotating rectifiers, there is no need of slip rings and it is also called *brushless* excitation system. In static excitation, all components are static or stationary. Figure 5.9 shows the brushless excitation system.

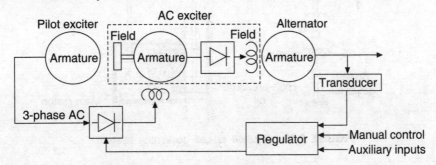

FIGURE 5.9 Brushless excitation system.

5.10 GOVERNING SYSTEM

The choice of governing system is influenced by whether generator is for independent factory or to the interconnected supply system. The fundamental difference is that the speed of a turbo-alternator supplying to industry will vary with the change in load, while the machine running in the interconnected electricity system is automatically tied to the frequency of the system irrespective of the load. Governing systems control the steam flow through the turbine to achieve one or more of the following basic functions:

(a) Maintain a nominally constant shaft speed at all the loads

(b) Maintain a nominally constant steam flow through the turbine

(c) Maintain a nominally constant pass-out steam pressure at all flows

(d) Maintain a nominally constant inlet steam pressure at all flows

(e) Maintain a nominally constant exhaust steam pressure at all flows

(f) Limit the power generated.

There are several methods of speed governing such as

1. Throttle governing

2. Nozzle control governing

3. By-pass governing

4. Fly ball speed governing etc.

Governing system has mainly four parts, namely, speed governor, amplifier, speed changer and linkage mechanism. Figure 5.10 shows the fly ball speed governing system.

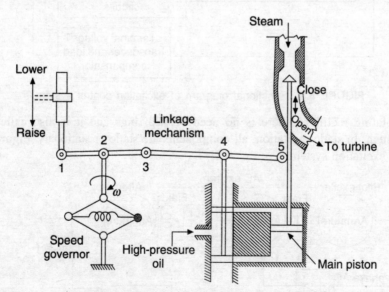

FIGURE 5.10 Fly ball speed governing system.

5.11 FUELS

Fuels, either in their natural or prepared forms, exist as solids, liquids and gases. Solid fuels include coals, lignites, cokes, woods and combustible wastes from many processing operations. Liquid fuels include alcohol, petroleum oils, etc., whereas gases are either natural or manufactured gases. The principal elements of any fuel are carbon (C) and hydrogen (H). Some fuels also have sulphur (S).

Coal, which is a mixture of carbon, hydrogen, oxygen, nitrogen, sulphur, moisture and ash, is mostly used in thermal power plants. Owing to the effect of time, pressure and temperature, the vegetation has been transformed into coal that is taken from the mines and ranges from fine dust to large lumps. Coal can be classified into several categories.

1. *Anthracite:* It is a very hard coal having a shiny black luster. It is non-coking and has a high percentage of carbon and less than 8% volatile matter. Anthracite coal burns either without flame or with very high bluish flames and desirable when smokeless combustion is essential.

2. *Semi-anthracite:* It occurs in small quantities and is not used for steam generation. The percentage of carbon is less and it burns with longer and more luminous flames. It contains 8–14% volatile matter and less luster.

3. *Semi-bituminous:* It is the highest grade of bituminous coal and burns with a very small amount of smoke. It is softer than anthracite and contains 14–22% volatile matters. Semi-bituminous coal has a tendency to break into small sizes during the storage and transportation.

4. *Bituminous:* This type of coal, which varies greatly in percentage of volatile matter, moisture, ash and sulphur, has high percentage of volatile matter and burns with long yellow and smoky flames. A high ash coal is usually designated as one having more than 10% ash. Bituminous coal is classified as free burning and caking or coking. Free burning coals do not swell and fuse together when ignite, as do the coking or caking coals.

5. *Sub-bituminous:* It is also known as black lignite and is low-grade bituminous coals. Sub-bituminous coals disintegrate when exposed to the air and require careful attention during the storage. Its volatile matter ranges from 35 to 45% and moisture contents from 17 to 20%.

6. *Lignite:* This is a transition state between peat and sub-bituminous grade of coal and has a woody or often a claylike appearance. It has low heat value, high moisture and high-ash contents.

A good-quality coal contains high percentage of fixed carbon, low moisture and less volatile matter. Fixed carbon refers to the combustible carbon left after the volatile matter has been driven off during heating. Two analyzes, namely, *proximate* analysis and *ultimate* analysis are performed to test the quality of coal. The proximate analysis gives essential information on moisture content, ash content, volatile content and fixed carbon, and helps to determine the general characteristic of fuel. On the other hand, ultimate analysis is the full chemical analysis of fuel and gives percentage of all its chemical constituents. The analysis can be carried on the basis of (a) fuel as received, (b) fuel as burned, (c) fuel air dries, (d) fuel dries and (e) fuel dried and ash free.

Indian coals, in general, have high ash contents up to 20%. Clean coal, which is also known as washing of coal, is used in several countries, which is sometimes difficult and costly.

Due to high ash contents, the efficiency of boiler is greatly reduced, thus the reduced efficiency of plant, due to unburnt coal, excessive clinker formation, etc. In most of the Indian thermal power plants, pulverized coal is used.

Liquid fuels such as oils are also used in boiler furnace to generate steam when it is cheaply available. It is easy in burning and controlling in heat. Even in coal thermal power station oils are used during the lighting up the boiler and in the case of emergencies.

Gaseous fuels are of two types: *natural* gas or *manufactured* gas. Methane and ethane are the main constituents of natural gas. They are preferred over coal power plants if cheaply available due to following advantages:

(a) They contain no ash or residue.

(b) They are easily mixed with oxygen and therefore no excess air is needed.

(c) They are adaptable to automatic controls.

(d) They are quickly responsive to load demands.

5.12 FLUIDIZED-BED COMBUSTION

Direct combustion of coal is best accomplished by fluidized bed combustion (FBC). If compressed gas is passed upward through a bed of inert particles at a sufficient velocity to overcome gravity, each particle will float on the gas stream in a boiling turbulent mass. This is known as *fluidized bed*. Coal particles are added to the inert mass and may constitute only 10% of the mass and thus cannot adhere to each other or agglomerate. Instead of inert particles such as ash and sand, lime stone or dolomite is widely used in proper proportional to combine with sulphur in coal and produce solid sulphate particles. The production of nitrogen oxides (NO_X) is also reduced greatly at lower combustion temperatures. Thus it has advantages: direct removal of sulphur during combustion; low NO_X emission, ability to burn a variety of fuels, and smaller size.

5.13 EFFICIENCY OF THERMAL POWER PLANTS

In thermal power plants there are three main important components: generator, turbine and boiler and based on their efficiencies the power plant efficiency can be obtained. The overall efficiency of thermal power plant can be defined as

$$\text{Overall efficiency of plant} = \begin{pmatrix} \text{Generator} \\ \text{efficiency} \end{pmatrix} \times \begin{pmatrix} \text{Efficiency of turbine} \\ \text{including the condenser} \end{pmatrix} \times \begin{pmatrix} \text{Boiler} \\ \text{efficiency} \end{pmatrix}$$

Generator is an electrical device and has high efficiency as compared to the mechanical devices such as turbine and boiler. The efficiency of synchronous generator varies between 96 and 99% that depends on size of machine and cooling system. The thermal efficiency of steam turbine varies between 24 and 32%, which depends on the number of factors such as temperature and pressure of steam, number of bleedings, exhaust steam pressure and temperature, etc. The efficiency of boiler with economizer and air preheaters may be taken as between 87 and 90%. Thus overall efficiency of the steam power plant will be between 18 and 24%.

5.14 Lubricating Systems

The purpose of lubrication is to prevent wear by friction and minimize frictional losses. Certain vegetable oils and mineral oils can be used for this purpose but due to inferior in stability, mineral oils are widely used for lubrication, which are also available in different forms. Different types of lubricants are oils, greases and solid lubricants such as graphite. Normally two types of lubricating mechanism are used as boundary film lubrications and hydrodynamic films lubrications.

5.15 Start-up Procedure of Thermal Units

The start-up procedure for thermal units depends on whether it is starting from cold state or hot state. The boiler is to be lighted up first but before that several checks and preparations are required. The main steps for cold start-up are as follows:

1. Clearances from all the maintenance units should be taken and the position of all the drains, valves must be in their required positions.
2. Feed tank must be filled using condensate transfer pump which pumps water from condensate storage tank to feed tank/condensate extraction pumps which pump condensate water from hot-well to feed tank.
3. Filling of boiler drum is done with the help of boiler feed pump (BFP) after checking the required conditions. BFP is an induction motor and consumes the highest power amongst the auxiliaries of power station.
4. One set of induced draught (ID) and forced draught (FD) fans are started and furnace drought is kept at –5 mm of water column. These fans are started only after checking required vane and damper positions, lubricating oil pressures, etc.
5. After checking the boiler protection and other arrangements, the boiler is lighted up with the help of 1 to 4 oil burners/guns, which may use fuel oil (FO), high-speed diesel (HSD), low diesel oil (LDO), etc., depending upon drum metal temperature.
6. As the drum pressure increases to 1.5–2.0 kg/cm^2, vent are closed. Further pressure-rising is done by increasing oil flows in burners or increasing the burners. At 18 kg/cm^2, super-heater drains are closed.
7. As pressure goes up to 30 kg/cm^2 pressure reducing de-super (PRDS) heating/charging is started.
8. Boiler pressure and temperature is raised up to the required value as per casing temperature of turbine. Colder the casing, lesser will be the pressure and temperature of steam to keep differential expansion in check.
9. Cooling-water (CW) pump is started before raising the vacuum in the condenser.
10. After PRDS has been charged, vacuum is started rising by taking an ejector in service. Main ejector is also taken into service to raise the vacuum up to the required level.
11. Before the rolling of turbine all protection should be checked and the desired main steam pressure and temperature are maintained at the inlet of turbine.

12. During the start-up, change in metal casing of turbine is carefully followed. Turbine lubricating oil pressure and temperature are properly monitored.

13. The turbine is rotated at 500 rpm and then 1000 rpm and all the parameters of the plant are properly monitored.

14. If all the parameters of the plant are in the prescribed range, turbine generator set can be rotated at 3000 rpm. The raising of speed from 1000 to 3000 rpm should be done continuously so that it should cross critical speed smoothly.

15. The parameters such as vibration of bearings, temperature of bearing oils, temperature difference of turbine casing, drum level, etc., are carefully monitored.

16. If all the parameters are normal, the generator can be synchronized as per guideline. Synchronization can be done manually or automatically.

17. As soon as unit is synchronized, coal mills are taken into the service. Primary air fans are started and coal feeding to boiler is also started. Oil is gradually reduced and then totally taken off after stabilization. Electrostatic precipitators are charged. Turbine drains are closed after main steam temperature reaches above 520°C.

18. The load is gradually increased keeping watch on differential expansion of turbine and turbo-supervisory parameters.

Chapter 6

Hydroelectric Power Plants

6.1 Introduction

Water is a boon for the living creatures. For the electricity generation, ample quantity of water is used where water-flow from higher level to a lower level is passed through a turbine. The energy of water utilized for electric power generation may be either kinetic or potential. When water is in motion, it has kinetic energy and is passed through the turbine for production of electricity. Potential energy available in form of the level difference of water (called *head*) is converted into kinetic energy that is used for rotating the generator to produce electricity. Water from the rain is collected in lakes and reservoirs at high altitude. Dams are constructed across the flowing streams, which require huge catchments area to store the water. After the generation, the water is let out into the river and gradually travels further and ultimately reaches the sea.

The hydraulic motors until the 19th century consisted of various types of waterwheels driven by the weight of the water or the kinetic energy of the current. The use of waterwheels as motors has several shortcomings, viz., they were cumbersome, had a low rotational speed and were very inefficient. Hydraulic turbines were developed in the beginning of the 19th century. Hydroelectric power was initiated in India in 1897 with a run-of-river scheme near Darjeeling. The first major hydroelectric development was Sivasamudram Scheme in Mysore with capacity of 4.5 MW, which was commissioned in 1902. In 1914, Khopoli project in Maharashtra was put into operation with a capacity of 50 MW for feeding power to Bombay, now called Mumbai, city. However there was not much growth till 1947 and hydroelectric power contribution in total installed capacity was only about 500 MW.

There are several advantages of hydropower.

(a) Water (also known as *white coal*) is non-wasting, self-replenishing. Supply of water is automatic and water utilized in one season is replenished by nature in the next season.

(b) Water reaches the powerhouse site on its own where no mining operation and transportation are involved as in the case of coal, oil and gas.

(c) After use of water in electricity production, it can be redirected for the further use of drinking and irrigation.

(d) Hydropower plant has very high efficiency (about 80%), that is much higher than thermal plants.

(e) Hydropower plants have very long life (even 50 years) compared to the thermal power plants.

(f) Maintenance is easy and less expensive compared to the thermal power plants.

(g) Hydropower plants are quick in start and shutdown.

(h) The cost of production of electricity is very small (only operation and maintenance cost).

(i) The percentage outage of hydropower plant is very low and thus more reliable.

(j) Hydropower also provides ancillary benefits such as recreation, fisheries, etc., in the case of run-of-river plants. It also controls the flood where a storage reservoir is contemplated.

(k) The modern developments in hydro turbines have made it possible to utilize a variety of turbines to suit a variety of conditions.

(l) It offers more flexibility in operation, control, etc.

The main drawbacks of hydroelectric plants are very initial capital intensive and high time of construction period. Due to construction of dams and reservoirs, a large portion of area is submerged into water, which leads to environmental and other social problems. Also the availability of water varies from year to year and in low rainfall years the capacity remains under utilized. However, the advantages far outweigh the disadvantages.

6.2 SELECTION OF SITE FOR HYDROELECTRIC POWER PLANTS

Selection of hydroelectric plants location depends on the following several factors:

Availability of water. Water energy can be available in the form of either potential energy or kinetic energy. To extract the potential energy, a reservoir or pondage is required whereas to extract the kinetic energy run-of-river project is used. In all the cases, a huge amount of water is required. Normally, water is collected in reservoirs during the rain and used for the electricity production throughout the years. Hilly areas are most suitable for hydropower plants.

Storage of water. When the kinetic energy of water is low it is preferable to have the reservoirs to collect the water for use of electricity production. Due to wide variation of rainfall during the year makes it necessary to have the reservoirs. The storage capacity of water is calculated by mass curve. The capacity of plants is based on the water energy available taking into the account of losses due to evaporation and percolation.

Head of water. The availability of head depends upon the topography of the area. High head means high potential energy. To get most economical and effective head, it is necessary to consider all possible factors, which affect it.

Distance from power station to the load centres. The generating stations are normally connected to the main grid through the transmission lines. The costs of transmission lines are also considered during the selection of site.

Accessibility of site. The site should be easily accessed by rail or road for transporting the plant equipments etc.

Others. When deciding the site, some other social factors are also considered, such as the reservoir area should have less impact on the relocation of the human beings from that area. The fertile land can be submerged into water. Also the construction of dams may affect several other impacts on the ecology. The reservoir should not be in seismic zone otherwise any happening may create the flooding of several area, damage of dam, equipments etc.

6.3 HYDROLOGY

Hydrology can be defined as the science that deals with the processes governing deletion and replenishment of water resources over and within the surface of earth. The cyclic movement, called *hydrologic cycle*, of water rotates water from the sea to the atmosphere by evaporation and then from there by precipitation to the earth and finally through streams, rivers, etc., back to the sea. The relationship between the elements of inflow and outflow is provided by the solution of the equations of mass, energy, momentum and state.

Hydrologic equation is simply the law of conservation of matter and can be written, during a given period, as

$$\text{Inflow} = \text{Outflow} + \text{Change in storage} \tag{6.1}$$

The main source of inflow is precipitation that includes rainfall, snowfall, mist, dew, frost, hail, sleet, etc. whereas sources of outflow are as follows:

1. *Surface runoff:* It is the portion of the precipitation, which appears as surface flow at the gauging site, after all losses.
2. *Evaporation:* It is the process by which water from liquid or solid state, is converted into vapour form.
3. *Infiltration:* It is the process by which water enters the surface strata of the soil and makes its way downwards to the water table.
4. *Transpiration:* It is the process whereby the moisture that has been absorbed by the roots of the trees.
5. *Interception:* It is the quantity of water that is intercepted by vegetation, buildings and other objects which subsequently evaporates without contributing to the runoff.

The change in the storage is the effect of changes in moisture of depression storage and detention storage.

Depression storage.   This is the quantity of water stored in small and large depressions, filling them to their overflow level. This quantity is lost gradually due to evaporation etc., without contributing to the surface runoff.

Detention storage.   Some of the water is accumulated on the land due to precipitation. The overland flow contributing to the runoff is possible if there is finite depth of flow over the surface. The volume of water corresponding to this depth is known as *detention* storage.

6.3.1 Mass Curve

Mass curve is a plot of cumulative volume of water that can be stored from a stream flow versus time in days, weeks or months. Figure 6.1 shows a mass curve. Maximum intercept between line *AB* and mass curve is known as *reservoir capacity*.

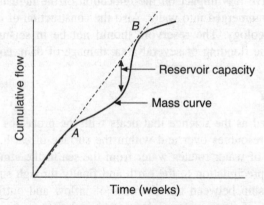

FIGURE 6.1   Mass curve.

The unit used for storage is either *cubic metre* or *day-second-metre*. A day-second-metre is the flow at the rate of 1 m^3/second for one day and equal to $60 \times 60 \times 24 = 86400$ m^3. The capacity of plant is based on the storage capacity, which can be modified by storage for the same mass curve. The water stored in dams is called *pondage* and water stored in upstream reservoirs is called *storage*. A small storage is used to meet the fluctuating demand for small period (one day). When powerhouse is away from the main storage, a small pondage is provided near the powerhouse. Sometimes surge tank is used. The capacity of reservoir, made for a period of deficiency to make available the flow of water at a required rate, is studied by mass curve.

6.3.2 Flow Duration Curve

Flow duration curve is a plot of discharge versus percentage of time for which the discharge is available. It is obtained from hydrograph data. The flow or discharge can be expressed as cubic metres per second, per week or other unit of time. If the head at which the flow is available is known, the discharge can be calculated in terms of the kilowatts power (P) using following equation.

$$P = \frac{0.736}{75} Q\rho h\eta \ \text{kW} \tag{6.2}$$

(since 75 kg-m/sec = 1 metric hp = 0.736 kW) where Q is the discharge in m^3/sec, ρ is the density of water ($=1000 \ \text{kg/m}^3$), η is the efficiency of plant and h is the available head in metres.

The flow duration curve becomes the load duration curve for hydroelectric plant and thus it is possible to know the total power available at the site. The maximum and minimum conditions of flow can also be obtained by the flow duration curve where minimum flow condition decides the maximum capacity of plant that can be improved by increasing the storage capacity. Figure 6.2 shows a flow duration curve. Flow duration curves are of no use where the time sequence of the flow is of importance such as in the study of floods.

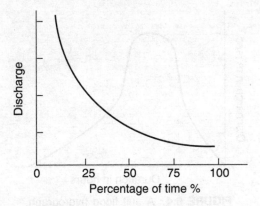

FIGURE 6.2   Flow duration curve.

6.3.3   Hydrograph

It is a plot between discharges versus time of the flow. Hydrograph is shown in Figure 6.3. Discharge is plotted on Y-axis and the corresponding time that may be months, hours, etc., is plotted on the X-axis. Hydrograph also indicates the available power from the stream at different times.

6.3.4   Unit Hydrograph

A unit hydrograph can be obtained from a hydrograph of the actual runoff where there is uniform rainfall intensity and a real uniform distribution. It is a hydrograph with a volume of 1 metre (or centimetre) of runoff resulting from a rainfall of specified duration and a real pattern. It was first proposed by L.K. Sherman in 1932 and is an extremely useful and powerful tool for flood calculations. Figure 6.4 shows a unit flood hydrograph.

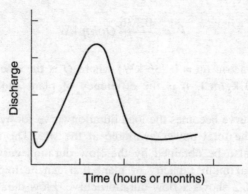

FIGURE 6.3   A hydrograph.

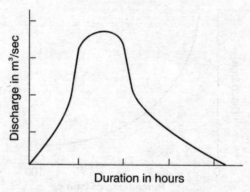

FIGURE 6.4   A unit flood hydrograph.

6.4   CLASSIFICATION OF HYDROELECTRIC PLANTS

Hydroelectric plants exhibit a great deal of variety. They can be classified on the basis of location and topographical features, the presence or absence of storage, the range of operating head, the hydraulic features of the plant, the operation features, etc. In some project, the main objective is not only the power production but also for different purposes such as water supply, irrigation, flood control, etc.

6.4.1   Classification Based on the Hydraulic Features

Based on the hydraulic principle in the basic design, hydroelectric plants can be categorized into the four types:

1. *Conventional hydroelectric plants:* These plants utilize the normal available hydraulic energy of the flowing water of rivers. Dams are constructed to collect the water and used for electricity production.

2. *Pumped storage plants:* Pumped storage power plants are used for meeting the peak demand. Such plants utilize the concept of recycling the same water by pumping the water back during off peak hours. It will be discussed later in this chapter.

3. *Tidal power plants:* Tidal power plants utilize the tidal energy of seawaters.

4. *Depression power plants:* It is a rare type of hydroelectric plant where hydropower is generated by diverting an ample amount of water such as seawater into a natural topographical depression that provides operating head for the plant. This type of plant exists in Egypt. The natural evaporation process controls the water level in the depression.

6.4.2 Classification on the Basis of Operation (Base or Peak)

A hydroelectric plant can be classified according to its operation in meeting the demand such as *base load plant* or *peak load plant*. A hydroelectric plant works as a base load plant if there is continuous power generation. If the conditions prevailing at the power station permit regulated release of water, plant can be used to generate peak power. Generally speaking, hydropower is quite suitable for peak load operation due to its quick starting and relative ease in picking up load. Pumped storage plants are necessarily peak load plants whereas run-of-river plants are the base load plants. Other types of hydroelectric power plants can be classified as per their operation.

6.4.3 Classification Based on Storage and Pondage

Hydroelectric power plants can also be classified on the consideration of whether they have a storage reservoir or not. Storage becomes necessary when the flow is uneven over the year. Without storage, the plants use only the natural normal flow. In such cases, there may be a mini-reservoir or pondage that takes care of day-to-day fluctuations. Some of the run-of-river plants have also mini-reservoir or pondage.

6.4.4 Classification Based on Location and Topography

A hydroelectric plant can be located in hilly areas or in plains. Plants in hilly areas are always associated with dams whereas plants in plain areas may have only weirs for the main structure. In plains the rivers are usually wide with large flood plains and may need ancillary river training works. Knowledge about the location and topography of a plant helps in appreciating these points.

6.4.5 Classification Based on Plant Capacity

Based on the capacity, hydroelectric plants are classified as

1.	Very low-capacity (midget) plants	up to 0.1 MW
2.	Low-capacity plants	up to 1.0 MW
3.	Medium-capacity plants	up to 10 MW
4.	High-capacity plants	more than 10 MW

Based on the capacity, hydroelectric power plants are also classified as

1.	Micro-hydro plants	<100 kW
2.	Mini-hydro plants	100 kW to 1 MW

3. Small-hydro plants   1 MW to a few MW
4. Hydro plants   More than a few MW
5. Super-hydro plants   More than 1000 MW

6.4.6 Classification Based on Head

It is difficult to give the exact range to classify hydroelectric plants based on the available head. Normally, it is classified as follows:

1. Low-head plants   <15 m
2. Medium-head plants   15–70 m
3. High-head plants   71–250 m
4. Very-high head plants   More than 250 m

High-head plants. Due to high head, small amount of water can produce a large amount of power. Therefore, these types of plants are very economical. Normally, the reservoirs are high up in the mountains and the powerhouse is at the foot, taking advantage of large level difference. The catchment area is small and if water from one stream is not sufficient, then water from neighbouring streams can be diverted to the lake through the pipelines or tunnels. The water is carried from main reservoir by tunnel to powerhouse via the surge tank. The length of conduit system may be 15 km or more. For heads above 500 m, Pelton turbines are used and Francis turbines are common for low head.

Medium-head plants. Larger volume of water is needed in such plants compared to high-head plants. Therefore, a reservoir of large capacity with large catchment area is required. In these plants, water is generally carried from main reservoir to the forebay and then to powerhouse through the short penstocks. There is no need of surge tank as forebay itself acts as surge tank. Generally there is one penstock per turbine. Francis, Kaplan and Propeller type of turbines are common for the medium head power plants.

Low-head plants. To generate same amount of power in such plants, water required is much larger than the high-head power plants. Generally run-of-river, tidal plants and midget plants fall into this category. The catchment area and the magnitude of peak flood are very large, the spillway length being considerable. Francis, Kaplan or Propeller turbines are used for low-head plants. The sizes of turbine and the powerhouse are large.

6.4.7 Classification Based on Constructional Features

Constructional feature is another way to classify the hydroelectric plants. They can be classified as follows:

Run-of-river plants. The dominant features of run-of-river plants are that these plants generate power on the rivers with a continuous flow throughout the year with small seasonal variations. Such plants neither have a large reservoir nor do they have a diversion of water away from the main channel. A typical run-of-river plant has a powerhouse located with a weir spanning the river that also serves as the river flow regulator. The site chosen should be on a stable reach of the river with stable bed and banks. The maximum flood anticipated should have low value and water should not carry much sediment. Based on the constructional arrangement of the powerhouse and weir, run-of-river plants can be further divided into four groups: block power plant, twin power plant, pier-head power plant and submersible power plant. These plants may or may not have the pondage. Run-of-river plants with pondage are more reliable and its generating capacity is less dependent on available rate of flow of water.

Valley dam plants. In valley dam plants, a dam is constructed for storing the water. Powerhouse is located at the toe of the dam. No diversion of the water from main river is involved. These are of medium- to high-head plants. The artificial head created will depend on the height of the dam. There are different arrangements of powerhouse location and spillway of the dam.

Diversion canal plants. A diversion canal with a flat slope in which the flow from the river is diverted through the canal to powerhouse. The water from powerhouse is drained back into the original river at downstream point. A weir is constructed at the end of the canal to create a small pool of water, called the *forebay*. The water from forebay is fed by means of penstocks to the powerhouse situated in the lower reach of the river.

High-head diversion plants. In these type of plants, water is diverted through a system of channels and tunnels. There are two ways to achieve it. (i) Water is diverted to another neighbouring river or basin which is at a much lower level than parent river. (ii) Water from river could be diverted along the tunnels from an upper stream point of river to a downstream point of same river. High-head diversion plants are more or less similar to low-head diversion canal plants. The main point of difference is, however, the elaborate conveyance system for the high-head plants.

Figure 6.5 shows the different types of hydroelectric plants.

6.5 Main Components of Hydroelectric Plants

The main components of a typical hydroelectric plant are: dam, reservoir, water conduit system, tailrace, surge tank, trash rack, and powerhouse (which consists of generator, prime mover, switchyards, etc.). Figure 6.6 shows a typical layout of high-head hydroelectric plant.

Dam or barrage. A dam or barrage is constructed to provide a head of water to be utilized in the water turbines. A dam across the river is a very important component in most of the high- and medium-head hydropower plants. Dams are also built on top of hills, in case of pump storage power plants, where is no inflow. Dams can be classified based on their (i) function, (ii) shape, (iii) material of construction and (iv) hydraulic and structural design. Table 6.1 shows the different types of dam classifications.

The main considerations in the choice of dam sites are safety and economy. Other important factors are

1. Geology of foundation,
2. Hydrological considerations and river diversion during the construction,

3. Construction material availability,
4. Accessibility of site to the rail/road,
5. Environmental degradation,
6. Human settlement etc.

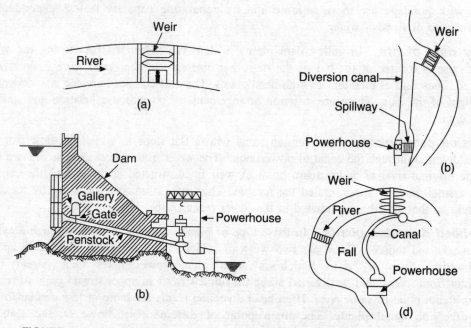

FIGURE 6.5 Types of hydroelectric plants: (a) run-of-river, (b) diversion canal, (c) valley dam, (d) high-head diversion.

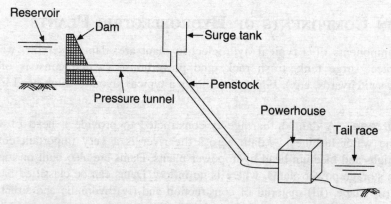

FIGURE 6.6 Typical layout of high-head hydroelectric plant.

Table 6.1 Classification of Dams

Classification based on	Types of dams
Function	(a) Storage dams
	(b) Diversion dams
	(c) Detention dams
Shape	(a) Trapezoidal dams
	(b) Arch dams
	(c) Multiple arch dams
Construction material	(a) Steel dams
	(b) Concrete dams
	(c) Stone masonry dams
	(d) Timber dams etc.
Design	(a) Gravity dams
	(b) Arch dams
	(c) Buttress dams
	(d) Embankment dams
	(e) Spillway dams
Hydraulic design	(a) Overflow dams
	(b) Non-overflow dams

Reservoir and forebay.   The main purpose of a reservoir is to store water which may be used to generate electricity and for irrigation purposes. The water is mainly stored during the rainy season. The capacity of reservoir is decided by the water requirement for power generation.

Forebay is a regulating reservoir storing water temporarily when the load on turbine is reduced and provide water when load is increased. It can be considered as the surge reservoir near the intake. This may be a pond behind the diversion dam or canal spread out.

Water-conduit system.   A water-conduit system carries water from the reservoir to the turbine of powerhouse through the pressure tunnel or pipes called *penstocks* those may be laid above ground or underground.

Tailrace.   Water is discharged into the tailrace after passing through the turbine, which carries it into the river. A *tailrace* is an open channel or a tunnel depending upon the powerhouse location. The discharge from all the turbines is collected in the tailrace at its beginning by means of branch channels. The tailrace may discharge into the original river itself or some other river.

Surge tank.   It is provided to act as pressure-release valve of the water-conduit system from the effect of water hammer. When an additional storage space[1] (called *surge tank*), near turbine is provided which stores water during the turbine load reduction and release water

---

1. The distance between the water source and turbine.

when sudden increase in load is required, it controls the pressure variation of penstock and prevents water hammer effect. It is analogous to the flywheel of internal combustion engine.

Different types of surge tanks are being used, namely, simple type, restricted orifice type, differential type, expansion chamber type and overflow type.

Trash rack. It is provided to stop the entry of debris, which might damage the gates and turbine runners or choking of nozzles of the impulse turbines. It is placed across the intake.

Prime mover. The head of water is converted into the kinetic energy in prime mover, which rotates the shaft of the electric power generators (normally synchronous alternators). Thus, a prime mover, also called a *turbine*, converts the kinetic and potential energy of water into the mechanical energy. The commonly used water turbines are Francis, Kaplan, Propeller, Pelton. Normally water turbines rotate on the vertical axis.

Powerhouse. Powerhouse is normally located near the foot of the dam. It may be underground or open type. Water is brought to the powerhouse with help of penstocks and passed to the turbines those rotate the alternators. The location of powerhouse is decided based on the maximum possible head at the turbine. In powerhouse there are several in-house auxiliaries and controls.

Spillway. It discharges the excess water of reservoir beyond the full permission level and acts as a safety valve of reservoir. If excess water is not discharged, water level of reservoir will be raised and water may start flowing over the dam, a phenomenon known as *overtopping*. The spillways can be classified as (a) overflow spillway, (b) side channel spillway, (c) emergency spillway, (d) chute or trough spillway and (e) shaft or siphon spillway.

6.6 CLASSIFICATION OF HYDRO TURBINES

Water turbines, which convert water energy into mechanical energy, can be considered as motors run by water. The main function of water turbines is to rotate the generator coupled to it to produce electricity.

Basically the water turbines can be divided into two main categories: the *impulse type* and *reaction type*. Water flows out of a nozzle, in case of impulse type, in the form of a jet such that all the pressure energy is converted into kinetic energy. The jet strikes the series of the buckets mounted on the periphery of the wheel. Because of the impact, the runner is rotated about the axis. Therefore the turbine is called the *impulse* turbine. Since the pressure throughout the turbine is at the atmospheric that is constant, the impulse turbine is also called a *constant pressure* turbine. Pelton turbine is an impulse turbine.

Reaction turbine works on the principle of reaction. Water enters the turbine at high pressure and low velocity, some pressure energy is converted into kinetic energy and water then enters the runner and pressure energy is successively converted into the kinetic energy. Water flowing through the runner creates a reaction on the runner vane and runner is rotated. In a reaction turbine, water is under pressure and turbine is filled with water when working. Therefore a casing is must in an impulse turbine so that water cannot splash out. Reaction water turbines usually have vertical arrangement. Since water can be admitted all over the runner at one time in a reaction turbine, it is sometimes also called a *full admission turbine*.

Propeller, Francis, Kaplan and more recently Deriaz turbines fall in this category. The efficiencies of various water turbines with respect to the full load are shown in Figure 6.7. The use of different types of water turbines based on the available head, flow direction, and specific speed is given in Table 6.2.

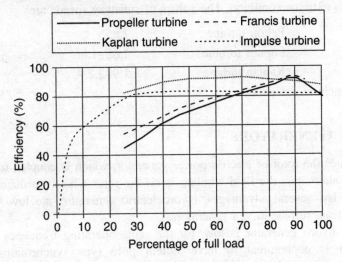

FIGURE 6.7 Typical efficiencies of various types of turbines.

Table 6.2 Use of Turbines for Different Purposes

Use based on	Classification	Turbine types
Head	(a) Low head, 2–15 m	(a) Propeller or Kaplan
	(b) Medium head, 16–70 m	(b) Kaplan or Francis
	(c) High head, 71–500 m	(c) Francis or Pelton
	(d) Very high head, > 500 m	(d) Pelton
Flow direction	(a) Radial inward or mixed flow	(a) Francis
	(b) Tangential flow	(b) Pelton
	(c) Axial flow	(c) Propeller or Kaplan
	(d) Diagonal flow	(d) Deriaz
Specific speed	(a) 4–70 rpm	(a) Pelton
	(b) 60–400 rpm	(b) Francis
	(c) 300–1100 rpm	(c) Kaplan
Output power	(a) Up to 33000 hp	(a) Pelton
	(b) Up to 15000 hp	(b) Kaplan
	(c) Up to 820000 hp	(c) Francis
	(d) Very large	(d) Francis
Discharge	(a) Low	(a) Pelton
	(b) Medium	(b) Francis
	(c) High	(c) Kaplan

Runaway speed is defined as the speed that the hydro unit will reach when the full load suddenly trips and the governor mechanism fails to close. This large increase in speed will increase the voltage and cause an electric breakdown. Due to high speed centrifugal force will be high and pole may fly off and bearing may be damaged. Therefore, the generator design has to be done for this extreme condition. The values of runaway speeds are:

Pelton turbine	$1.85N$
Francis turbine	$1.65–1.8N$
Kaplan turbine	$1.9–2.2N$

where N is the synchronous speed.

6.7   HYDRO GENERATORS

Water turbine rotates the rotor of electric power generator, which is coupled to the turbine. In all electric power alternators the field winding is on the rotor whereas armature is stationary. This arrangement has several advantages. Hydroelectric generators are low speed machines compared to the steam turbine driven generators.

As speed of hydro generator is low, for the same operating frequency the number of poles is high. It is economical to have salient pole type synchronous machine. To accommodate the large number of poles, the diameter of the rotor has to be large enough. However, the axial length of the poles may be comparatively low.

To avoid hunting and ensure the stability under transient and fault conditions, a proper value of flywheel effect is necessary. It is also useful in taking care of sudden load change of system. The flywheel effect is defined as equal to Wk^2, where W is the weight of rotating part in kg and $k = 2 \times$ radius of gyration.

Nowadays, the size of hydro generating units is more than 250 MW. As size increases, a number of problems arises, such as:

(a) Heat loss increases and additional cooling capacity has to be provided.

(b) Vibration is likely to increase and supporting structure must be made more robust.

(c) Thrust bearing must be specially designed for heavy duty and should be provided with high efficiency cooling.

(d) Machine becomes smaller for the same output, the value of Wk^2 decreases and lesser energy storage capacity is available to cope with the load fluctuations.

6.8   PUMP STORAGE PLANTS

The pumped storage power plants are a special type of power plants which work as ordinary conventional hydropower stations for the part of the time. These plants generate electricity during the peak load hours, called *generating phase*, and pump water back from the tailrace side to the high reservoir during off peak hours, called *pumping phase*. The pumped storage plants have the following advantages:

(a) As compared to other peaking units, pump storage plants are economical.

(b) The pumped storage plant is as rugged and dependable as conventional hydropower station and can pick up load quickly.

(c) Such power stations are readily adaptable to automation as well as remote control.

(d) Free from environmental pollution.

(e) It offers great flexibility in operation.

(f) These plants allow other units to run as base load and thus improve the overall efficiency of the system.

But these plants suffer from following drawbacks:

(a) They have to be operated in narrow range of rated capacity to obtain the maximum efficiency.

(b) Time interval required is about six hours to fully load from the complete shut down.

(c) Machine is idle for several hours.

The pumped storage plants can be classified in two ways: based on the duration of operating cycle and based on the inflow. The operating cycle may be daily, monthly or seasonal. Based on the type of inflow, pumped storage plant can be classified as (a) recirculating or pure type and (b) mixed type.

Example 6.1 If the catchment area of a reservoir is 50 km^2 and average rainfall is 150 cm/year, find the power in kW for which station having mean head of 40 metre should be designed. Only 75% of rainfall is utilized and expected load factor of station is 75%. Assume the turbine and generator efficiencies are 88% and 93% respectively.

Solution Total available water for electricity production = $50 \times 10^6 \times 1.50 \times 0.75$

$$= 56.25 \times 10^6 \text{ m}^3$$

Taking the uniform discharge

$$\text{The quantity available} = \frac{56.25 \times 10^6}{8760 \times 60 \times 60} = 1.784 \text{ m}^3/\text{sec}$$

Using the Equation (6.2), the power in kW will be

$$P = \frac{0.736}{75} Q\rho h \eta$$

$$= \frac{0.736}{75} \times 1.784 \times 1000 \times 40 \times 0.88 \times 0.93$$

$$= 572.23 \text{ kW}$$

Since the load factor is 75%,

$$\text{Installed capacity of the generators} = \frac{572.23}{0.75} \cong 760 \text{ kW}$$

Example 6.2   The average weekly discharge (Q) measured at a site is given below:

Week	1	2	3	4	5	6	7	8	9	10
Q(m³/sec)	500	500	350	200	300	800	1100	900	400	200

(a) Calculate the average discharge available.

(b) Plot the hydrograph.

(c) Plot flow-duration curve.

(d) Plot mass curve.

Solution   (a) We have

$$\text{Total discharge during 10 weeks} = 500 + 500 + 350 + 200 + 300$$
$$+ 800 + 1100 + 900 + 400 + 200$$
$$= 5250 \text{ m}^3/\text{sec}$$

and

$$\text{Average weekly discharge} = \frac{5250}{10} = 525 \text{ m}^3/\text{sec}$$

(b) The hydrograph is drawn as in Figure 6.8.

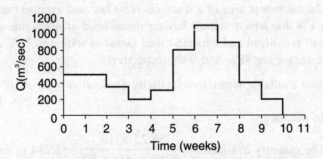

FIGURE 6.8   Hydrograph (Example 6.2).

(c) Since the flow-duration curve (Figure 6.9) is a plot of discharge versus percentage of time for which discharge is available which can be obtained from the hydrograph data as given below:

Discharge (m³/sec)	Period (No. of weeks)	Percentage of total period
1100	1	10
900 and above	2	20
800 and above	3	30
500 and above	5	50
400 and above	6	60
350 and above	7	70
300 and above	9	90
200 and above	10	100

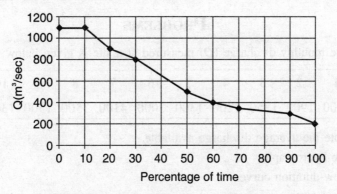

FIGURE 6.9 Flow duration curve (Example 6.2).

(d) Mass curve as in Figure 6.10 is obtained from the data presented in the following table.

Week	Weekly flow (m³/sec)	Weekly volume (day-sec-metre)	Cumulative flow (day-sec-metre)
1	500	3500	3500
2	500	3500	7000
3	350	2450	9450
4	200	1400	10850
5	300	2100	12950
6	800	5600	18550
7	1100	7700	26250
8	900	6300	32550
9	400	2800	35350
10	200	1400	36750

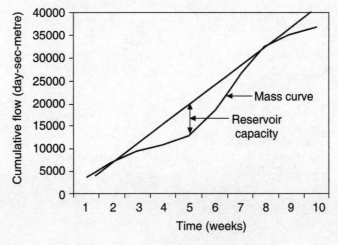

FIGURE 6.10 Mass curve (Example 6.2).

PROBLEMS

6.1   The average monthly discharge (Q) measured at a site is given below:

Week	1	2	3	4	5	6	7	8	9	10	11	12
Q(m³/sec)	1800	1900	1350	1200	1300	3000	4100	3500	1500	1300	1100	1000

    (a) Calculate the average discharge available.

    (b) Plot the hydrograph.

    (c) Plot flow-duration curve.

    (d) Plot mass curve.

6.2   Using the data as given in Problem 6.1, find the maximum and average power that can be developed in the hydroelectric plant having the mean head of 50 m, if the efficiency of the plant is 85%. Also, calculate the load factor of the machine.

Chapter 7

Nuclear Power Plants

7.1 INTRODUCTION

The consumption of electric energy in residential, commercial and industrial sector, all over the world has increased in many folds. Coal, natural gas and oil provide most of the world's energy. Petroleum currently accounts for 40% of the world's energy, natural gas provides 24%, and coal provides about 26% of the world's energy and generates about 37% of the world's electricity.

Since fossil fuels are a natural resource, there will eventually be a shortage of them in near future. The International Energy Agency is predicting oil to run out by the year 2020 with the increased demand and the global economy expands. Some predictions expect an oil supply crisis sometime within the next two decades when global demand will exceed the oil supply. Natural gas is expected to remain for up to 65 more years and the coal supply could last up to 200 years at current consumption rates. With the world population increasing to a predicted 8 billion by the year 2050, the end could come sooner.

7.2 ADVERSE EFFECTS OF FOSSIL FUELS

Fossil fuel greenhouse gases are among major contributors to the problem of global warming. Not only the burning of fossil fuels damages the environment, but every stage in the production of a fossil fuel also exposes the environment to potential harm. For example, at the drill site, leaks and spills may infiltrate the groundwater. During transportation and filling, spills and accidents leak oil into the environment. At the refinery more toxic leakage occurs. Local gas stations and boating docks contribute additional spills. Vaporization and underground tank leakage add even more chemicals to the environment. And of course, automobile exhaust gases pollute the air and contribute to respiratory ailments such as the increasing levels of asthma in children. Motor vehicles account for 50% of all hazardous air pollutants and about 90% of carbon mono-oxide found in the air.

Burning of fossil fuels causes air pollution. Pollution is the smog we see over cities, as well as, airborne contaminants that are not visible to the naked eye. These contaminants can make you sick, burn your eyes and nose, give you an itchy, irritated throat, and cause trouble with your breathing. The chemicals in polluted air can cause cancer, brain and nerve damage, birth defects, lung injury, and breathing problems. Air pollution harms the environment, and the people, animals, forests, streams and lakes that reside within it.

7.3 PROS AND CONS OF NUCLEAR POWER GENERATION

Pros

Nuclear fuel is inexpensive, more abundant than fossil fuels, and easy to transport. The energy generated is very efficient and the remaining waste is compact. Nuclear reactors need little fuel and it must only be changed approximately once every three years. The amount of waste produced is billions of time smaller that the volume of waste produced from a coal-burning plant. Nuclear reactors are safe in comparison to fossil fuel methods. Each year, about 50,000 people die due to respiratory illnesses in America caused by burning of coal. The chance of a nuclear accident that would cause that kind of damage to human life is 1 in every 250 years. Most of all, it is a clean source of energy because it does not contribute to the greenhouse effect or to acid rain.

Cons

Even though the cost of fuel is low, the actual cost of producing energy is higher than other forms of energy because of emergency, containment, and radioactive waste storage systems. High-level radioactive waste must be stored in underground containment permanently. It must remain deep below the surface of the earth for millions of years until it looses its radioactivity. Uranium and thorium are mostly used as fuel in nuclear reactors. The mining of uranium itself can cause serious problems in the environment and to the people living near the mining site. During mining, large amounts of air contaminated with radon and dust are blown into the open air which increases the levels of radon concentrations. The incidence of lung cancer increases in these areas. Groundwater from the mines contaminates rivers and lakes.

The meltdown of a reactor not only causes severe immediate danger, it can also contaminate the area for years after the disaster. Increased incidences of thyroid cancer along with numerous other serious health problems accompany a nuclear meltdown. Crops grown in the area can contain high levels of radioactive elements, and fish populations in nearby lakes cannot regenerate, etc. It is even hypothesized that a properly functioning reactor can emit toxic levels of radioactivity to the population in the surrounding area.

Economics of nuclear power

- Nuclear power is cost competitive with other forms of electricity generation, except in regions where there is direct access to low-cost fossil fuels.
- The decreasing cost of fossil fuels in the past decade has eroded nuclear power's previous cost advantage in many countries.
- Fuel costs for nuclear plants are a minor proportion of total generating costs and often about one-third those for coal-fired plants.
- In assessing the cost competitiveness of nuclear energy, decommissioning and waste disposal costs are taken into account.

The relative costs of generating electricity from coal, gas and nuclear plants vary considerably depending on location. Coal is, and will probably remain, economically attractive in countries such as India, China, USA and Australia with abundant and accessible domestic coal resources. Gas is also competitive for base-load power in many places, particularly with combined-cycle plants. Nuclear energy is, in many places, competitive with fossil fuel for electricity generation, despite relatively high capital costs and the need to internalize all waste disposal and decommissioning costs. If the social, health and environmental costs of fossil fuels are also taken into account, nuclear is outstanding. Nuclear energy averages 0.4 euro cents/kWh, much the same as hydro, coal is over 4.0 cents (4.1–7.3), gas ranges 1.3–2.3 cents and only wind shows up better than nuclear, at 0.1–0.2 cents/kWh average.

7.4 SELECTION OF SITE FOR NUCLEAR POWER PLANTS

There are several factors, which are considered in selecting the site for the nuclear power station. The selection of site is similar to the thermal power station as water is used as working fluid i.e. steam.

1. *Availability of water:* As in the case of steam power stations, nuclear power stations also requires ample amount of water for cooling and steam generation.
2. *Disposal of waste:* It is one of the very important considerations in the nuclear power station due to dangerous waste/residue of the nuclear substances. Hence an extra care is needed in this respect. The storage of waste, which is to be disposed deep under the ground in sea so that radioactive effect is eliminated.
3. *Away from populated area:* Although there is always tight safety but still there are chances of radioactive radiation, which affects the health of people. Therefore, it must be away from the populated areas.
4. *Nearest to the load centres:* Since the transportation and storage requirements are less compared to the coal fired plants. It is preferred to construct the nuclear power plant near the load centres so that transportation of energy at minimum cost can be achieved.
5. *Other factors:* Accessibility to the road and rail are the general consideration of almost all the power plants as heavy equipments are to be transported to the sites during the construction. The fuels are also required to transport from the mines during the operation.

7.5   COST OF ELECTRICITY

The basic attraction of nuclear energy is its low cost compared with coal, oil and gas fired plants. Uranium, however, has to be processed, enriched and fabricated into fuel elements, and at least three quarters of the cost is due to enrichment and fabrication. Allowances must also be made for the management of radioactive spent fuel and the ultimate disposal of this spent fuel or the wastes separated from it. The total fuel cost of a nuclear power plant is typically about one-third that of a coal-fired plant and between one-fourth and one-fifth of those for a gas combined-cycle plant. In the USA, they account for 0.1–0.2 cent/kWh, which is no more than 5% of the cost of the electricity produced.

The cost of nuclear power generation has remained steady over the last decade. This is because declining fuel (including enrichment), operating and maintenance costs have been offset by rising investment costs. In general, the construction cost of a nuclear power plant is significantly higher than a coal- or gas-fired plant because of added and sophisticated safety features, back-up control equipment and other materials used. These can contribute up to half the nuclear generation cost. This has sometimes been exacerbated by long construction period, pushing up cost further. In Asia, time taken to construct a nuclear power plant is shorter, for instance the new-generation 1300 MWe Japanese reactors, which began operating in 1996 and 1997, were built in a short period of four years.

Figure 7.1 shows the cost of electricity generation based on fuel plus operation and maintenance costs only. This cost excludes capital, since this varies greatly among utilities and states, as well as with the age of the plant.

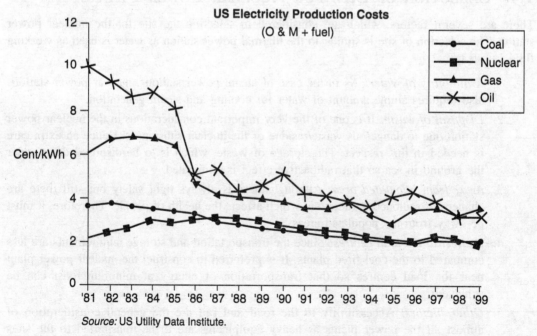

FIGURE 7.1 Production cost of electricity in USA.

The future competitiveness of nuclear power will substantially depend on the additional cost which may accrue to coal-generating plants. It is uncertain how the real cost of meeting targets for reducing sulphur dioxide and greenhouse gas emissions will be attributed to fossil fuel plants. Overall, and under current regulatory measures, it is expected to remain economically competitive with fossil fuel generation, except in regions where there is direct access to low-cost fossil fuels. In Australia, for example, coal-fired generating plants are close to both the mines supplying them and the main population centres, and large volumes of gas are available on low cost, long-term contracts.

Plant choice is likely to depend on a country's balance of payments situation. Nuclear power is very capital-intensive while fuel costs are relatively much more significant for systems based on fossil fuels. Therefore, if a country such as Japan or France has to choose between importing large quantities of fuel and spending a lot of capital at home, simple costs may be less important than wider economic considerations. Development of nuclear power, for instance, could provide work for local industries, which build the plant and also minimize long-term commitments to buying fuels from abroad. Overseas purchases over the lifetime of a new coal-fired plant in Japan, for example, may be subject to price rises which could be a more serious drain on foreign currency reserves than less costly uranium.

Table 7.1 presents electricity generating cost (cents/kWh) in different countries for 2005–2010.

Table 7.1 Some Comparative Electricity Generating Cost for 2005–2010

Country	Nuclear	Coal	Gas
France	3.22	4.64	4.74
Russia	2.69	4.63	3.54
Japan	5.75	5.58	7.91
Korea	3.07	3.44	4.25
Spain	4.10	4.22	4.79
USA	3.33	2.48	2.33–2.71
Canada	2.47–2.96	2.92	3.00
China	2.54–3.08	3.18	–

Source: OECD/IEA NEA 1998.

7.6 COMPONENTS OF NUCLEAR POWER PLANT

A nuclear power plant is almost similar to the coal-fired power plant except the steam generation part where nuclear energy is used for the steam generation. Some safety devices are also used. The basic circuit of a liquid coolant nuclear power plant is shown in Figure 7.2. The boiler of a conventional steam power station is replaced by the nuclear reactor and the heat exchanger. Reactor is the main part of a nuclear plant where a coolant is used to generate the steam to run the turbine and thus electricity is produced.

7.7 BASIC REVIEW OF NUCLEAR PHYSICS

Atoms. An *atom* consists of a positively charged nucleus having neutrons and protons, and a number of much lighter negatively charged electrons orbiting the nucleus. Protons are positively

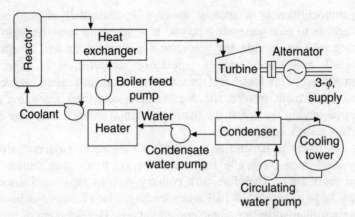

FIGURE 7.2 Nuclear power plant using a heat exchanger.

charged and its magnitude is equal to the magnitude of charge that is negative on an electron. The charge on each proton is 1.602×10^{-19} coulomb. Thus an atom is electrically uncharged as the number of protons is equal to the number of electrons.

The number of protons in a nucleus is called the *atomic number*, which is normally represented as Z. The total number of protons and neutrons in the nucleus is called *mass number* and is normally denoted by A. Therefore, the number of neutrons in the atom will be $(A - Z)$. The nuclear symbol is written as

$$_A X^Z \quad \text{or} \quad {}^Z_A X$$

where X is chemical symbol. The chemical nature of an element is determined by its atomic number. Hydrogen ($^1_1 H$) has one nucleus composed of 1 proton, no neutron and 1 electron.

Most of the weight of an atom is concentrated in the nucleus. The radius of a nucleus is of the order of 10^{-16} m and that of atom is 10^{-11} m. The weight of a proton, electron and neutron are represented in terms of the atomic mass unit (amu), which is (1/16)th of the weight of the oxygen atom. One atomic mass unit is equal to 1.66×10^{-27} kg.

$$\text{Proton mass } (m_p) = 1.007277 \text{ amu} = 1.673 \times 10^{-27} \text{ kg}$$

$$\text{Neutron mass } (m_n) = 1.008665 \text{ amu} = 1.674 \times 10^{-27} \text{ kg}$$

$$\text{Electron mass } (m_e) = 0.0005486 \text{ amu} = 9.107 \times 10^{-31} \text{ kg}$$

The atoms having the same number of protons (or electrons) have similar chemical properties. They differ mainly in their masses. Such atoms are called *isotopes*. Some of the isotopes of some elements are unstable and disintegrate spontaneously. Many isotopes do not appear in nature and are synthesized in the laboratory or in nuclear reactors. Two other particles are of importance, namely, the *positron* and *neutrino*. The positron is a positively charged electron having the symbols $_{+1}e^0$, e^+ or β^+, whereas the symbol for electron is $_{-1}e^0$, e^- or β^-. The neutrino is a tiny, electrically neutral particle, ejected along with β particle during the nuclear fission.

Radioactivity. Most of the isotopes starting with $Z \geq 81$ are not stable due to small binding energy per nucleon and emit radiation till a more stable nucleus is reached. Thus, a spontaneous disintegration process is called *radioactive decay,* which is accompanied by the radioactive rays (α, β and γ). The resulting nucleus is called the *daughter* and the original nucleus is called the *parent.* The radioactivity is always accompanied by a decrease of mass or liberation of energy. Radioactive isotopes, both natural and man-made, emit (a) α particles, (b) β particles, (c) γ radiation, (d) neutrons and (e) neutrinos. They also undergo positron decay and orbital electron absorption, called *K-capture.*

These terms are defined as follows:

α decay. Alpha particles are helium nuclei ($_2He^4$), normally emitted by a heavier radioactive nuclei at high velocity of about 3×10^7 m/s or (1/10)th of the speed of light and accompanied by γ radiation.

β decay. It is equivalent to the emission of an electron and raised the atomic number by one while keeping the mass number the same. The mass of β particle is same as mass of electron. The emitted velocity of β particles is of velocity of light. The penetrating power of β particles are more than α particles but lesser than γ rays.

γ radiation. γ rays are the electromagnetic waves of short wavelength and very high frequency and so very high energy ($\varepsilon = h\nu$). When an α or a β particle is emitted from the nucleus and smaller nucleus is till in an excited state, the excess energy is emitted in the form of γ rays. γ radiation is highly penetrating and does not affect either the atomic or mass number.

Neutron emission. If a nucleus possesses extremely high-excitation energy, it may emit a neutron. The binding energy of a neutron varies with mass number but on an average it is 8 MeV. If the excitation energy is 8 MeV or more, there may be neutron emission. In neutron decay, the daughter is an isotope of parent.

Positron decay. When a radioactive nucleus has an excess of protons, β^+ (positron) decay occurs and proton is converted into the neutron. Therefore, the daughter nucleus has one less proton than the parent nucleus. To maintain the electric charge neutrality of the atom, one electron has to be released. These positron and electron are annihilated (added) producing gamma energy equivalent to the sum of their rest masses, i.e. $2 \times 0.00055 \times 931 = 1.024$ MeV. The reverse of annihilation process is called *pair production.* A γ photon having an energy exceeding 1.024 MeV can form positron–electron pair, converting energy into mass in an endothermic process.

K-capture. This occurs when a nucleus having an excess of photons but does not have the threshold energy of 1.024 MeV to emit a positron and it captures an orbital electron from the rear most or k-shell. A proton in the nucleus changes into a neutron by K-capture, which is accompanied by X-ray emission.

Radiation or nuclear disintegration occurs at a definite rate, which is often expressed in the form of half-life that is the time in which half of an original atom disintegrates. The rate of decay is also called *activity.* The half-life is defined as

$$t_{1/2} = \frac{\ln 2}{\lambda} = \frac{0.6931}{\lambda} \qquad (7.1)$$

where λ is *decay constant*. If N_0 is the number of nuclei of one specimen, half of the N_0 decay after one half-life; one-half of the remaining atom or 1/4 of N_0 decays during the second half-life and so on. Table 7.2 presents several radioactive materials with their emissions, product isotopes and half-lives.

The rate of release of radiation by a radioisotope is dependent on the activity, a, which is the number of disintegrations per second. Since the decay constant λ is the change of decay each second, then with N nuclei present, the activity is

$$a = \lambda N$$

where

$$N = \frac{\text{Avogadro's constant } (= 6.023 \times 10^{23})}{\text{Atomic mass}}$$

The useful unit of activity is the curie (Ci). One curie is equivalent of 3.7×10^{10} disintegration/second.

Table 7.2 Selected Radioactive Isotopes

Isotopes	Half-life	Principal radiations	
		Type	Energy (in MeV)
Neutron	10.6 minutes	β	0.782
Hydrogen-3 (tritium)	12.33 years	β	0.0186
Carbon-14	5730 years	β	0.155
Sodium-24	15.03 hours	β	1.389
		γ	1.369, 2.754
Potasium-40	1.28×10^9 years	β	1.325
Cobalt-60	5.27 years	β	0.318
		γ	1.173, 1.332
Krypton-85	10.7 years	β	0.672
		γ	0.517
Iodine-131	8.04 days	β	0.606
Cesium-137	30.17 years	β	0.512
Radium-226	1.60×10^3 years	α	4.78
Uranium-235	7.038×10^8 years	α	4.40
Uranium-238	4.468×10^9 years	α	4.20
Plutonium-239	2.41×10^4 years	α	5.16

Binding energy and mass defects.   In nuclear physics, the energy is expressed in mega-electron-volt (MeV) and mass is in atomic mass unit (amu). One electron volt is the energy gained by an electron passing through the potential difference of one voltage. Since the charge on electron is 1.602×10^{-19} C,

$$1 \text{ eV} = 1.602 \times 10^{-19} \text{ Joule}$$

$$1 \text{ MeV} = 10^6 \times 1.602 \times 10^{-19} = 1.602 \times 10^{-13} \text{ J}$$

According to Einstein mass-energy relation ($E = mc^2$, where m is mass in kg, E is energy in joules and c is the velocity of light in metre/second), the energy corresponding to 1 amu ($= 1.66 \times 10^{-27}$ kg) will be as follows:

$$1 \text{ amu} = 1.66 \times 10^{-27} \times (3 \times 10^8)^2 = 1.494 \times 10^{-10} \text{ J}$$

or

$$1 \text{ amu} = \frac{1.494 \times 10^{-10}}{1.602 \times 10^{-13}} \text{ MeV} = 931 \text{ MeV}$$

The sum of masses of the protons and neutrons exceeds the mass of the atomic nucleus. This difference in the mass is called *mass defect*. The energy associated with the mass defect is known as the *binding energy* of the nucleus, which is a direct measure of nuclear stability. The energy can be released in two ways:

1. By combining the light nucleus and the energy released, known as *fusion*.
2. By breaking the heavy nucleus and the energy released, known as *fission*.

Fission is most widely used in nuclear power stations. The materials fissionable by thermal or low speed neutrons are $_{92}U^{233}$, $_{92}U^{235}$ and $_{94}Pu^{239}$.

7.8 MAIN COMPONENTS OF REACTORS

The nuclear furnace is termed as *reactor* or *pile*. The purpose of a nuclear reactor of power plant is to produce electricity. Mass is converted into energy. A mass of fissile material such as uranium is brought together in the form of fuel rods and inserted into the core of the reactor. This energy from fission heats the core. To cool the core, and remove the heat so that it can be used to generate power, a coolant is run through the system and taken to a heat exchanger, which removes the heat to a separate system. It is then used to generate steam, which runs turbines, which in turn drives electric generators.

Fuel rods. A *fuel rod* is a zircaloy tube, filled with pellets of uranium. These fuel assemblies can be lifted into and out of the reactor mechanically, allowing fuel replenishment while the reactor is in operation. This is a typical fuel rod assembly.

Shielding. *Shielding* is used to give the protection against the α, β and γ radiations during the process of fission in reactor.

Moderator. A *moderator* is used to slow down the neutrons released during fission. Graphite, heavy water or beryllium can be used as a moderator for natural uranium; however, ordinary water is used with enriched uranium.

Control rods. To prevent the melting of fuel rods, disintegration of coolant, destruction of reactor due to excessive energy release, control the chain reaction at steady state value during the operation of reactor, it is necessary to have controls. Chain reaction can be controlled either by removing the fuel rods or by inserting neutron absorbing material. These rods are made of boron carbide, cadmium or hafnium and are inserted from the bottom of the core to absorb neutrons, which controls the rate of fission. Additional main control rods are inserted from the top down and provide automatic, manual or emergency control.

Coolant. Coolants are used for transferring heat produced inside the reactor to a heat exchanger for utilization of power generation. The commonly used coolants are gas (carbon dioxide, air, hydrogen, helium), ordinary water, heavy water, liquid metals (sodium or potassium) and some other organic liquids. Coolant flows through and around the reactor. There is also an emergency core cooling system, which will come into operation if either coolant circuit is interrupted.

Steam separator. Steam from the heated coolant is fed to turbines to produce electricity in the generator. Ninety-five per cent of the heat from fission is transferred through the coolant. The steam is then condensed and fed back into the circulating coolant.

Containment. The reactor core is located in a concrete lined cavity that acts as a radiation shield. The upper shield or pile cap above the core is made of steel and supports the fuel assemblies.

7.9 Description of Fuel Sources

The energy to power a nuclear reactor is created through nuclear fission. Fission takes place when an atom splits in two and releases a lot of energy as heat.

In order to use a naturally occurring uranium ore as fuel, it must go through the purification process. An ore is a rock containing recoverable concentrations of uranium. It is mined, crushed and grinded into slurry. The slurry is leached with sulphuric acid, which dissolves the uranium, and it is then extracted. It then goes through a solvent extraction (or precipitation) process and uranium comes out in the form of a bright yellow solid. It goes through a high-temperature drying process and turns into a *khaki* (or soil) colour. It is then shipped out and is ready to go into the fuel rods.

Uranium is the most frequently used element in the fission process. An isotope of uranium can split into two very easily. When its nucleus is hit by a slow neutron, the fission process is started. It continues as several fast electrons are split from the nucleus. In order to continue the reaction, these electrons must be slowed by a moderator (often water). Control rods are used to regulate the rate of the reaction. When the reaction takes place in the core of a reactor it creates energy that can be used for power generation. The uranium is loaded into the core in the form of pellets encased in stainless steel tubes. These tubes are then surrounded by a moderator. The entire core is enclosed in a very thick steel or concrete pressurized vessel. The heat is then used to make steam, which in turn is put through a turbine which generates electricity.

Spent fuel assemblies are replaced one-third at a time, once a year, before they cause the reactor to lose energy. Fuel lasts for about three years until the build up of fission products starts slowing down the reaction.

7.10 Types of Reactors

A nuclear reactor can be classified in different ways such as on the basis of types of core used, moderator used, coolant used, fuel used and neutron energy. The classification of reactors is given in Table 7.3.

Table 7.3 Classification of Reactors

Basis of classification	Types of reactors
Type of core used	• Homogeneous reactors • Heterogeneous reactors
Moderator used	• Graphite reactors • Beryllium reactors • Light water (ordinary) reactors • Heavy water reactors
Coolant used	• Ordinary water cooled reactors • Heavy water cooled reactors • Gas cooled reactors • Liquid metal cooled reactors • Organic liquid cooled reactors
Neutron energy	• Thermal reactors • Fast reactors
Fuel material used	• Enrich uranium • Natural uranium • Plutonium • Thorium

A heterogeneous reactor has a large number of fuel rods with the coolant circulating around them and carrying away the heat produced during the fission process. In a homogeneous reactor, the moderator and fuel are mixed together. The solution is critical in the core. The other advantages are:

- No need of control rods
- Need not be shut down for removal of fission products
- Simple in design
- Cheaper
- Core power density is higher due to better heat transfer capability.

Due to difficulties in maintenance, induced radioactivity, erosion and corrosion, homogeneous reactors are not commonly used. Natural uranium also cannot be used. Light water cooled and moderated reactors using slightly enriched uranium fuel are the most commonly used for power production.

7.10.1 Pressurized Water Reactor (PWR)

Water can be used as a moderator and coolant for power reactors. Figure 7.3 shows the pressurized water reactor power plant. The fuel used is slightly enriched uranium in the form of thin rods or pallets and cladding is either of stainless steel or zircaloy. Water under pressure is used as both moderator and coolant. This type of reactor, as shown in Figure 7.4, is extensively

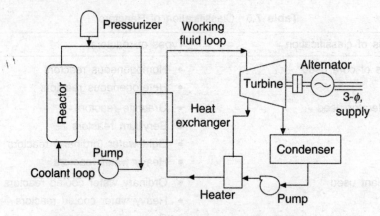

FIGURE 7.3 Schematic diagram of a PWR power plant.

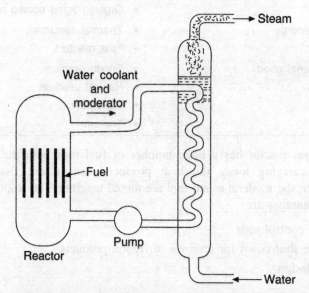

FIGURE 7.4 Pressurized water reactor (light water).

developed in USA. The most important limitation in PWR is the critical temperature of water. The coolant pressure must be greater than the saturation pressure to suppress boiling which is maintained at about 155 bars. A circulating pump is used to maintain the water round the core, which absorbs heat. The PWR power plant is composed of two loops in series, the *coolant* loop, also called *primary* loop and the water-steam or working fluid loop. The coolant picks up the heat from the reactor and transfers it to the working fluid to generate steam to run the turbine–generator system similar to the steam power plant.

A pressurizer and surge tank, which is tapped into the pipe loop, is used to maintain the constant pressure in the water system throughout the load range. There is also some modification to increase the efficiency of the cycle by inclusion of an oil-fired superheater between main heat exchangers and the turbine. There is also an economizer along with some feed water heaters. Since the water passing through the reactor becomes radioactive and therefore the entire primary circuit including the heat exchanger has to be shielded. The main advantages and disadvantages are given as follows:

Advantages

- It is cheap as ordinary water is used as moderator and coolant.
- It is very compact in size compared to other reactors.
- Power density of reactor is relatively high.
- There is a possibility of breeding plutonium by providing a blanket of U-238.
- Reactor takes care of the load variation by using the pressurizer and surge tank.

Disadvantages

- Low thermal efficiency (approximately 20%).
- Greater heat loss due to use of heat exchanger.
- Due to high pressure, a strong pressure vessel is required.
- There is lack of flexibility in recharging.
- More safety device is required.
- Expensive cladding material is required to avoid corrosion.

7.10.2 Boiling Water Reactor (BWR)

Boiling water reactor also uses water as a moderator and coolant but in this case the steam is generated in the reactor itself, as shown in Figure 7.5. There is no need of heat exchanger. Steam is separated and dried by mechanical devices located in the upper part of the pressure vessel assembly. Thus water serves the triple functions of coolant, moderator and working fluid. In this reactor, enriched uranium is used as fuel. Figure 7.6 shows a schematic diagram of boiling water reactor power plant. The advantages and disadvantages of BWR are given as follows:

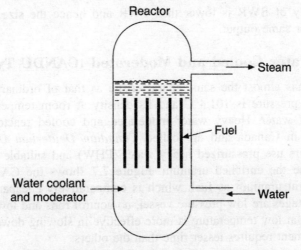

FIGURE 7.5 Boiling water reactor (light water).

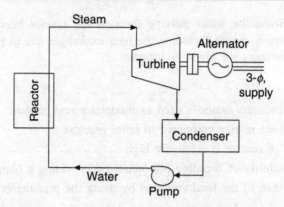

FIGURE 7.6   Schematic diagram of a BWR power plant.

Advantages

- Less costlier than PWR due to reduction in cost of heat exchanger.
- It is more efficient than pressurized water reactor as there is no heat loss component in the heat exchanger.
- The pressure of vessel is less compared to the PWR as water is allowed to boil in reactor. It also reduces the cost of vessel.
- A BWR is more stable than a PWR.
- The temperature of metal surface is lower as compared to the PWR.

Disadvantages

- Since steam is produced from water, which is passing through the reactor, the radioactive contamination of turbine mechanism is possible. Better steam pipes are required to avoid the radioactive fear.
- Waste of steam will also lower the efficiency of the plant.
- It is not suitable for meeting a sudden load increase.
- Power density of BWR is lower than PWR and hence the size of vessel is larger than PWR for same output.

7.10.3   Heavy Water Cooled and Moderated (CANDU Type) Reactor

Heavy water (D_2O) has almost the same characteristic as that of ordinary water. Its boiling point at atmospheric pressure is 101.4°C and its density at room temperature is only 10% above the density of water. Heavy water moderated and cooled reactors are extensively developed and used in Canada and are called *Canadian Deuterium Uranium* (CANDU) reactors. These reactors use pressurized heavy water (PHW) and suitable for those countries which do not produce the enriched uranium. Figure 7.7 shows the CANDU reactor. This reactor uses the natural uranium as fuel, which is comparatively cheaper than the enriched uranium. Other advantages are low-pressure vessel, no control rods and low-fuel consumption. The moderators being at low temperature is more effective in slowing down the neutrons. The construction of equipment requires lesser time than the others.

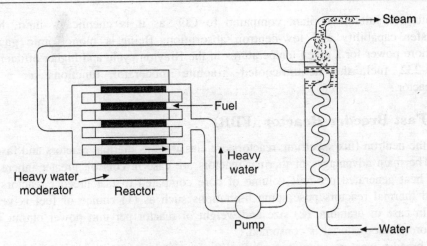

FIGURE 7.7 Heavy water reactor.

The main drawback of this type of reactor is its cost, as the cost of heavy water is extremely high. There is also a problem of leakage, therefore, a proper safety design is needed.

7.10.4 Gas-cooled Reactor

In gas-cooled reactors, gas is used as a coolant and graphite is used as a moderator, as shown in Figure 7.8. The inherent advantage of gas-cooling is that the maximum temperature and pressure of the working fluid can be selected independently; raising temperature does not necessarily imply raising of coolant pressure, as with the liquid cooled reactors. Normally carbon dioxide or helium is used as coolant. Although gases are inferior to water in heat transfer, but offers several advantages such as safer than water-cooled reactors, less severe corrosion problem and natural uranium can be used as fuel.

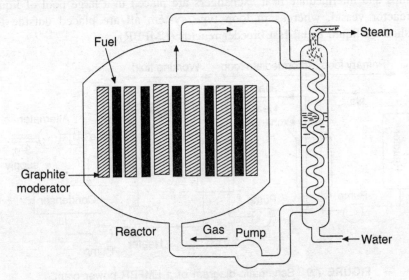

FIGURE 7.8 Gas-cooled reactor.

Helium, a suitable coolant compared to CO_2 as it is chemically inert, has good heat transfer capability and low-neutron absorption. Being a monoatomic gas, it can produce more power for a given temperatures in the Brayton cycle and higher efficiency. With U-233/Th-232 fuel, the helium-cooled graphite moderator functions as a thermal breeder reactor.

7.10.5   Fast Breeder Reactor (FBR)

Based on the neutron flux spectrum, reactors are classified as thermal reactors and fast breeder reactors. The main advantages of thermal reactors are ease in control, greater inherent safety and more heat generated per unit volume of core compared to fast breeder reactors. On the other hand thermal reactors pose some limitations such as (1) choice of fuel is very much restricted in case of uranium, (2) size and weight of reactor per unit power output is higher and (3) more fissile material is consumed.

Fast breeder reactors convert more fertile material to fissile material and therefore fuel consumption is less compared to the thermal reactors. Most produce fissile plutonium from fertile U-238. The fuel rod in core region thus contains a mixture of fissile Pu-239 and U-238. The active core region is surrounded by a blanket of fertile U-238. This region captures neutrons that would otherwise be lost through leakage, thus producing additional fissile material.

A coolant with excellent heat-transfer properties is required to minimize the temperature-drop from the fuel surface to the coolant and also it must be non-moderating. This rules out water, and the best coolants for fast breeder reactors are liquid metals such as sodium (Na). Such reactors are also called *liquid metal cooled reactors* (LMCR). Due to induced radioactive of liquid sodium, an intermediate loop also uses Na or NaK as coolant between the primary radioactive coolant and the steam cycle. Therefore, there is a need of two heat exchangers. The primary loop design can be either pool type or loop type. In pool type system, the reactor core, primary pumps and intermediate heat exchangers are placed in a large pool of liquid sodium contained reactor vessel, whereas in loop type system all are placed outside the vessel. Figure 7.9 shows a liquid metal fast breeder reactor (LMFBR).

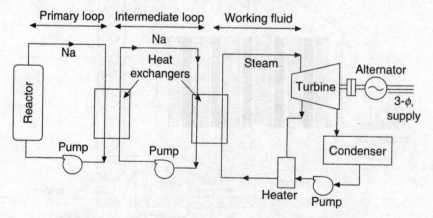

FIGURE 7.9 Schematic diagram of a LMFBR power plant.

7.10.6 Fusion Reactor

Fusion is a process where small nuclei are combined together to form heavy nucleus. During this process huge energy is released. There are several possible reactions. A positively charged nucleus is accelerated with high kinetic energy to overcome the repulsive forces, by raising the very high temperature resulting in a plasma. The four possible reactions involving deuterium are:

$$_1H^2 + _1H^2 \rightarrow _2He^3 + _0n^1 \qquad 3.2 \text{ MeV per reaction}$$

$$_1H^2 + _1H^2 \rightarrow _1H^3 + _1p^1 \qquad 4.0 \text{ MeV}$$

$$_1H^2 + _1H^3 \rightarrow _2He^4 + _0n^1 \qquad 17.6 \text{ MeV}$$

$$_1H^2 + _2He^3 \rightarrow _2He^4 + _1p^1 \qquad 18.3 \text{ MeV}$$

The main advantages of the fusion power plants are:

- Deuterium is available in abundant
- No radioactive waste production
- Safer in operation
- High efficiency
- Low heat rejection to the environment.

Now the commercially suitable technology is not developed.

7.11 NUCLEAR POWER PROGRAMME IN INDIA

In India, nuclear power is developed by Nuclear Power Corporation that installs powerhouses and generates electricity. Till 2007, the installed capacity of nuclear power station was 4120 MW. India uses pressurized heavy water reactors (PHWR) because of several advantages. It uses natural uranium as fuel that is available in India and heavy water as moderator and coolant.

The existing operating power stations of the Company are:

1. Tarapur Atomic Power Station Units—1&2 (TAPS—1&2) (Maharashtra)
2. Rajasthan Atomic Power Station Unit—2–4 (RAPS—2–4) (Rajasthan)
3. Madras Atomic Power Station Units—1&2 (MAPS—1&2) (Tamil Nadu)
4. Narora Atomic Power Station Units—1&2 (NAPS—1&2) (UP)
5. Kakrapara Atomic Station Units—1&2 (KAPS—1&2) (Gujarat)
6. Kaiga Atomic Power Station (Kaiga—1&2) (Tamilnadu)

Table 7.12 gives the nuclear history of India.

Table 7.4   India's Nuclear History

Year	Developments
1947	India gains independence from Britain.
1948	Indian government passes the Atomic Energy Act (the beginning of its nuclear program).
1955	• Canada agrees to supply India with a powerful 40 MW research reactor, known as the Canadian–Indian Reactor, CIR.
	• With British assistance, construction begins on India's first reactor, the 1 MW Apsara research reactor.
1956	• USA agrees to supply heavy water for CIR, now called CIRUS.
(March)	• Apsara becomes India's first operational reactor.
1960	CIRUS starts operating.
1962	India predicts nuclear energy will generate 20 to 25 GW of electricity by 1987.
1969	India predicts its nuclear generated electricity will be 43.5 GW by 2000.
1972	Work begins on a pilot scale Fast Breeder Test Reactor. It was expected to become operational in 1976, but it was delayed until October 1985.
1974	India explodes its first nuclear device at Pokhran and claims the explosion was for
(May)	peaceful purposes.
1975	The Nuclear Suppliers Group, an international organization that aims to reduce nuclear weapons proliferation, forms in response to India's nuclear tests.
1987	India's nuclear generated electricity capacity is 950 MW.
1998	• India conducts a second set of test explosions (11–13 May).
	• Pakistan responds by exploding its own nuclear devices (28–30 May).
2000	• President Bill Clinton visits India, the first US president to do so in 22 years.
	• India's nuclear generated electricity capacity is 2.7 GW.
	• For the first time, the Fast Breeder Test Reactor operates continuously for 53 days.
2001	USA lifts sanctions that were imposed on India and Pakistan after the 1998 tests.
2004	Construction begins on India's first industrial-scale breeder reactor, the Prototype Fast Breeder Reactor.
2006	• The Indian Department of Atomic Energy predicts it will be able to generate 20 GW of nuclear energy by 2020 and more than 200 GW by 2052.
	• President George W. Bush approves a controversial law that could eventually allow India to buy American nuclear reactors and fuel.
	• In March, Bush and Manmohan Singh sign a nuclear agreement to provide fuel and technology.
2007	India and Pakistan sign an agreement to reduce the risk of accidental nuclear war.
2010	Anticipated date of completion of Prototype Fast Breeder Reactor.

7.12 EFFECTS OF RADIATION ON HUMANS BEINGS AND THE BIOSPHERE

Radiation refers to the frequency of an electromagnetic spectrum related to electromagnetic radiation. It is the emission of energy through space in the form of waves. Radiation is not an anthropogenic process. Natural background radiation is emitted from radioactive chemicals that are naturally occurring, such as uranium, radon, potassium and other elements. Radiation is sometimes referred to as alpha, beta or gamma radiation.

Uranium itself does not contain much radioactive material, but it must be carefully handled in the mining process. Most of the radioactive material is left in the tailings, after the uranium is extracted, and never goes into the fuel. Small or natural doses of radiation are not harmful to humans or the biosphere. A dose of 100 mrems per year is considered to be the average human exposure. A dose of over 200 mrem all at once could cause radiation sickness. The naturally occurring radioactive material becomes hazardous through human intervention, such as, mining and using it in the fission reaction process. Through these activities, radioactive chemicals are introduced to food, air and water.

Radioactive fission products are variant forms of ordinary chemicals and are produced in nuclear reactors. It is also possible for the fission chain reaction to form activation products which can lead to contamination. This happens when already existing chemicals in the nearby air or water absorb energy and slightly vary in structure to become radioactive. As they return to normal state over hundreds of thousands of years, they release ionizing radiation. Gamma radiation is released from isotopes of bismuth and lead. They can be toxic to the kidney if they build up, but are usually released through the urine. As radon decays, it emits alpha radiation. Radon gas is released during the mining of uranium. Alpha particles do not normally penetrate the human skin, but they can damage the skin. If they enter the body through ingesting, inhaling or absorbing radioactive chemicals, they can cause serious damage to the organs. For example, if alpha particles (or beta particles) discharge in the lungs they can cause lung cancer. If they are attached to the bone, they can cause bone cancers or leukemia. That is why it is harmful to have our water, food and air in contact with these materials.

Safe disposal of radioactive waste

After all the fuel in the rod has gone through the fission process, the rods are said to be 'spent'. At that time, they are the most radioactive material on earth! Since they emit gamma radiation, they must not come in contact with the biosphere, so they are shielded with water and thick lead walls. If they were to come in contact with humans, they would cause certain death! These fuel rods must go through a process to remove the radiation. The outer cladding is dissolved in nitric acid and the radioactive debris is stored, in the liquid form, in large carbon or stainless steel drums. After it solidifies, it is permanently buried in a repository. Waste of lower radioactivity is buried in dirt trenches or pumped out to sea. This is not hazardous because this waste is of low concentration.

Over time, a nuclear power plant becomes contaminated even though most of the fission fragments are safely kept inside the fuel rods. Activation products are formed in the air, water and pipes of the building, and the plant eventually becomes unusable. It is then deactivated, dismantled and disposed off as a radioactive waste. The radioactive waste in the mining process is contained in a dam. The solids that remain after the uranium is extracted are called *tailings*. They are pumped as slurry to the specially engineered dam to retain them securely.

What happens in a meltdown?

The term *meltdown* refers to the actual melting of the fuel in the reactor. This occurs when the temperature in the core reaches 2800°C. A significant amount of melting has occurred in several cases: Three Mile Island and Chernobyl. The worst-case scenario of a meltdown would happen in this sequence: the reactor loses coolant water and the core is exposed, the fuel assemblies would corrode and the fuel would be exposed and would then melt its way through the containment. In less severe cases, the release of radioactive materials to the environment does not always occur. This will only happen if there is over-pressure of the containment due to 20% melting of fuel, a steam explosion, and failure of the containment cooling and spraying systems. Even if the fuel does begin to melt, it would take hours to make its way through the containment. Therefore, workers have plenty of time to restore coolant to the core.

Redesigned reactors

The nuclear industry has learnt from the mistakes that lead to the disasters at Chernobyl, Three Mile Island and other close calls. Improvements and new designs have been made to help ensure that the world will never again come close to a nuclear meltdown. Redesigned plans include strengthened containment in order to decrease the potential for leakage, and a new heating/cooling system. This new system involves an emergency evacuation of heat (when the core is damaged), a stabilizing/cooling process for this heat, and a decrease in the quantity of free hydrogen that could further increase the fission process.

Control rods have been improved to fit the entire length of the core and the insertion time was lowered, making it easier to control the rate of the fission reaction, therefore, not allowing it to get out of control. Improvements to the emergency protection system include incorporating a four-time redundant checking system.

7.13   Uranium as a Source of Energy

Uranium has the advantage of being a highly concentrated source of energy, which is easily and cheaply transportable. The quantities needed are very much less than for coal or oil. One kilogram of natural uranium will yield about 20,000 times as much energy as the same amount of coal. It is, therefore, intrinsically a very portable and tradable commodity. The fuel's contribution to the overall cost of the electricity produced is relatively small, so even a large fuel price escalation will have relatively little effect. For instance, a doubling of the 2000 U_3O_8 price would increase the fuel cost for a light water reactor by 30% and the electricity cost about 7% (whereas doubling the gas price would add 70% to the price of electricity).

There are other possible savings. For example, if spent fuel is reprocessed and the recovered plutonium and uranium are used in mixed oxide (MOX) fuel, more energy can be extracted. The cost of achieving this is large, but is offset by MOX fuel not needing enrichment and particularly by the smaller amount of high-level wastes produced at the end. Seven UO_2 fuel assemblies give rise to one MOX assembly plus some vitrified high-level waste, resulting in only about 35% of the volume, mass and cost of disposal.

7.14 SAFETY OF NUCLEAR POWER REACTORS

There have been two major accidents in the history of civil nuclear power generation:

- *Three Mile Island*, United States, in 1979, where the reactor was severely damaged but radiation was contained and there were no adverse health or environmental consequences.
- *Chernobyl*, Ukraine, in 1986, where the destruction of the reactor by a steam explosion and fire killed 30 people and had significant health and environmental consequences.

Safety is also a prime concern for those working in nuclear plants. Radiation doses are controlled by using remote handling for many operations in the core of the reactor, by shielding, and by limiting workers' time in areas with significant radiation levels. Continuous monitoring of individual doses and the work environment back up these procedures, and ensure very low radiation doses compared with those in other industries. By any comparison, nuclear energy applied to electricity generation is extremely safe. There are over one thousand deaths each year in coal mines, mostly providing fuel for the main alternative to nuclear energy. There are also health hazards from the actual use of fossil fuels.

To achieve an optimum safety, nuclear plants in the western countries operate with a 'safety-in-depth' approach, with multiple safety systems. These include a series of physical barriers between the radioactive reactor core and the environment, the provision of multiple safety systems, each with backup and designed to accommodate human error. Safety systems account for about one quarter of the capital cost of such reactors.

Besides the control rods, which are inserted to absorb neutrons and the backup cooling systems to remove excess heat, most reactors are designed with an inherent feature called a *negative void coefficient*. This means that beyond an optimal level, as the temperature increases, the efficiency of the reaction decreases (especially if any steam has formed in the cooling water). This is due to a decrease in moderating effect so that less neutrons cause fission, hence the reaction slows down automatically.

Other physical features also enhance safety. For instance, in a typical reactor, the fuel is in the form of solid ceramic (UO_2) pellets. The radioactive fission products remain bound inside the fuel pellets. The pellets are inside zirconium alloy tubes, forming fuel rods. The rods are inside a large steel pressure vessel with walls about 20-cm thick. This in turn is enclosed inside a robust concrete containment structure with walls a metre or more thick.

In 1996, the Nuclear Safety Convention came into force. It is the first international legal instrument on the safety of nuclear power plants worldwide. It commits participating countries to maintain a high level of safety by setting international benchmarks to which they subscribe and against which they report. It has 65 signatories and has been ratified by 41 states.

Example 7.1 Find the binding energy in MeV of ordinary helium $_2He^4$ for which atomic mass is 4.002603 amu. Given that $m_p = 1.007277$ amu, $m_n = 1.008665$ amu and $m_e = 0.00055$ amu.

Solution Molecule of helium has 2 protons, 2 electrons and 2 neutrons. Therefore

$$\text{Mass defect, } \Delta m = 2 \times 1.007277 + 2 \times 0.00055 + 2 \times 1.008665$$
$$- 4.002603$$
$$= 0.030381 \text{ amu}$$

$$\text{Binding energy} = 0.030381 \times 931 = 28.285 \text{ MeV}$$

$$\text{Binding energy per nucleon} = \frac{28.285}{4} = 7.071 \text{ MeV}$$

Example 7.2 The decay constant of radium (atomic mass = 226.095) is 1.3566×10^{-11} s^{-1}. Find the (a) half-life and (b) the initial activity of 1 g of radium-226.

Solution   (a) From Equation (7.1)

$$\text{Half-life} = \frac{0.6931}{\lambda} = \frac{0.6931}{1.3566 \times 10^{-11}} = 5.10909 \times 10^{10} \text{ sec}$$

Therefore

$$\text{Half-life} = \frac{5.10909 \times 10^{10}}{365 \times 24 \times 60 \times 60} = 1620.08 \text{ yr}$$

(b) Number of atoms per gram of radium-226 is

$$\frac{\text{Avogadro's constant}}{\text{Atomic mass}} = \frac{6.023 \times 10^{23}}{226.095} = 2.6639 \times 10^{21}$$

and

$$\text{Activity } a = \lambda N = 1.3566 \times 10^{-11} \times 2.6639 \times 10^{21}$$

$$= 3.614 \times 10^{10} \text{ disintegration/second}$$

$$= 0.977 \text{ Ci}$$

Example 7.3 Assuming 80% of neutrons are absorbed by U-235 cause fission and rest being absorbed by the non-fission capture to produce an isotope U-236, estimate the fuel consumption of U-235 per hour to produce 100 MW of power. Each fission of U-235 yields 190 MeV of useful energy.

Solution   Since

$$190\text{-MeV energy in terms of joule} = 190 \times 10^6 \times 1.60 \times 10^{-19}$$

$$= 3.04 \times 10^{-11} \text{ J}$$

Number of fission required to produce one joule of energy is

$$\frac{1}{3.04 \times 10^{-11}} = 3.29 \times 10^{10}$$

The number of nuclei burnt during 1 hour per MW of power is

$$\frac{10^6 \times 3.29 \times 10^{10} \times 3600}{0.80} = 1.48026 \times 10^{20} \text{ absorption/hr}$$

Mass of U-235 consumed to produce 1-MW power is

$$\frac{1.48026 \times 10^{20} \times 235}{\text{Avogadro's constant } (=6.023 \times 10^{23})} = 0.0577555 \text{ g/hr}$$

Therefore, fuel consumption of U-235 to produce 100 MW will be 5.7756 g/hr.

Chapter 8

Gas Power Plants

8.1 INTRODUCTION

Gasoline, oil and natural gas are all fossil fuels, which were formed over millions of years as carbon-based life forms died and decomposed. After many years, layers of sand and clay formed above organic layers. The pressure from the upper layers hardened organic material to form into the substances known as coal or crude oil. Crude oil is used to make gasoline, which are used daily to power cars and some generators. Natural gases are mined in a similar way. The natural gas is trapped between the crude oil below and the limestone above. Natural gas is used in homes and in major factories and corporations to heat and energize the facilities.

Gas-turbine (GT) based technology is of great interest to the developing countries because it is the most efficient technology for converting fossil fuels into electricity and because of ongoing research and development to make it even more efficient. In addition, gas-turbines generate relatively low level of greenhouse gases (GHG), such as carbon dioxide. Finally, GT based technology has the flexibility to deal with the situations where natural gas is not readily available (a situation that frequently occur in developing countries) because it can handle a wide variety of low calorific value and contaminated fuels, the latter requiring a lot of care for their successful operation.

8.2 SIMPLE GAS-TURBINE PLANT

A simple gas-turbine plant consists of a combustor, an air compressor, a turbine and several auxiliaries for lubrication, speed control, fuel supply and starting. There are several practical limitations such as blade temperature, blade speed, compressor efficiency, turbine efficiency and heat transfer, are encountered in gas-turbine operation.

In the operation of gas turbine, compressed air is delivered to the combustor where fuel is supplied in steady flow and a continuous flame is maintained. A spark makes the original ignition. The heated air in the combustor expands through nozzles and develops a high velocity. Some of the kinetic energy of air stream is delivered to the blades of the turbine. Part of this energy is used to drive the compressor and the remainder is available for shaft work. A combustion chamber connects the compressor air outlet and the gas turbine gas inlet. When unit runs, air enters the compressor inlet from the atmosphere. Air pressure and temperature rise as the compressor forces the air through its outlet. The compressed air then enters the combustion chamber or furnace where fuel oil or gas also enters and burns in the compressed air, raising its temperature. The heated air and the product of combustion, comprising a mixture of gases, then enter the turbine and produce the shaft work. The gas pressure drops as it flows through the turbine and the gas finally exhausts at atmospheric pressure into the surrounding air. Figure 8.1 shows the simple gas-turbine plant.

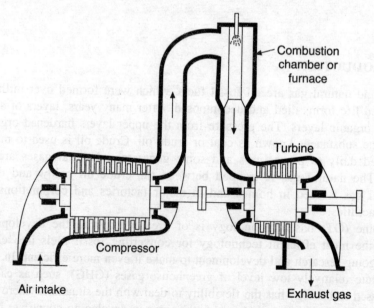

FIGURE 8.1 Simple gas-turbine plant.

Besides its use in aircraft, the gas turbine has its widest application as pumping engine in the petroleum industries. The successful use of pulverized coal as fuel can also be used for gas-turbine plants. Gas-turbine plant offers inherent advantages of its simplicity, compactness, low space, low first cost and low cooling water requirement. Some of the advantages of gas turbine over the reciprocating engines for aircraft are: use of kerosene or distillate, less fire hazard, no unbalance forces, simple cooling system, fewer moving parts, easy installation, small frontal area, not being limited by propeller characteristics and less weight per horsepower.

8.3 ADVANTAGES OF GAS-TURBINE PLANT OVER STEAM-POWER PLANT

Gas-turbine plants offer several advantages over the steam-power plants. Some of them are listed below:

1. Gas-turbine system is compact and required less space compared to steam-power plant of same capacity.
2. It requires fewer auxiliaries and installation takes less time.
3. There is no condenser maintenance.
4. It requires a simple lubricating system, light foundation.
5. It can be easily controlled.
6. It can be quickly started as compared to the steam-power plant.
7. The fuel consumption is low during the starting and shutting down.
8. There is clean exhaust and there is no stack required.
9. Due to fewer auxiliaries, the required personnel to run the plant are also less.
10. In the case of no run plant, personnel required are almost nil.
11. Virtually, there is no water requirement.
12. Gas-turbine plants have low weight power ratio.
13. It is also economical to operate below a given power factor and thus saving of cost.
14. The capital cost is comparatively smaller than that of steam-power plant.

The main problem with the gas-turbine plant is that the compressor must be started before the unit starts which requires the additional external driving power to start the turbine. However, in the case of a steam-power station, it is also necessary to run the several auxiliaries before the starting of the units such as boiler-feed pump, ID and FD fans, etc. After the unit is started, the turbine is used to drive the compressor and total work available is less.

8.4 SIMPLE GAS-TURBINE CYCLE

Brayton, in 1873, presented simple gas-turbine cycle that is basis of gas-turbine analysis. Figure 8.2 shows the gas-turbine cycle which consists of isentropic compression (1 to 2), constant-pressure energy addition (2 to 3), isentropic expansion (3 to 4) and constant-pressure energy release (4 to 1).

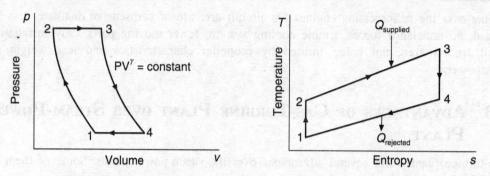

FIGURE 8.2 *p–v* and *t–s* diagrams of simple gas-turbine cycle.

It is reversible cycle and efficiency would be

$$\eta = \frac{Q_{\text{supplied}} - Q_{\text{rejected}}}{Q_{\text{supplied}}} = \frac{mC_P(T_3 - T_2) - mC_P(T_4 - T_1)}{mC_P(T_3 - T_2)} = 1 - \frac{T_4 - T_1}{T_3 - T_2} \qquad (8.1)$$

where m is the mass of the air flow and C_P is the specific heat at constant pressure. Now since

$$\frac{T_2}{T_1} = \left(\frac{v_1}{v_2}\right)^{\gamma-1} = \left(\frac{v_4}{v_3}\right)^{\gamma-1} = \frac{T_3}{T_4}$$

Equation (8.1) can be written as

$$\eta = 1 - \frac{T_1}{T_2} = 1 - \left(\frac{v_2}{v_1}\right)^{\gamma-1} = 1 - \frac{1}{(p_2/p_1)^{(\gamma-1)/\gamma}} \qquad (8.2)$$

In practice the actual cycle efficiency may deviate from the ideal cycle due to following reasons.

1. Air is not a perfect gas.
2. The medium is not pure air since fuel has been added.
3. The quantity of medium may change due to leakage, fuel injection and bleed air for cooling.
4. Compression and expansion are not isentropic.
5. Pressure losses occur throughout the system.
6. Not all energy supplied in fuel is released on combustion.
7. Energy escapes from the system (non-adiabatic).
8. Exhaust velocity is not used.

The efficiency of simple gas turbine is very low. There are three methods to increase the thermal efficiency of the cycle, which are: *regeneration*, *reheating* and *intercooling*.

Regeneration. Recovering waste heat from the high-temperature exhaust gases of a gas turbine is a means of improving the cycle efficiency. It is similar to the air preheater in the case of thermal power plants. The device used for extracting the heat from the heated gas is called *regenerator* or *heat exchanger*. These are either tabular or rotary plate type in construction. Figure 8.3 shows a line diagram of gas turbine with regenerator.

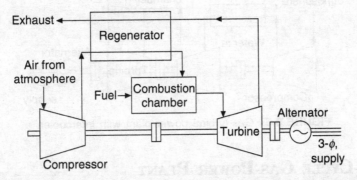

FIGURE 8.3 Layout of a gas-turbine power plant with a regenerator.

The use of a regenerator in a gas turbine presents three problems: necessity of large area of tube surface, maintenance of clean surfaces, and increased resistance flow. The effectiveness of a regenerator is transferring all the energy available from the exhaust gases to the air, which is to be heated.

Reheating. Partially expanded high-temperature gas in turbine can be reheated so that it can be expanded further to produce additional work. There may be several stages of heating. If only one turbine is there, then there will be no use of reheating. In two-stage turbine, one reheater can be used, as shown in Figure 8.4. It improves the performance of the gas-turbine plant.

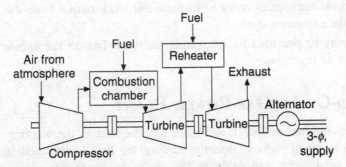

FIGURE 8.4 Gas-turbine power plant with reheater.

Intercooling. Compressor consumes very high energy and therefore two compressors are used with intercooling, which acts as a heat exchanger, as shown in Figure 8.5. The power required to run the compressor could be reduced because reduction in the volume of air-cooled. The number of stages of compressors are decided based on the cost and energy saving. Intercooling results in the enhancement of thermal efficiency, air rate and work ratio. Therefore, overall size of the power plant is reduced for same capacity. Normally, air or water is used to cool the compressor.

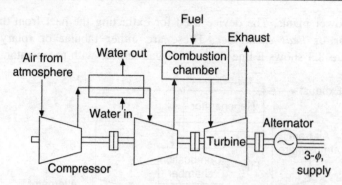

FIGURE 8.5 Gas-turbine power plant with intercooler.

8.5 OPEN-CYCLE GAS-POWER PLANT

Open cycle is the simplest form of gas turbine where air is taken from the atmosphere, compressed, heated at constant pressure (usually by combustion of fuel in the air) and expanded in the turbine. Gases coming out of the turbine are exhausted in the atmosphere. It suffers from the disadvantage that its efficiency is moderate. A number of simple additions can therefore be made to the cycle which, at the expense of some increase in complexity, increase either its efficiency or its specific output. They are as follows:

(a) It is possible to divide the compression units into two or more stages and to provide intercooling between each stage.

(b) The turbine can also be split into two or more stages and heat added using reheaters between the turbines in order to increase the work output from the lower pressure-end of the expansion cycle.

(c) Means may be provided for recovering the waste heat in the turbine exhaust, which is known as regenerator.

8.6 CLOSED-CYCLE GAS-POWER PLANT

In closed-cycle gas-turbine, as shown in Figure 8.6, the heat to the working medium (air or any suitable gas) is given without directly burning the fuel in the medium and the same working fluid is used again and again in the cycle. In gas-power plant, the combustion chamber is just like the boiler, intercooler is as condenser and air-heater corresponds to the water heater of the steam power plant. Closed-cycle gas-turbine plants are not yet used for the generation of electricity due to large size of required heat exchangers. A comparison of open cycle and close cycle is given in Table 8.1.

In order to gain the partial advantages of smaller equipments and to reduce the cost of air heater, semi-closed-cycle gas-turbines are proposed, where closed cycle handles the clean air only.

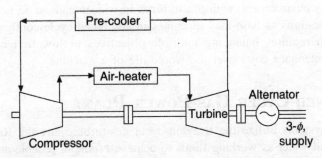

FIGURE 8.6 Layout of a closed-cycle gas-turbine power plant.

Table 8.1 Comparison of Open-cycle and Closed-cycle Gas-turbine Plants

Open cycle	Closed cycle
Combustion product flows through the turbine. Thus there is a danger of fouling.	Instead of combustion chamber there is an air heater to warm the working air. Therefore, there is no danger of fouling.
It is not possible to use the denser air and therefore larger size is required.	Due to closed operation, cycle can work on high pressure and thus the physical size of equipments are reduced and their performance improved considerably.
There is no need of pre-coolers between turbine exhaust and the compressor inlet.	Pre-coolers are required to get rid of the unavailable energy by cooling the working air to the lowest possible temperature.
It is a simple cycle.	It becomes complex due to the addition of air heater and pre-cooler those are needed.
Less cooling water is required.	Ample cooling water is required.
Better quality of fuel is used.	Inferior fuel or solid fuel can be used.

8.7 Gas-Turbine for Power Generation

In the 1950s, when gas turbines were first used for power generation in large numbers, they were applied almost exclusively to peaking duty. Designs were required for this mode of service that featured low specific cost and good starting reliability. Through the 1960s and early 1970s, continuing advances in efficiency, reliability and availability facilitated a wider range of applications for gas turbines. Today, with the addition of low emissions, overall low life-cycle cost and fast installation time, the gas-turbine-based power plant has become the most widely used method for power production.

With the increasing operating hours, the cost of fuel has assumed greater significance in optimizing machine design. As operating (or fuel) cost has become more important, technology development has been focussed on improving efficiency, primarily through increasing firing temperature. But higher operating temperatures can drive design engineers to use more expensive parts that may affect operating and maintenance practices.

So, in today's environment, with gas turbines in widespread use in power generation and cogeneration applications as base-load machines in combined-cycle configurations, optimizing gas-turbine design requires balancing multiple objectives of low first cost, fuel cost, and operation and maintenance costs over the whole life of a machine.

8.8 COMBINED-CYCLE GAS-POWER PLANT

Combined-cycle systems utilize the Brayton-cycle gas-turbine and the Rankine-cycle steam system with air and water as working fluids to achieve efficient, reliable and economic power generation. Flexibility provided by these systems satisfies both utility-power generation and industrial-cogeneration applications. Current commercially available power-generation combined-cycle plants achieve net plant thermal efficiency typically in the 50–55% range. Further development of gas-turbine, high-temperature materials and hot-gas path, metal-surface cooling technology shows promise for near-term future power generation combined-cycle systems capable of reaching 60% or greater plant thermal efficiency. Additional gas-turbine technological development, as well as increases in steam-cycle pressure and temperature and steam turbine stage-design enhancement, is expected to achieve further improvement in combined-cycle efficiency.

8.9 FEATURES OF COMBINED-CYCLE GAS-TURBINE

The combination of the Brayton-cycle gas-turbine and the Rankine-cycle steam-power system complements each other to form efficient combined-cycles. The Brayton cycle has high source temperature and rejects heat at a temperature that is conveniently used as the energy source for the Rankine cycle. The most commonly used working fluids for combined cycles are air and steam. Other working fluids (organic fluids, potassium vapour, mercury vapour, and others) have been applied on a limited scale. Combined-cycle systems that utilize steam and air-working fluids have achieved widespread commercial application due to:

- High thermal efficiency through application of two complementary thermodynamic cycles.
- Heat rejection from the Brayton cycle (gas turbine) at a high temperature that can be utilized in a simple and efficient manner.
- Working fluids (water and air) that are readily available, inexpensive and nontoxic.

Industrial gas turbine (GT) is a well-established technology. GTs, in combination with the waste heat recovery steam generators to supply steam to steam-turbines (thus forming a combined-cycle plant), are already reaching efficiencies of well over 50%, with efficiencies projected to approach 60% over the next few years. In addition, GT based plants are of interest because of the modularity of the technology (i.e. phased plant construction and commissioning can be staged in accordance with the demands of the power system), their relatively low level of greenhouse gas (GHG) emissions, such as carbon dioxide as well their ability to handle a wide variety of low calorific value and contaminated fuels, the latter requiring a lot of care for their successful operation. Finally, GTs are especially attractive because of current low fuel prices. Main features of the combined-cycle power plants are:

1. *High thermal efficiency:* Combined-cycle thermal efficiency is higher than that of other conventional power generation systems.

2. *Low installed cost:* Combined-cycle equipment is pre-engineered and factory packaged to minimize installation time and cost. All major equipments, such as gas-turbine generator, heat recovery steam-generator (HRSG), and steam-turbine generator, can be shipped to the field as assembled and tested components. Auxiliary equipments, such as condensers, can be shipped factory-tubed and hydro-tested. This greatly reduces the inventory of parts that must be managed in the field and minimizes installation cost. The combined-cycle equipment cost is higher than that of conventional steam plants due to pre-engineering; however, combined-cycle plant installation costs are significantly lower, resulting from the reduced installation cycle.

3. *Fuel flexibility:* Combined-cycle plants are efficiently operated by burning a wide range of fuels, ranging from clean natural gas and distillate oil fuels to ash-bearing crude oil and residual oil fuels. Operation with coal-derived gas fuels has been applied in many commercial-size combined-cycle systems.

4. *Flexible duty cycle:* Combined-cycle systems provide flexibility in operation for both base load and mid-range duty with daily startup. Gas turbines in multi-shaft, combined-cycle configuration can be started quickly, bringing about two-third of plant power online, typically in less than 60 minutes. Combined-cycle plants also provide efficient operation at part load, particularly for multiple gas-turbine combined-cycle systems. Modulating compressor inlet guide vanes are standard features of many gas-turbine models, enabling high efficiency operation at part load through reduction in turbine airflow. This is accomplished at a nearly constant turbine exhaust temperature, so that design steam conditions and low stack loss can be maintained to provide an excellent part-load efficiency.

5. *Short-installation cycle:* Combined-cycle plants can be installed and operated in lesser time than that required for conventional steam plants. Again, this is primarily due to the pre-engineering and packaging of major components in the factory. Phased installation of the plant, when gas turbines are installed and operated in the simple-cycle mode during the steam-cycle equipment installation, enables the user to generate power and revenue in as little as a year from order date.

6. *High reliability/availability:* High reliability operation results from evolutionary design development that improves parts and components, and quality manufacturing programs that offer operational factory testing. High availability is achieved through development of sound operation and maintenance practices, which reside principally with the user.

7. *Low operation and maintenance costs:* Low operation and maintenance costs are achieved through quality design, prudent operation and equipment design that allow convenient access for component inspection.

8. *High efficiency in small-capacity increments:* Gas-turbine generators are designed and manufactured in discrete frame sizes.

8.10 MICROTURBINES

Microturbines operate on the same principles as traditional gas turbines. Air is drawn into the compressor where it is pressurized and forced into the cold side of the recuperator. Here, exhaust heat is used to preheat the air before it enters the combustion chamber. The combustion chamber then mixes the heated air with fuel and burns it. This mixture expands through the turbine, which drives the compressor and generator (typically at high speeds such as from 70,000 to 120,000 rpm). Since the generator is mounted on the same shaft as the turbine, it rotates at the same speed. The combusted air is then exhausted through the recuperator before being discharged at the exhaust outlet.

The generator thus produces high-frequency AC-power that is converted to 50–60 Hz by power electronics devices. Typical power ratings range from 25–500 kW although multiple units may be directly interconnected to provide up to 10 MW. Typical capital costs are in the 500–1000 \$/kW range and electrical efficiencies are 27–32%. Utilizing the exhaust, heat can improve the overall efficiency up to 80%. Footprint size is of 60 kW/m^2 area, where operating costs (i.e. the cost to produce electricity) are estimated between 6 and 8 cents/kWh and NO$_X$ emissions are around 0.1 lb/BTU. Typically, microturbines use natural gas as fuel, but other fuels, such as diesel, propane and kerosene are possible. Flare gas from wellheads has even been used as a source of fuel. However, the quality of the fuel (particulates, etc.) must be controlled due to the narrow paths within the turbine.

8.11 INTEGRATED GASIFICATION COMBINED-CYCLE (IGCC) PLANTS

IGCC plants consist of three main sections: the 'gas island' for conversion of coal and refinery residues (such as heavy fuel oil, vacuum residues or petroleum coke) including gasification and downstream gas purification (removal of sulphur and heavy metal compounds in accordance with required emissions levels), the air separation unit and the combined-cycle plant. The modular design (of gas generation, gas-turbine system, HRSG and the steam-turbine system) offers the possibility of phased construction as well as retrofitting of CC plants with a gasification plant, thus replacing the 'standard' gas-turbine fuels (natural gas or fuel oil) by syngas produced from coal or refinery residues. IGCC is, in principle, a combination of two mature technologies. However proper integration is the key to the success of the IGCC projects from lessons learnt from more than 350 gasifiers operating commercially worldwide. IGCC can be expected to be a field of commercial application in developed countries, such as Italy, for residual refinery fuels and gasified coal. However, a great care needs to be taken in implementing a commercialization strategy for developing countries. The total potential of refinery-based integrated coal gasification combined-cycle (IGCC) plants is estimated to be 135 GW, by 2015. Currently, over 6 GW of coal and refinery residue based IGCC projects are either under construction or planned.

Biomass gasification-combined cycle technology offers several advantages relative to direct combustion-steam cycle and other biomass power technologies. The principal advantage of IGCC plants is its potential for a higher power-generation efficiency in the smaller size range appropriate for biomass power projects. This higher efficiency is important because the delivered cost of biomass fuel is often higher than that of fossil fuels, and biomass power projects are generally smaller (10–60 MW) and hence encounter diseconomies of scale relative to fossil fuel power projects (250–330 MW and larger for coal-based direct combustion and IGCC plants). The size of biomass power projects is limited by the maximum transport distance at which it is economic to harvest and transport biomass fuel to a power plant (50–75 miles) and the biomass crop production potential of the land area around the plant. Figure 8.7 shows the process flow sheet of atmospheric pressure gasification combined cycle power plant.

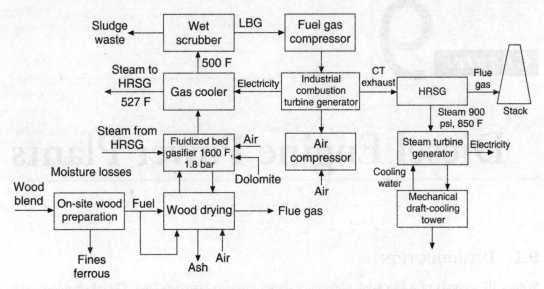

FIGURE 8.7 Atmospheric pressure gasification combined-cycle power plant.

Chapter 9

Diesel Engine Power Plants

9.1 Introduction

Within 10 seconds of a blackout, stationary diesel engines start working. Diesel engine-driven electric generators serve as emergency backup power for hospitals, business and individuals nationwide and provide the electric utility industry crucial services during power failures. Portable rental power units are used in critical situations as a temporary source of power. During preparations for the "Y2K" computer crisis, diesel generators served as a critical backup strategy for individuals and businesses.

In addition, diesel generators are used as backup power by most of the nuclear power plants due to their reliability and ability to maintain plant safety in emergencies. Coal-fired power plants also rely on diesel for emergency auxiliary systems. Hydroelectric, nuclear, wind and solar power are also used to provide backup power generation. Still, most of these alternatives rely on diesel engines at some point in the power production process. Hence, diesel engines will continue to be an integral part of power generation for the foreseeable future.

In June 2005, US Environmental Protection Agency (EPA) proposed new regulations that would put stationary diesel engine emissions on track to achieve near-zero emissions levels in the next few years. In the interim, engine manufacturers and the utility industry have risen to these new challenges and are already producing and designing engines and diesel generators to meet these new regulations. The diesel industry is confident that the new emissions standards can be met without disruptive impacts on power output, reliability, ease of maintenance, and fuel economy of diesel engines.

To help businesses and cities protect critical facilities during a power outage, the following measures can be taken to ensure backup power in a crisis.

- *Assess the risk:* Identifying your facility's critical loads is an important first step. Assign a cost to the risks associated with utility power interruptions, production losses and downtime.
- *Install a standby generator:* Frequent outages of a few seconds, a few minutes, or more can often disrupt performance and have significant cost implications to businesses. While other fuel sources take up to two minutes to engage, diesel-powered standby generators are uniquely qualified to provide power quickly during a power outage and offers the most effective source of reliable backup power available.
- *Have sufficient fuel storage:* The chemical structure of diesel fuel allows more energy to be released per unit than any other source of commonly used power. This greater power density means less fuel consumption than other sources. Still, it is important to make sure that you have sufficient fuel storage capacity on-site for an extended outage of several days.
- *Maintain your equipment:* As required by electrical codes, standby generators should be "exercised" monthly to ensure that they operate as designed in the event of an emergency.
- *Contract rental power:* If installing your own standby generation is not feasible for your business, you might consider contracting with a firm to reserve rental generator power for use in the event of an extended outage.

9.2 Advantages of Diesel Power Plants

Diesel power plants offer several advantages as follows.

- The capital cost per kW is low.
- Design and installation are simple and cheap.
- These can be easily procured, installed and commissioned in less time.
- Compared to the thermal-power plants, less space is required for sitting and fuel storage.
- Starting time and stopping time are very less. Thus, they can be put into service and taken out quickly.
- These have good efficiency (approximately 40–45%), which is higher than thermal power plants. Moreover, the working efficiency at part loads does not fall so much as that of a steam plant.
- Small diesel generators can be portable and can be put near any load requirement. However, a big size diesel power plant can be located near load centres as it requires less space.
- These power plants are free from ash and require less water for cooling system.
- The operation is simpler, and lesser operating and supervising staff is needed than a thermal power plant.

9.3 Disadvantages of Diesel Power Plants

Diesel power plants have several disadvantages as well. They are as follows.

- The operating cost of it is very high as diesel is more costly than coal.
- The size of diesel unit is limited and very large capacity is not possible with these prime movers.
- Their repair and maintenance costs are high.
- The useful life is very less (approximately 5–10 years).
- They have limited overload capacity.
- The noise and air pollution is more.

9.4 Applications of Diesel Power Plants

The size limitations notwithstanding, the escalating oil prices have made the operation of diesel electric plants very uneconomical. As a result, they play a minor role in electric power generation. The existing plants are operated only when absolutely necessary. Their fields of application are as follows:

- *Emergency plant:* A countless number of industries all over the country have installed diesel electric plants in their premises to maintain essential services when supply from the grid is not available.
- They are used for starting auxiliaries in steam power stations.
- *Mobile plants:* Mobile diesel electric plants mounted on trailers are used for temporary and emergency purposes.
- *Peak load plant:* A diesel plant can be started and loaded quickly. As such, these plants can be used as peak load plants.
- *Standby plants:* They can be used as standby plants when supply from grid is not available.
- They can be used in remote locations where supply from the grid is not available. The use of diesel electric plants during the construction stages of thermal and hydroelectric power plants is very common.

9.5 Diesel Engine Power

The ideal thermal cycle of the diesel engine is shown in Figure 9.1. Beginning with working medium at state 1, it is first polytropically compressed to state 2, then the heat is added during limited isobaric expansion, after which a polytropic expansion to the initial volume reduced the pressure to state 4. The processes 1–2 and 3–4 in ideal cycle are the isentropics with air as the fluid. The area 1–2–3–4–1 is the work produced by the cycle, and effective pressure is its average height.

The ideal air standard efficiency (η) will be

$$\eta = 1 - \frac{1}{\gamma r^{(\gamma-1)}} \left[\frac{(v_3/v_2)^\gamma - 1}{(v_3/v_2) - 1} \right] \tag{9.1}$$

and ideal mean effective pressure will be

$$P_{av} = p_1 r \left[\frac{\gamma r^{(\gamma-1)} \left((v_3/v_2) - 1 \right) - \left((v_3/v_2)^\gamma - 1 \right)}{(\gamma - 1)(r - 1)} \right] \tag{9.2}$$

where r is the compression ratio (v_1/v_2) and for air standard performance $\gamma = 1.4$.
From Equation (9.1), it can be seen that higher efficiency can be achieved by high compression ratio and low cutoff ratio (v_3/v_2). The engine size (which is proportional to the P_{av} is increased as R decreases. The requirement of adequate fuel consumption imposes a limitation on maximum cutoff ratio (R) that can be used.

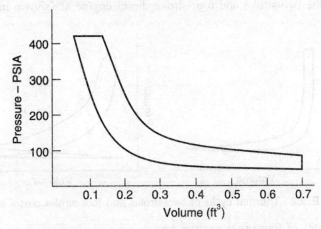

FIGURE 9.1 Ideal thermal cycle of diesel engine.

9.6 DIESEL PLANT EQUIPMENT

In the modern age, diesel engines are extensively used for driving small electric generators. The electric equipment in the diesel plant, however, is influenced greatly by the diesel engine characteristics. Besides engine, diesel plants need the following equipment for their operation.

(a) *Governing system.*
(b) *Air-intake system:* Air filters, ducts, super charger.
(c) *Exhaust system:* Connecting ducts, silencers, mufflers, water heaters.
(d) *Starting systems:* Battery, air compressor, electric motor.
(e) *Engine cooling system:* Pumps, spray-pond, heat-exchanger, water-treatment, piping.
(f) *Engine lubricating system:* Oil tanks, oil pumps, relief valves, filters, purifiers, coolers, piping.

(g) *Fuel system:*   Fuel storage tanks, pumps, strainers, oil filters, meters, heaters, piping.

(h) *Alternators with exciters.*

(i) *Instrumentation.*

(j) *Switchgear and control equipment.*

9.6.1   Diesel Engines

The diesel engine, for a diesel electric plant, may operate on a two-stroke or four-stroke cycle. In a two-stroke cycle, there is a combined expansion and exhaust stroke (backward stroke) and a combined intake and compression stroke (forward stroke) to complete one revolution of the crankshaft. In a two-stroke engine, the cycle of operations is completed in four-stroke (two revolutions), the four strokes being intake (suction), compression, expansion (working) and exhaust. A two-stroke engine develops more power for the same speed and piston displacement and costs less than a four-stroke engine. However, a four-stroke engine has higher efficiency, lower specific fuel consumption and more effective lubrication than a two-stroke engine. The thermal cycles of the two-stroke and four-stroke diesel engine are shown in Figure 9.2.

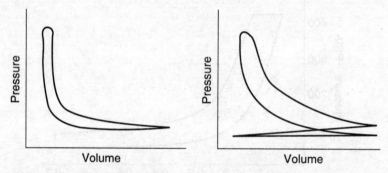

FIGURE 9.2   Thermal cycle of two-stroke and four-stroke diesel engine.

The major advantages of four-cycle engines are:

(a) Cylinder scavenging is performed throughout one stroke and therefore more efficiently performed, and the fuel consumption is slightly reduced.

(b) Lubrication is more effective, and during the expansion and exhaust strokes, the pressure on the main gear is relieved. Thus, the oil film automatically reinforces itself in the bearing, etc. The engine can be designed with higher bearing pressure.

(c) Scavenging pumps are not necessary.

(d) Combustion and expansion occur once in four-strokes and therefore cooling is better and the heat stress is lower.

(e) There are no ports in the cylinder liner.

The major advantages of two-cycle engines are:

(a) More power can be developed for a given size of cylinder.

(b) The weight, cost and size of engine per BHP is less.

(c) More flexible engine and simple design.

Two types of ignition system (compression ignition or spark ignition) are used. The diesel engines are mostly compression ignition type. In compression ignition engine, combustion starts by spontaneous ignition of fuel and air because of high temperature developed by the compression of the air, whereas a spark ignition engine uses a spark plug to ignite the fuel air mixture. Large diesel engines intended for continuous service and long life are usually low-speed units. Thus, units ranging from 1000 to 3500 hp, the speed of 400 to 600 rpm are common and the piston speeds range from 1200 rpm to 1600 rpm. The smaller units have speed up to 900 rpm or 1200 rpm.

The selection of engine size depends on the capacity of the plant. The overload capacity of the plant is very low and its operation at loads less than full loads is uneconomical. Therefore, the determination of plant capacity is very important. To determine plant capacity, an estimate of essential connected loads (which must be supplied under emergency conditions) is necessary. It is also necessary to estimate the demand factor and the diversity factor. The connected load multiplied by demand factor and divided by diversity factor gives the plant capacity. The size and number of engines depends on plant capacity, the purpose for which the plant is being set up and the load characteristics. For small-scale industries only one or two engines are sufficient. It is advisable to calculate the generation cost and overall plant economy for more than one alternative and select the best one. The total space available in the installation is also an important consideration in determining the number and size of units.

9.6.2 Governors

The speed regulation is defined as

$$S = \frac{\text{No load speed } (N_0) - \text{Full load speed } (N_f)}{\text{Full load speed } (N_f)} \tag{9.3}$$

Modern diesel engines are equipped with either non-isochronous or isochronous governors. A non-isochronous governor may be either a mechanical governor in which the power to regulate the fuel flow is obtained from flyweights, or it may be a relay type employing a hydraulic or electric (including electronic) system. Isochronous governors are relay type and usually supplied for the diesel engine having parallel operation. When voltage and frequency (single generator operation) are not so important, the regulation of 6% is acceptable. All diesel engines should be supplied with emergency over speed governors to stop the units when the speed exceeds by 10%.

9.6.3 Air-intake System

Air requirements of diesel plants are high (around 4–8 m^3 per kWh). Small engines take air from the engine room, but for large engines, air is drawn from outside the engine room and delivered to the inlet manifold through the air filters, which remove the dust and other suspended impurities from air. Filter types include dry, oil bath, viscous impingement and electrostatic precipitator filters. In cold climates, the intake air is heated, by using the heat from exhaust gases, before injection. Supercharging is usually employed to increase the pressure of intake air above atmospheric pressure.

9.6.4 Exhaust System

The diesel engine takes considerable amount of air, and this air comes out from the exhaust system. The function of the exhaust system is to discharge the engine exhaust to the atmosphere outside the building. A good exhaust system should keep the noise at a low level, exhaust well above the ground level to reduce the air pollution at breathing level, and isolate the engine vibrations from the building by using a flexible section of the exhaust pipe. The exhaust pipe is provided with a muffler to reduce pressure in the exhaust line and eliminate much of the noise. The exhaust system must carry around 0.17 to 0.23 m^3 of air per minute per horse power developed. The waste heat of exhaust gases may be used to raise low-pressure steam, or heat the oil or ventilating air for the plant, or to heat the buildings.

9.6.5 Starting System

Because of high compression pressures, even a small diesel engine in a power plant cannot be started by hand cranking. Small diesel engines can be started by electric starter driven by batteries. Air motors may be used for medium sized units. Compressed air system is mostly used for starting diesel engine in power plants. Compressed air from air tank, at about 20 times atmospheric pressure, is admitted to a few of the engine cylinders, making them work like reciprocating air motors to turn the engine shaft. Fuel admission to the remaining cylinders causes the engine to start. A motor-driven compressor is used to supply air to the compressed air tank. A 0.45 m^3 tank with air at 20 atmospheric pressure is sufficient for starting a 1200 hp engine 5 to 7 times without being recharged.

9.6.6 Cooling System

The extra heat, not used for doing useful work, has to be removed from the engine. Otherwise, this extra heat may disintegrate the lubricating oil film on the cylinder walls and damage the cylinder liners, heads, walls, piston and rings. Small engines may be air-cooled but large engines mostly employ forced water cooling. The cold water is sent through the cylinder jacket with the help of a pump. The hot water is cooled in a spray pond and re-circulated. It is necessary to keep the exit temperature of the cooling water around 70°C. If this temperature is too low, the lubricating oil film will not spread properly and will result in cylinder and piston wear. If this temperature is too high, the lubricating oil burns. This necessitates a control of the flow of cooling water according to the load on the engine. The cooling water requirement of a diesel engine (for 10°C temperature rise) is around 2 to 4 litres per bhp per minute. It is possible to utilize the heat of exit cooling water for heating oil or buildings. It is necessary to treat the make-up water to remove the scale forming impurities. Zeolite softener or lime or lime-soda-ash treatment is employed.

9.6.7 Lubricating Oil System

Lubricating oil consumption is one of the important elements in the diesel power costs which is around 3% of the fuel costs. Therefore, a proper lub-oil system is a must. High pressure and small clearances necessitate a good lubrication system for a diesel engine. The life of the engine and the efficiency depend largely on the lubrication system. In addition to lubricating the moving parts, the lubricating oil removes heat from the cylinder and bearings, carries away the solid matter from rubber moving parts and helps piston rings to seal gases in the cylinder. The parts of the engine which need lubrication include piston and cylinders, gears, crank-shaft and connecting rod, bearings etc. Piston and cylinder need special lubricating oil. The forced feed lubrication is mostly used, and the equipment for this purpose includes pumps, oil cooler, oil cleaner, sump oil tank etc. The lub-oil pumps are driven by engine shaft. An oil system should have a strainer to remove larger impurities, and filters are used to remove smaller particles.

9.6.8 Fuel Oil System

In a small engine, the fuel is stored in a small tank mounted on the engines. Whereas the fuel received by the large plant is stored in bulk storage tanks which are situated outdoors for safety. Oil is drawn from these tanks by pumps, daily or at suitable intervals, and delivered through strainers and meters to small storage tanks called day tanks which feed engines. The function of the engine fuel admission system is to supply correct amount of fuel to each cylinder in advance of the working stroke at proper time even with varying load conditions. Nowadays, all diesel power plant engines use mechanical injection system in which fuel at a pressure of around 100 kg/cm^2 is delivered mechanically, through the atomiser nozzle, into the compressed air.

9.6.9 Diesel Engine Alternator

The diesel engine alternators are of rotating field, salient pole construction, the number of poles varying from 6 to 28 and capacities from 25 to 35000 kVA at 0.8 p.f. lagging. Generally they are rated at 440 volt, though larger machines may have a voltage rating of 2.2 kV. The alternators are directly coupled to the engines. Special attention as regards mechanical design of the alternator is necessary to avoid setting up of torsional vibrations due to uneven turning moment of the engine. They are provided with automatic voltage regulators to permit close voltage regulation and satisfactory parallel operation. Almost all diesel engine alternators are provided with damper windings. Each alternator is provided with its own exciter usually coupled to the engine shaft either directly or through a belt to increase speed. The voltage rating of exciter is 115 V or 230 V and power rating 2 to 4% of the alternator rating.

9.6.10 Instrumentation

A diesel plant must have a number of instruments to ensure satisfactory operation. These instruments are:

(a) *Temperature measurements:* Thermometers (or pyrometers) for measurement of exhaust temperature, jacket water temperature, lubricating oil temperature, fuel oil temperature and injection air compressor temperature.

(b) *Pressure measurements:* Pressure gauges to gauge both final and inter-stage pressure of starting air system, lubricating oil system before and after cooler, cooling water, jacket water and fuel oil before and after strainer.

(c) Energy meter, wattmeter, voltmeter and ammeter.

(d) Synchronising equipment, if operating with grid.

(e) Alarm systems to give warning in the event of high lubricating oil temperature, high jacket water temperature, low jacket water pressure, low lubricating-oil pressure, incorrect starting and blower motor over current.

9.6.11 Substation Equipment

The various pieces of substation equipment include bus bars, station transformers, circuit breakers, over-current, over-voltage and under-voltage relays etc. The switchgear is grouped in the form of a switch board, which is placed in the engine hall on the alternator end of the engine. A mimic diagram with lamp type semaphores indicates the position of the circuit breakers and also indicates whether the bus bar is alive or dead. The engine governors can be controlled from the switchboard to enable easy synchronizing of the alternators. Figure 9.3 shows the diagram of a diesel engine.

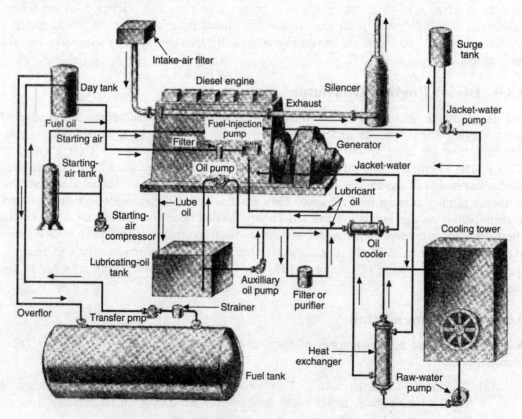

FIGURE 9.3 Schematic diagram of a diesel engine.

9.7 RECENT ADVANCES IN DIESEL PLANTS

The following new diesel plant technologies are being developed. Diesel-combined-cycle plants and bio fuel-based diesel engines are becoming popular. In the diesel-combined-cycle plant, the exhaust gas temperatures are higher due to the combination of design and tuning. This technology used hot combustion process for combustion instead of the conventional process. In hot combustion process, the diesel engines cooling losses are reduced, thus increasing the temperature of hot exhaust gases. The waste heat of exhaust gases is used in steam generation, which is used to generate electricity thus improving the plant efficiency. DCC plant is equipped with nitrogen oxide catalytic converter and desulphurisation system to keep the pollution level low. Using plants for production of diesel can be used for power generation. A low cost method of converting wood and other bio fuels into liquid bio fuels is being developed.

10

Transmission Line Parameters (Constants) Calculations

10.1 INTRODUCTION

The main function of a transmission line is to transfer bulk amount of power to load centres and industrial users up to the primary distribution lines. A transmission system consists of structures, wires, switching and conversion stations. It forms the bone of the power system, which connects the generating stations with the load points. Transmission systems are interconnected due to economic, security and reliability reasons. The transmission line requirement is decided based on the system planning. Whenever a generating plant is added to the system, a transmission line is a must to evacuate the power from the generating station. Each country has certain sets of rules for the voltage and number of lines for evacuation. The requirement of other transmission lines is also assessed so that no line gets overloaded even during the outage of some critical lines. While deciding the transmission system, following factors need to be considered:

1. Voltage level
2. Right-of-way requirements
3. Type and size of a conductor
4. Line regulation and voltage control
5. Corona loss
6. Efficiency
7. Compensation requirement
8. System performance including the power flow, stability, etc.
9. System fault levels at different bus bars and requirement of new circuit breakers for the same.
10. Protection system for new lines and a change in setting of the same for other lines, if any.
11. Grounding
12. Insulation coordination
13. Mechanical design
    (a) Sag and stress calculations
    (b) Conductor composition
    (c) Conductor spacing
    (d) Insulator configurations
14. Structure design
    (a) Structure types
    (b) Stress calculations
15. Economics of the system

10.2 Types of Conductors

Conductors used for electrical system are those having less resistance, low weight, high-tensile strength, low cost and low coefficient of expansion. Normally, we use aluminium and copper as conductors for the same. The main advantages of aluminium conductors over copper conductors are:

- low weight
- high conductivity (less resistance) and less corona loss
- low cost

The main problems with aluminium conductors are:

- low tensile strength
- high coefficient of expansion
- large area (thus high wind pressure)

Normally, conductors for ac transmission system are used in the form of *stranded* except for smaller cross-section. Stranded conductors are electrically parallel and spiralled together. The main reason for stranding the conductors is to reduce the skin effect. The size of conductors is decided based on the voltage and the current carrying capacity. A general formula for the total number of strands (N) for n layers (including the centre strand) of strands in a conductor, if each strand is uniform, is

$$N = 3n^2 - 3n + 1 \tag{10.1}$$

The overall outer diameter of the conductor (D), if the diameter of one strand is d, will be

$$D = (2n - 1)d \tag{10.2}$$

To increase the tensile strength of the conductor, one or more central conductors (of different materials) are used, which have a high tensile strength. In modern overhead transmission systems, bare aluminium conductors are used which are classified as

AAC: all-aluminium conductor

AAAC: all-aluminium alloy conductor

ACSR: aluminium conductor steel reinforced

ACAR: aluminium conductor alloy reinforced

In most applications, ACSR conductors are used for both distribution lines and transmission lines. Reasons for these are given as follows:

(a) Steel core aluminium conductors are normally cheaper than copper conductor of equal resistance which is obtained without sacrificing efficiency, durability or length of useful life.

(b) By high mechanical strength, the length of span can be increased and cost of erection and maintenance can be reduced.

(c) Corona loss (to be discussed) and skin effect are reduced.

The name of various ACSR conductors used in India are given in Table 10.1. It should be noted that these are the names of animals.

Table 10.1 Names of ACSR Conductors

Names	Size (mm)	Names	Size (mm)
Mole	6/1/1.50*	Wolf	30/7/2.59
Squirrel	6/1/2.11	Panther	30/7/3.00
Weasel	6/1/2.59	Zebra	54/7/3.00
Rabbit	6/1/3.55	Moose	54/7/3.53
Raccoon	6/1/4.09	Bersimis	42/4.57 (Al) + 7/2.54 (steel)
Dog	6/4.72 (Al) + 7/1.57 (steel)		

* number of strands/no. of steel strands/diameter of strands

10.3 REPRESENTATION OF LINE

For analysis purposes, a single-phase transmission line can be represented by series combination of ac resistance (r) and inductance (L) and shunt combination of conductance (g) and capacitance (C), as shown in Figure 10.1, where small sections of lines are added together to form the full-length line. The conductance of transmission line represents the leakage loss at the insulators of the supports. Three-phase transmission line can also be represented as a single-phase equivalent representation, if the line is balanced. These parameters are distributed in nature and are usually represented on loop-length basis in case of two-wire transmission system and on per conductor basis in case of three-phase transmission systems.

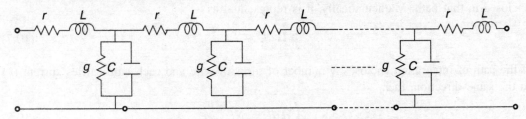

FIGURE 10.1 Distributed line parameters.

The transmission capacity of a line mainly depends on the inductance and the capacitance, as resistance and conductance are very small. The resistance used for analysis of transmission line performance is the effective (or ac) resistance. The direct current resistance (R_{dc}) of a conductor is defined as

$$R_{dc} = \frac{\rho l}{A} \text{ ohm} \tag{10.3}$$

where ρ = conductor resistivity, l = conductor length and A = conductor cross-section area. The ac resistance is more than dc resistance due to skin effect.

10.4 INDUCTORS AND INDUCTANCE

An *inductor* is a device that stores energy in a magnetic field. The *inductance* (L) is defined as the flux linkages per unit current. Mathematically it can be written, if the flux linkage linearly changes with the current, as

$$L = \frac{\text{Total magnetic flux linkage}}{\text{current, } I} = \frac{\lambda \, (= N\psi_m)}{I} \tag{10.4}$$

where λ is the total flux linkages (weber-turns) and ψ_m is the flux linkage in the coil. When the flux linkage does not linearly change with the current, inductance is defined as the ratio of infinitesimal change in flux linkage to infinitesimal change in current producing it and can be written as

$$L = \frac{d\lambda}{dI} \tag{10.5}$$

Mutual inductance between two circuits is defined as the ratio of flux linkages of one circuit to the current in the second circuit. If λ_{12} is flux linkage with circuit 1 produced by current I_2, the mutual inductance will be

$$M_{12} = \frac{\lambda_{12}}{I_2} \text{ henry}$$ (10.6)

10.5 AMPERE'S LAW

The line integral of magnetic flux intensity (**H**) around a closed path is equal to the current enclosed in that path. Mathematically, it is represented as

$$\oint \mathbf{H}\, dl = I$$ (10.7)

If the path of integration encloses N number of turns of wire and each wire carries current (I) in the same direction, then

$$\oint \mathbf{H}\, dl = NI$$ (10.8)

Using the Ampere's law, the magnetic field intensity (ampere-turn/metre) due to a long current carrying conductor as shown in Figure 10.2 can be derived as follows:

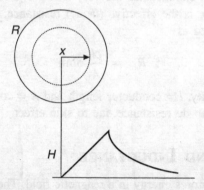

FIGURE 10.2 Variation of magnetic field intensity of a long conductor.

Let us assume that current is uniformly distributed in the conductor of radius R and the return path for the current in this conductor is so far away that magnetic field of the conductor is not affected. Magnetic field intensity will be different within and outside the conductor as the flux linkages due to internal flux and external flux are different.

Magnetic field intensity outside the conductor

Let us calculate the magnetic field intensity ($\mathbf{H}_x$) using Ampere's law at a distance x (>R). The length of enclosed path will be $2\pi x$ and the enclosed current is I. Using Equation (10.7),

$$\oint \mathbf{H}_x dl = I \quad \text{or} \quad \mathbf{H}_x 2\pi x = I$$ (10.9)

or

$$\mathbf{H}_x = \frac{I}{2\pi x} \tag{10.10}$$

This shows that magnetic field intensity is inversely proportional to the distance x, outside the conductor.

Magnetic field intensity inside the conductor

Let us calculate the magnetic field intensity ($\mathbf{H}_x$) using Ampere's Law at a distance x ($< R$). The length of enclosed path will be $2\pi x$ (Figure 10.2). Since the current density ($I_x/a' = I/a$) is same throughout the conductor where a' and a are the area of the conductor at radius x and R respectively, the enclosed current at x inside the conductor will be

$$I_x = I\frac{\pi x^2}{\pi R^2} \quad \text{or} \quad I_x = I\left(\frac{x}{R}\right)^2 \tag{10.11}$$

Using Ampere's law,

$$\oint \mathbf{H}_x dl = I_x \quad \text{or} \quad \mathbf{H}_x 2\pi x = I\left(\frac{x}{R}\right)^2 \tag{10.12}$$

or

$$\mathbf{H}_x = \frac{Ix}{2\pi R^2} \tag{10.13}$$

This indicates that magnetic field intensity at a distance x inside the conductor is directly proportional to the distance from the centre of the conductor. Following observation can be made from above calculations:

1. Magnetic field intensity at surface of the conductor is the highest.
2. Magnetic field intensity at the centre of the conductor is zero.
3. The presence of earth will affect the magnetic field geometry insignificantly.
4. Even the volume of the conductor is small, magnetic field energy ($W_e = 0.5\,\mu H^2$) stored is not small.

10.6 INDUCTANCE OF A CONDUCTOR

Inductance of a conductor is defined as the flux linkage per ampere. Since there are two flux linkages: one is due to the internal flux and second is due to the external flux, inductances corresponding to these fluxes are calculated separately. Following assumptions are made:

(a) Current density in the conductor is uniform
(b) Relative permeability of conductor material is unity.

Inductance due to internal flux linkages. Magnetic flux density (**B**) can be written using Equation (10.13) as

$$\mathbf{B} = \mu \mathbf{H} = \mu_0 \mu_r \mathbf{H} = \mu_0 \frac{Ix}{2\pi R^2}$$

This shows that flux density varies with the distance from the centre. Refer to Figure 10.3.

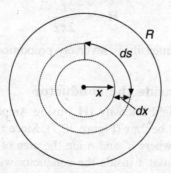

FIGURE 10.3 Cross-section of conductor.

Let us take magnetic field density ($\mathbf{B}_x$) is constant for small distance of dx at x from the centre. The flux ($d\phi$) passing through a small cylindrical shell of radii x and $x + dx$ will be

$$d\phi = \mathbf{B}_x dx l = \mu_0 I_x dx l/(2\pi R^2) \text{ Wb}$$

where l is the length of the wire. Since this flux links only the current enclosed in the radius of x, the flux linkage will be product of flux and number of turns. Thus

$$d\lambda = d\phi \left(\frac{x}{R}\right)^2 \quad \left(\text{since } \frac{I_x}{I} = \frac{\pi x^2}{\pi R^2}\right)$$

or

$$d\lambda = \mu_0 \frac{Ix}{2\pi R^2} \left(\frac{x}{R}\right)^2 dx \quad \text{(if length of wire } l = 1 \text{ metre)}$$

Thus total flux linkage will be

$$\lambda = \int_0^R d\lambda = \frac{I\mu_0}{2\pi R^4} \int_0^R x^3 dx = \frac{I\mu_0}{8\pi}$$

Inductance due to internal flux linkage (L_{int}) will be

$$L_{int} = \frac{\lambda}{I} = \frac{\mu_0}{8\pi} = \frac{10^{-7}}{2} \text{ H/m} \tag{10.14}$$

Inductance due to external flux linkages. Let us calculate the flux linkage between two points A and B at distances d_1 and d_2 respectively from the centre of the conductor. The flux density ($\mathbf{B}_x$) at distance x from the centre of the conductor, as shown in Figure 10.4, can be expressed using Equation (10.10) as

$$\mathbf{B}_x = \mu_0 \mu_r \mathbf{H}_x = \frac{\mu_0 I}{2\pi x} \text{ Wb/m}^2 \quad (\text{taking } \mu_r \cong 1)$$

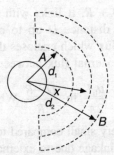

FIGURE 10.4 Flux linkage between two points.

Thus flux in the concentric circle shell will be

$$d\phi = \mathbf{B}_x dxl = \frac{\mu_0 I}{2\pi x} dx \, l \text{ Wb}$$

This flux links the current I and thus the total flux linkage between points A and B will be

$$\lambda = \frac{I\mu_0}{2\pi} \int_{d_1}^{d_2} \frac{1}{x} dx$$

$$= \frac{I\mu_0}{2\pi} \ln \frac{d_2}{d_1} \text{ Wb-T/m length of conductor}$$

Therefore, the inductance due to external flux will be

$$L_{\text{ext}} = \frac{\lambda}{I} = \frac{\mu_0}{2\pi} \ln \frac{d_2}{d_1} \text{ H/m} \tag{10.15}$$

10.7 INDUCTANCE OF A SINGLE-PHASE (TWO-WIRE) CONDUCTOR

Figure 10.5 shows an arrangement of one-phase two-wire system in which one conductor is used as return path. X denotes current passing through the conductor normal to the paper and the return current coming out of the paper is denoted by dot.

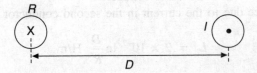

FIGURE 10.5 Single-phase two-wire system.

For conductor-1, there are two fluxes. One is due to the internal flux and other is due to external flux. The inductance due to internal flux will be the same as in Equation (10.14). The external flux will be from the distance R (radius of conductor) to $D + R$ but it should be noted that the flux links up to a distance $D - R$ (at the surface of the second conductor) with a current I and between $D - R$ and $D + R$, it links with varying current from I to zero. For simplicity, we can take the average distance D up to centre of the second conductor. For distances greater than D, there is no flux which encloses the conductor as sum of the current is zero. Therefore, flux linkage due to external flux between $D - R$ to R will be

$$\lambda_{\text{ext}} = \frac{\mu_0 I}{2\pi} \ln \frac{D - R}{R} \text{ Wb-T/m}$$

Normally, the radius of conductor is very small compared to the distance between the conductors ($R \ll D$). Thus $D - R \cong D$. The flux linkage due to external flux can be written as

$$\lambda_{\text{ext}} = \frac{\mu_0 I}{2\pi} \ln \frac{D}{R} \text{ Wb-T/m}$$

Total flux linkage of conductor-1 will be

$$\lambda = \lambda_{\text{int}} + \lambda_{\text{ext}} = \frac{\mu_0 I}{8\pi} + \frac{\mu_0 I}{2\pi} \ln \frac{D}{R} \text{ Wb-T/m} \tag{10.16}$$

Total inductance of the circuit due to the current in conductor-1 only is

$$L_1 = \frac{\lambda}{I} = \frac{\mu_0}{8\pi} + \frac{\mu_0}{2\pi} \ln \frac{D}{R}$$

$$= 2 \times 10^{-7} \left(\frac{1}{4} + \ln \frac{D}{R} \right)$$

$$= 2 \times 10^{-7} \left(\ln e^{1/4} + \ln \frac{D}{R} \right)$$

$$= 2 \times 10^{-7} \ln \frac{D}{e^{-1/4} R}$$

$$= 2 \times 10^{-7} \ln \frac{D}{R'} \text{ H/m} \tag{10.17}$$

Since $e^{-1/4}$ is equal to 0.7788, therefore R' (called as geometric mean radius G.M.R.) is equal to $0.7788R$. This multiplying factor of 0.7788 adjusts the radius in order to account for internal flux linkages, which applies to solid round conductor.

Similarly, inductance due to the current in the second conductor will be

$$L_2 = 2 \times 10^{-7} \ln \frac{D}{R'} \text{ H/m}$$

The inductance will be given by

$$L = L_1 + L_2 = 4 \times 10^{-7} \ln \frac{D}{R'} \text{ H/m} \tag{10.18}$$

Equation (10.18) can also be derived with the help of total flux linkages. The total flux linkages due to both the conductors will be the sum of the flux linkages caused by the currents flowing in both the conductors. Since the current in both the conductors is same, the total flux linkages will be double of Equation (10.16). The total inductance will be the total flux linkages divided by the current as

$$L = \frac{\lambda_1 + \lambda_2}{I}$$

$$= \frac{2\lambda}{I}$$

$$= \frac{\mu_0}{4\pi} + \frac{\mu_0}{\pi} \ln \frac{D}{R}$$

$$= 4 \times 10^{-7} \left(\frac{1}{4} + \ln \frac{D}{R} \right)$$

$$= 4 \times 10^{-7} \ln \frac{D}{R'} \text{ H/m}$$

This inductance is called *inductance per loop length* which is double of the inductance per conductor in a single-phase line.

10.8 FLUX LINKAGES IN A COMPOSITE CONDUCTOR—SELF AND MUTUAL GMD

Let us consider a group of n composite conductors electrically parallel, as shown in Figure 10.6. There will be two types of flux linkages: one due to current in conductor itself and second due to currents in the other conductors. If the currents carried by individual composite conductor are I_1, I_2, I_3, ..., I_n, their sum will be zero. The respective distance between each conductor and the point P that is very far from them as shown in the figure. Stranded conductors are also a type composite conductor and each strand shares equal current but the sum of currents are not zero.

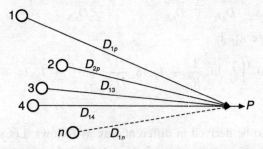

FIGURE 10.6 Group of n-composite conductors.

The flux linkage (internal and external) of conductor-1 (Equation 10.16), which is of radius R_1, due to its own current I_1, up to point P will be

$$\lambda_{1P1} = \frac{\mu_0 I_1}{8\pi} + \frac{\mu_0 I_1}{2\pi} \ln \frac{D_{1P}}{R_1} = 2 \times 10^{-7} I_1 \ln \frac{D_{1P}}{R_1'}$$

The flux linkage with conductor-1 due to current in conductor-2 within limiting distance D_{2P} and D_{12} will be

$$\lambda_{1P2} = 2 \times 10^{-7} I_2 \ln \frac{D_{2P}}{D_{12}}$$

Similarly, flux linkages with conductor-1 due to the currents in other conductors can be written. The total flux linkages with conductor-1 due to current in all the conductors will be

$$\lambda_{1P} = \lambda_{1P1} + \lambda_{1P2} + \lambda_{1P3} + \lambda_{1P4} + \cdots + \lambda_{1Pn}$$

$$= 2 \times 10^{-7} I_1 \ln \frac{D_{1P}}{R_1'} + 2 \times 10^{-7} I_2 \ln \frac{D_{2P}}{D_{12}} + \cdots + 2 \times 10^{-7} I_n \ln \frac{D_{nP}}{D_{1n}}$$

$$= 2 \times 10^{-7} \left(I_1 \ln \frac{1}{R_1'} + I_2 \ln \frac{1}{D_{12}} + \cdots + I_n \ln \frac{1}{D_{1n}} \right)$$

$$+ 2 \times 10^{-7} \left[I_1 \ln D_{1P} + I_2 \ln D_{2P} + \cdots + I_n \ln D_{nP} \right] \tag{10.19}$$

Since sum of the currents in all the conductors is zero, the current in the nth conductor can be written as $I_n = - (I_1 + I_2 + I_3 + \cdots + I_{n-1}]$. Putting this value in Equation (10.19) and simplifying, we get

$$\lambda_{1P} = 2 \times 10^{-7} \left(I_1 \ln \frac{1}{R_1'} + I_2 \ln \frac{1}{D_{12}} + \cdots + I_n \ln \frac{1}{D_{1n}} \right)$$

$$+ 2 \times 10^{-7} \left(I_1 \ln \frac{D_{1P}}{D_{nP}} + I_2 \ln \frac{D_{2P}}{D_{nP}} + \cdots + I_{n-1} \ln \frac{D_{(n-1)P}}{D_{nP}} \right)$$

As point P is very far away from composite conductors, the ratios

$$\frac{D_{1P}}{D_{nP}} \cong \frac{D_{2P}}{D_{nP}} \cong \cdots \cong \frac{D_{(n-1)P}}{D_{nP}} = 1$$

Thus, the net flux linkage λ_{1P} is

$$\lambda_{1P} = 2 \times 10^{-7} \left(I_1 \ln \frac{1}{R_1'} + I_2 \ln \frac{1}{D_{12}} + \cdots + I_n \ln \frac{1}{D_{1n}} \right) \text{Wb-T/m} \tag{10.20}$$

Alternate method

Equation (10.20) can also be derived in different way as follows. Let us take three conductors as shown in Figure 10.7.

Flux linkages of conductor-1 due to its own current I_1 will be (external flux due to current in conductor-1 will extend from R to infinity)

$$\lambda_{11} = \frac{I_1 \mu_0}{2\pi} \int_{R_1}^{\infty} \frac{dx}{x} + \frac{I_1 \mu_0}{8\pi}$$

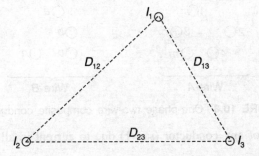

FIGURE 10.7 Flux linkage of one conductor in group of three conductors.

Flux linkages of conductor-1 due to current I_2 in conductor-2 will be (flux due to current in conductor-2 will be enclosed from D_{12} to infinity),

$$\lambda_{12} = \frac{I_2 \mu_0}{2\pi} \int_{D_{12}}^{\infty} \frac{dx}{x}$$

Similarly, flux linkages of conductor-1 due to current I_3 will be

$$\lambda_{13} = \frac{I_3 \mu_0}{2\pi} \int_{D_{13}}^{\infty} \frac{dx}{x}$$

Total flux linkages of conductor-1 will be

$$\lambda_1 = 2 \times 10^{-7} \left(I_1 \ln \frac{\infty}{R_1'} + I_2 \ln \frac{\infty}{D_{12}} + I_3 \ln \frac{\infty}{D_{13}} \right)$$

$$= 2 \times 10^{-7} \left(I_1 \ln \frac{1}{R_1'} + I_2 \ln \frac{1}{D_{12}} + I_3 \ln \frac{1}{D_{13}} \right) + 2 \times 10^{-7} \left[(I_1 + I_2 + I_3) \ln \infty \right]$$

Since $I_1 + I_2 + I_3 = 0$, thus second term will be vanished

$$\lambda_1 = 2 \times 10^{-7} \left(I_1 \ln \frac{1}{R_1'} + I_2 \ln \frac{1}{D_{12}} + I_3 \ln \frac{1}{D_{13}} \right)$$

This equation can be generalized as Equation (10.20) for n conductors in a group.

10.9 INDUCTANCE OF ONE-PHASE TWO-WIRE (COMPOSITE-CONDUCTORS) LINE

Let us assume, two wires A and B consist of respectively m and n composite conductors, as shown in Figure 10.8. The current in each conductor of wire-A will be I/m and of wire-B will be $-I/n$. One group of conductors acts as a 'go' conductors for single-phase line and the other as the 'return' conductors.

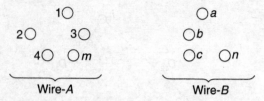

FIGURE 10.8 One-phase two-wire composite conductors.

The flux linkages of any conductor (say 1) due to current in all conductors will be

$$\lambda_1 = 2 \times 10^{-7} \left(\frac{I}{m} \ln \frac{1}{D_{11}} + \frac{I}{m} \ln \frac{1}{D_{12}} + \cdots + \frac{I}{m} \ln \frac{1}{D_{1m}} \right)$$

$$+ 2 \times 10^{-7} \left(-\frac{I}{n} \ln \frac{1}{D_{1a}} - \frac{I}{n} \ln \frac{1}{D_{1b}} - \cdots - \frac{I}{n} \ln \frac{1}{D_{1n}} \right)$$

$$= 2 \times 10^{-7} \, I \, \ln \frac{\sqrt[n]{D_{1a} D_{1b} \cdots D_{1n}}}{\sqrt[m]{D_{11} D_{12} \cdots D_{1m}}}$$

The inductance of conductor-1 in wire-*A* will be

$$L_1 = \frac{\lambda_1}{I/m} = 2m \times 10^{-7} \ln \frac{\sqrt[n]{D_{1a} D_{1b} \cdots D_{1n}}}{\sqrt[m]{D_{11} D_{12} \cdots D_{1m}}}$$

Similarly, the inductance of conductor-2 in wire-*A* will be

$$L_2 = \frac{\lambda_2}{I/m} = 2m \times 10^{-7} \ln \frac{\sqrt[n]{D_{2a} D_{2b} \cdots D_{2n}}}{\sqrt[m]{D_{21} D_{22} \cdots D_{2m}}}$$

The average inductance of *m* conductors in wire-*A*

$$L_{\text{avg}} = \frac{L_1 + L_2 + \cdots + L_m}{m}$$

Since wire-*A* consist of *m* conductors electrically in parallel, the inductance of wire-*A* will be

$$L_A = \frac{L_{\text{avg}}}{m} = \frac{L_1 + L_2 + L_3 + \cdots + L_m}{m^2}$$

$$= 2 \times 10^{-7} \ln \frac{\sqrt[mn]{(D_{1a} D_{1b} \cdots D_{1n})(D_{2a} D_{2b} \cdots D_{2n}) \cdots (D_{ma} D_{mb} \cdots D_{mn})}}{\sqrt[m^2]{(D_{11} D_{12} \cdots D_{1m})(D_{21} D_{22} \cdots D_{2m}) \cdots (D_{m1} D_{m2} \cdots D_{mm})}} \quad (10.21)$$

where $D_{11}, D_{22}, \ldots, D_{mm}$ represent the 0.7788 times the radius of conductors 1, 2, ..., *m* respectively.

The numerator of argument of natural log (*mn*th root of the product of the *mn* distances between *m* conductors of wire-*A* and *n* conductors of wire-*B*) is called *geometric mean distance* (GMD, often called *mutual GMD*) and denoted by D_m. The denominator of argument of log, which is the m^2 root of m^2 distances, i.e. the distances of the various conductors from one conductor and the radius of the same conductor, is called *geometric mean radius* (GMR, also called *self GMD*) and denoted by D_s. Then, the inductances of conductors will be

$$L_A = 2 \times 10^{-7} \ln \frac{D_m}{D_{sA}} \text{ H/m} \tag{10.22}$$

Inductance of wire-*B* can also be obtained as

$$L_B = 2 \times 10^{-7} \ln \frac{D_m}{D_{sB}} \text{ H/m}$$

The total inductance of composite conductors of both wires will be

$$L = L_A + L_B = 2 \times 10^{-7} \ln \left(\frac{D_m}{D_{sA}} \frac{D_m}{D_{sB}} \right) \text{ H/m}$$

If the wires *A* and *B* are identical, $D_{sA} = D_{sB}$.

10.10 INDUCTANCE OF THREE-PHASE TRANSMISSION LINE

A single circuit, 3-phase system as shown in Figure 10.9, is having three wires (conductors) *a*, *b* and *c* with current I_a, I_b and I_c respectively. Let us assume that radius of each conductor is *R*. The flux linkage of conductor *a* due to currents I_a, I_b and I_c, using Equation (10.20), can be written as

$$\lambda_a = 2 \times 10^{-7} \left(I_a \ln \frac{1}{R'} + I_b \ln \frac{1}{D_{ab}} + I_c \ln \frac{1}{D_{ac}} \right)$$

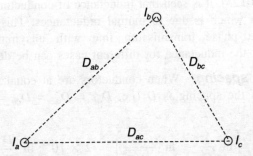

FIGURE 10.9 Three-phase transmission line with unsymmetrical spacing.

Similarly λ_b and λ_c can be expressed as

$$\lambda_b = 2 \times 10^{-7} \left(I_a \ln \frac{1}{D_{ab}} + I_b \ln \frac{1}{R'} + I_c \ln \frac{1}{D_{cb}} \right)$$

and

$$\lambda_c = 2 \times 10^{-7} \left(I_a \ln \frac{1}{D_{ac}} + I_b \ln \frac{1}{D_{cb}} + I_c \ln \frac{1}{R'} \right)$$

If currents in phases are symmetrical, the phase current I_b and I_c can be represented in terms of phase current I_a, as follows:

$$I_b = I_a \angle -120° = \alpha^2 I_a \quad \text{and} \quad I_c = I_a \angle 120° = \alpha I_a$$

where $\alpha^2 = -0.5 + j0.866$. Putting the values of I_b and I_c in the expression of I_a, we have

$$\lambda_a = 2 \times 10^{-7} \left[I_a \ln \frac{1}{R'} + I_a(-0.5 - j0.866) \ln \frac{1}{D_{ab}} + I_a(-0.5 + j0.866) \ln \frac{1}{D_{ac}} \right]$$

Thus inductance of conductor a will be

$$L_a = \frac{\lambda_a}{I_a} = 2 \times 10^{-7} \left[\ln \frac{\lambda_a}{R'} + (-0.5 - j0.866) \ln \frac{1}{D_{ab}} + (-0.5 + j0.866) \ln \frac{1}{D_{ac}} \right]$$

$$= 2 \times 10^{-7} \left(\ln \frac{1}{R'} - \ln \frac{1}{\sqrt{D_{ab} D_{ac}}} - j\frac{\sqrt{3}}{2} \ln \frac{D_{ac}}{D_{ab}} \right) \tag{10.23}$$

Similarly

$$L_b = 2 \times 10^{-7} \left(\ln \frac{1}{R'} - \ln \frac{1}{\sqrt{D_{ab} D_{cb}}} - j\frac{\sqrt{3}}{2} \ln \frac{D_{ab}}{D_{cb}} \right) \tag{10.24}$$

and

$$L_c = 2 \times 10^{-7} \left(\ln \frac{1}{R'} - \ln \frac{1}{\sqrt{D_{ac} D_{cb}}} - j\frac{\sqrt{3}}{2} \ln \frac{D_{cb}}{D_{ac}} \right) \tag{10.25}$$

From Equations (10.23–10.25), it is seen that inductance of conductors a, b and c are unequal and have imaginary part which is due to mutual inductances. This is a general derivation for single circuit, three-phase transmission line with unsymmetrical spacing. From Equations (10.23–10.25), the inductance for different cases can be derived as follows:

Conductors at equal spacing. When conductors are at equal spacing, they are called *symmetrically* spaced. If the spacing is D (i.e. $D_{ab} = D_{ac} = D_{cb} = D$), the inductance of conductors will be

$$L_a = 2 \times 10^{-7} \left(\ln \frac{1}{R'} - \ln \frac{1}{\sqrt{DD}} \right) = 2 \times 10^{-7} \ln \frac{D}{R'} = L_b = L_c$$

This indicates that if spacing between the conductors is same, whether they are transposed or not, the inductance of each phase is equal and there is no imaginary components.

Line is transposed. Transposing of power conductors means changing the position of phase conductors at regular interval along the line so that each conductor occupy others positions over an equal distance, as shown in Figure 10.10. If transmission lines are not transposed, the voltage drop in the transmission line will not be the same due to unequal inductances. Another problem is the radio interference because external flux outside the conductors is not zero.

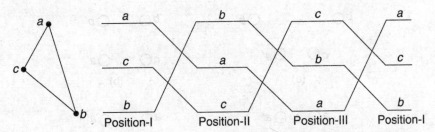

FIGURE 10.10 Transposition of lines.

Normally, modern power lines are not transposed, however, it is done at the stations. The effects of difference in inductance are very small in the case of asymmetrical spacing. The inductance of untransposed line is taken as average value of inductances.

If a line is transposed, each line will take all the three positions for the one-third length of the line. The average value of inductance will be

$$L = \frac{L_a + L_b + L_c}{3} = \frac{2}{3} \times 10^{-7} \left(3 \ln \frac{1}{R'} - \ln \frac{1}{\sqrt{D_{ab}D_{cb}D_{ab}D_{ac}D_{ca}D_{cb}}} \right)$$

$$= 2 \times 10^{-7} \left(\ln \frac{1}{R'} - \frac{1}{3} \ln \frac{1}{D_{ab}D_{bc}D_{ca}} \right)$$

$$= 2 \times 10^{-7} \ln \frac{\sqrt[3]{D_{ab}D_{bc}D_{ca}}}{R'} \text{ H/m}$$

Thus GMD will be

$$D_m = D_{eq} = \sqrt[3]{D_{ab}D_{bc}D_{ca}}$$

For the equilateral spacing $D_m = D$.

10.11 INDUCTANCE OF A THREE-PHASE DOUBLE-CIRCUIT LINE

To increase power transfer from one point to another point, transmission lines run in parallel, normally on the same tower, are called *double circuit*. There are different configurations possible: symmetrically spaced and asymmetrically spaced. If these circuits are on the same tower, the effect of self and mutual inductance are more than if they are on the different towers. The main aim to run more than one circuit is to reduce the inductance of the equivalent circuit. It can be seen from Equation (10.22) that for low inductance, the D_m should be low and D_s should be as high as possible. Therefore, the rule is to separate the individual conductors of a phase as widely as possible and keep the distance between the phases small. So, in the case of double circuit line, arrangement of Figures 10.11(a) and 10.11(b) are preferred to the arrangements as shown in Figures 10.11(c) and 10.11(d). Conductors a and a' are connected in parallel and form one phase of supply.

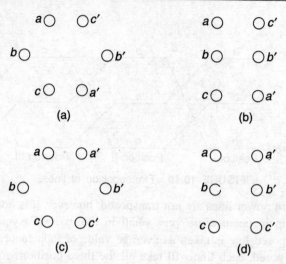

FIGURE 10.11 Three-phase, double-circuit arrangements.

Inductance with symmetrical spacing

Inductance can be calculated from the basic theory of flux linkages or with GMD and GMR concepts. For symmetrical spacing, the conductors must be placed at the vertices of a regular hexagonal, as shown in Figure 10.12. Conductors a, b and c belongs to one circuit and a', b' and c' are of second circuit. The words a, b, c denoted the respective phases of the system. From Figure 10.12,

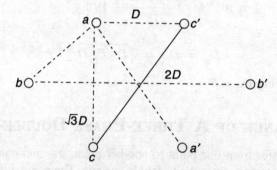

FIGURE 10.12 Three-phase, double-circuit with symmetrical spacing.

$$D_{ab} = D_{bc} = D_{ac'} = D_{c'b'} = D_{ca'} = D_{b'a'} = D$$

$$D_{ac} = D_{b'c} = D_{c'a'} = D_{bc'} = D_{ba'} = D_{ab'} = \sqrt{3}D$$

$$D_{aa'} = D_{bb'} = D_{cc'} = 2D.$$

Let us assume a balance case, i.e. $I_a + I_b + I_c = 0$ and radius of each conductor is R.

Method 1: Flux linkages approach.

Flux linkage of conductor a

$$\lambda_a = 2 \times 10^{-7}\left[I_a\left(\ln\frac{1}{R'} + \ln\frac{1}{2D}\right) + I_b\left(\ln\frac{1}{D} + \ln\frac{1}{\sqrt{3}D}\right) + I_c\left(\ln\frac{1}{\sqrt{3}D} + \ln\frac{1}{D}\right)\right]$$

$$= 2 \times 10^{-7}\left[I_a\left(\ln\frac{1}{2DR'}\right) + I_b\left(\ln\frac{1}{\sqrt{3}D^2}\right) + I_c\left(\ln\frac{1}{\sqrt{3}D^2}\right)\right]$$

$$= 2 \times 10^{-7}\left[I_a\left(\ln\frac{1}{2DR'}\right) + (I_b + I_c)\left(\ln\frac{1}{\sqrt{3}D^2}\right)\right]$$

Substituting the value of $I_b + I_c = -I_a$, we get

$$\lambda_a = 2 \times 10^{-7}\left[I_a\left(\ln\frac{1}{2DR'}\right) - I_a\left(\ln\frac{1}{\sqrt{3}D^2}\right)\right]$$

$$= 2 \times 10^{-7}\left[I_a\left(\ln\frac{\sqrt{3}D^2}{2DR'}\right)\right]$$

$$= 2 \times 10^{-7}\,I_a\left(\ln\frac{\sqrt{3}D}{2R'}\right) \text{ Wb-T/m}$$

Hence the inductance of conductor a will be

$$L_a = \frac{\lambda_a}{I_a} = 2 \times 10^{-7}\left(\ln\frac{\sqrt{3}D}{2R'}\right) \text{ H/m} \tag{10.26}$$

Since the conductors of a phase are in parallel, the inductance of phase a will be $L_a/2$.

Method 2: GMR and GMD approach.

Mutual GMD of phase a is

$$\sqrt[8]{D_{ab}D_{ac}D_{ab'}D_{ac'}D_{a'b}D_{a'c}D_{a'b'}D_{a'c'}} = \sqrt[8]{D\sqrt{3}D\sqrt{3}D\,D\sqrt{3}DD\,D\sqrt{3}D} = \sqrt[4]{3}D$$

and

Self-GMD (or GMR) of phase $a = \sqrt[4]{R'D_{aa'}D_{aa'}R'} = \sqrt[4]{R'2D2DR'} = \sqrt{2DR'}$

Inductance of phase a using Equation (10.22) will be

$$L_A = 2 \times 10^{-7}\left(\ln\frac{D_m}{D_{sA}}\right) = 2 \times 10^{-7}\left(\ln\frac{\sqrt[4]{3}D}{\sqrt{2DR'}}\right)$$

$$= 2 \times 10^{-7}\left(\frac{1}{2}\ln\frac{\sqrt{3}D}{2R'}\right) = 1 \times 10^{-7}\left(\ln\frac{\sqrt{3}D}{2R'}\right) \text{ H/m}$$

Inductance of each conductor will be $2 \times L_A$ which will be

$$2 \times 10^{-7} \left(\ln \frac{\sqrt{3}D}{2R'} \right) \text{H/m}$$

It is same as in Equation (10.26). It must be noted that using GMD and GMR concept, inductance of phase (not conductor) is calculated.

Inductance with unsymmetrical spacing (transposed lines)

Since the conductors are not symmetrically placed, to calculate the inductance of the line, the line should be assumed to be transposed. If transposition is not there, there will be imaginary terms in inductance. Figure 10.13 shows the possible arrangement of transposed lines.

To remember the sequence of the transposition, the position of phases of first circuit will move downward in cycle and the phases of second circuit will move upward cyclically.

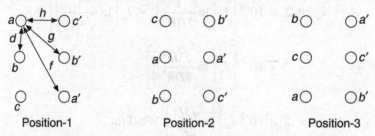

FIGURE 10.13 Three-phase double-circuit arrangements.

Method 1: Flux linkages approach. Flux linkages of conductor a in position-1

$$\lambda_{a1} = 2 \times 10^{-7} \left[I_a \left(\ln \frac{1}{R'} + \ln \frac{1}{f} \right) + I_b \left(\ln \frac{1}{d} + \ln \frac{1}{g} \right) + I_c \left(\frac{1}{2d} + \ln \frac{1}{h} \right) \right]$$

$$= 2 \times 10^{-7} \left[I_a \left(\ln \frac{1}{R'f} \right) + I_b \left(\ln \frac{1}{dg} \right) + I_c \left(\ln \frac{1}{2dh} \right) \right]$$

Similarly, flux linkages of conductor a in position-2 and position-3 will be

$$\lambda_{a2} = 2 \times 10^{-7} \left[I_a \left(\ln \frac{1}{R'} + \ln \frac{1}{h} \right) + I_b \left(\ln \frac{1}{d} + \ln \frac{1}{g} \right) + I_c \left(\ln \frac{1}{d} + \ln \frac{1}{g} \right) \right]$$

$$= 2 \times 10^{-7} \left[I_a \left(\ln \frac{1}{R'h} \right) + I_b \left(\ln \frac{1}{dg} \right) + I_c \left(\ln \frac{1}{dg} \right) \right]$$

$$\lambda_{a3} = 2 \times 10^{-7} \left[I_a \left(\ln \frac{1}{R'} + \ln \frac{1}{f} \right) + I_b \left(\ln \frac{1}{2d} + \ln \frac{1}{h} \right) + I_c \left(\ln \frac{1}{d} + \ln \frac{1}{g} \right) \right]$$

$$= 2 \times 10^{-7} \left[I_a \left(\ln \frac{1}{R'f} \right) + I_b \left(\ln \frac{1}{2dh} \right) + I_c \left(\ln \frac{1}{dg} \right) \right]$$

The average flux linkages of conductor $a(\lambda_a)$ will be $(\lambda_{a1} + \lambda_{a2} + \lambda_{a3})/3$. Hence

$$\lambda_a = \frac{2 \times 10^{-7}}{3}\left[I_a\left(\ln\frac{1}{R'fR'hR'f}\right) + I_b\left(\ln\frac{1}{dgdg2dh}\right) + I_c\left(\ln\frac{1}{2dhdgdg}\right)\right]$$

$$= \frac{2 \times 10^{-7}}{3}\left[I_a\left(\ln\frac{1}{R'fR'hR'f}\right) + (I_b + I_c)\left(\ln\frac{1}{2dhdgdg}\right)\right]$$

Substituting the value of $I_b + I_c = -I_a$, we get

$$\lambda_a = \frac{2 \times 10^{-7}}{3}\left[I_a\left(\ln\frac{1}{R'fR'hR'f}\right) - I_a\left(\ln\frac{1}{2dhdgdg}\right)\right]$$

$$= \frac{2 \times 10^{-7}}{3}\left[I_a\left(\ln\frac{2dhdgdg}{R'fR'hR'f}\right)\right]$$

$$= 2 \times 10^{-7} I_a\left(\ln\frac{2^{1/3}dg^{2/3}}{R'f^{2/3}}\right)$$

Hence inductance of conductor a will be

$$L_a = \frac{\lambda_a}{I_a} = 2 \times 10^{-7}\ \ln\left[2^{1/3}\left(\frac{d}{R'}\right)\left(\frac{g}{f}\right)^{2/3}\right] \text{H/m} \qquad (10.27)$$

Since the conductors of a phase are in parallel, the inductance of phase a will be $L_a/2$.

Method 2: GMR and GMD approach. Mutual GMD of phase a in position-1,

$$\text{GMD}_1 = \sqrt[4]{D_{ab}D_{ac}D_{ab'}D_{ac'}} = \sqrt[4]{d(2d)gh}$$

Similarly, mutual GMD of phase a in position-2 and position-3 can be written as

$$\text{GMD}_2 = \sqrt[4]{D_{ab}D_{ac}D_{ab'}D_{ac'}} = \sqrt[4]{ddgg}$$

and

$$\text{GMD}_3 = \sqrt[4]{D_{ab}D_{ac}D_{ab'}D_{ac'}} = \sqrt[4]{2ddhg}$$

(Note that GMD_1 is of conductor a only and for a' it will be the same. Therefore, the effective GMD of phase a will be equal to the GMD of conductor a.)

Self-GMD (or GMR) of phase a in position-1,

$$\text{GMR}_1 = \sqrt[2]{R'D_{aa'}} = \sqrt{R'f}$$

Similarly self-GMR of phase a in position-2 and position-3 can be written as

$$\text{GMR}_2 = \sqrt{R'D_{aa'}} = \sqrt{R'h} \quad \text{and} \quad \text{GMR}_3 = \sqrt{R'D_{aa'}} = \sqrt{R'f}$$

The equivalent GMD (D_m) and GMR (D_s) of the system will be

$$
\begin{aligned}
D_m &= \sqrt[3]{\text{GMD}_1 \times \text{GMD}_2 \times \text{GMD}_3} \\
&= \sqrt[3]{(d \times 2d \times g \times h)^{1/4}(d \times d \times g \times g)^{1/4}(2d \times d \times h \times g)^{1/4}} \\
&= 2^{1/6} d^{1/2} g^{1/3} h^{1/6}
\end{aligned}
$$

and

$$
\begin{aligned}
D_s &= \sqrt[3]{\text{GMR}_1 \times \text{GMR}_2 \times \text{GMR}_3} \\
&= \sqrt[3]{(R'f)^{1/2}(R'h)^{1/2}(R'f)^{1/2}} \\
&= R'^{1/2} f^{1/3} h^{1/6}
\end{aligned}
$$

Inductance of phase a using Equation (10.22) will be

$$L_A = 2 \times 10^{-7}\left(\ln\frac{D_m}{D_{sA}}\right) = 2 \times 10^{-7}\left(\ln\frac{2^{1/6} d^{1/2} g^{1/3} h^{1/6}}{R'^{1/2} h^{1/6} f^{1/3}}\right) = 2 \times 10^{-7}\left(\ln\frac{2^{1/6} d^{1/2} g^{1/3}}{R'^{1/2} f^{1/3}}\right)$$

Inductance of each conductor will be $2L_A$. Therefore,

$$L_a = 2 \times 10^{-7}\left(\ln\frac{2^{1/3} d g^{2/3}}{R' f^{2/3}}\right)$$

It is same as in Equation (10.27).

It should be noted that GMD concept could not be applied to non-homogeneous conductors. If the current is not uniformly distributed over the section of conductor, GMD approach will not be suitable. It is defined as GMD of a point with respect to a number of points, which is the geometric mean distance between that point and other points. It can also be applied to the area.

10.12   BUNDLED CONDUCTORS

Stranded or composite conductors touch each other, however, bundled conductors are separated from each other by 30 cm or more and conductors of each phase are connected by conducting wires at particular length. Figure 10.14 shows the stranded and bundled conductors. For the voltage rating more than 230 kV, it is not possible to use the round conductors due to excessive corona loss. It is preferred to have the hollow conductor, normally in substations, and bundled conductors in transmission lines. The main advantages of using bundled conductors are:

- Reduced corona loss
- Reduced voltage gradient at the surface of the conductor
- Low reactance due to increase in the self-GMD

- Reduced radio interference
- Increase in capacitance
- Larger loading capability and
- Increase surge impedance loading.

The reactance of bundled conductors can be calculated with the help of GMD and GMR approach.

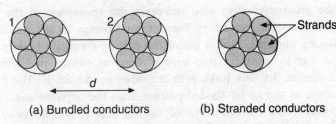

(a) Bundled conductors   (b) Stranded conductors

FIGURE 10.14 Bundled and stranded conductors.

10.13 SKIN EFFECT

The alternating current distribution in a wire is not uniform. The current density near the surface is more than near to the centre. It is affected by the frequency of the current. If the frequency of current is more, the current distribution is more non-uniform. This effect is known as *skin effect*. Due to this effect the effective resistance (or ac resistance of the conductors) becomes more than the direct current (dc), where the current distribution is uniform, resistance (called the dc resistance). This can be understood by an example.

Consider a solid current carrying conductor of circular cross-section, as shown in Figure 10.15. This can be replaced by a large number of conductors bunched together with small radii. These conductors occupy the same cross-sectional area. If the current is same, the loss can be calculated in both the cases and thus the effective resistance. In n strands, each of resistance nR ohm carries a uniformly distributed current (of I/n ampere). The loss will be same as a single conductor (I^2R). Let us assume half of the conductors ($n/2$) carry currents of $[(I/n) + \Delta I]$ ampere and the other half ($n/2$) carry $[(I/n) - \Delta I]$ ampere. The total loss is

$$\frac{n}{2}\left(\frac{I}{n} + \Delta I\right)^2 nR + \frac{n}{2}\left(\frac{I}{n} - \Delta I\right)^2 nR = \frac{n^2R}{2}\left[2\left(\frac{I}{n}\right)^2 + 2\Delta I^2\right] = I^2R + n^2R\Delta I^2$$

which is greater than I^2R. This indicates that the effective resistance will be more than the dc resistance if current distribution is not uniform.

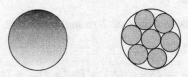

FIGURE 10.15 Skin effect.

Due to non-uniformity of current, skin effect, the flux linkages are reduced and thus skin effect reduces the effective internal reactance. The inner filaments carrying currents give rise to flux which links the inner filaments only whereas the flux due to the current carrying outer filaments enclose both inner and outer filaments.

10.14 PROXIMITY EFFECT

Like skin effect, the *proximity effect* also increases the resistance of the conductor. The alternating flux in a conductor caused by the current flowing in neighbouring conductors gives rise to circulating currents, which cause the non-uniformity of the current and thus increases resistance. Let us consider two-wire system, as shown in Figure 10.16. When conductor A carries current, its flux links with the other conductor B. The flux linkages are nearer to the conductor, as shown by shaded portion, than the opposite side. If the current in conductor B is opposite to the current in A, the current density will be more in the adjacent portion of the conductor. If the current direction is same, the current density will be more in the remote part of the conductor. Due to this non-uniformity, the effective resistance is more than the dc resistance.

FIGURE 10.16 Proximity effect.

This effect is more pronounced in cable where the phase conductors are nearer to each other. The proximity effect is negligible in overhead transmission line. Both skin effect and proximity effect depend on the conductor size, frequency of the supply, resistivity and permeability of the conductor material. For the circular conductors, the increase in effective resistance is proportional to $d^2 f \mu_r / \rho$, where d is the diameter of the conductor.

10.15 GUY'S THEOREM

If the number of strands is more, it is very cumbersome to calculate the effective radius of the conductor. These can be calculated by Guy's Theorem. It is stated as:

1. GMD between n conductors symmetrically placed on the periphery of a circle of radius r will be $r \times (n)^{1/(r-1)}$.
2. GMD of any point inside the circle from a line or point placed on the periphery of a circle of radius r will be r.

Example 10.1 Find the equivalent radius of 7-strand conductor. The radius of each strand is r.

Solution From Figure 10.17,

$$D_{12} = D_{23} = D_{34} = D_{45} = D_{56} = D_{17} = D_{27} = D_{37} = D_{47} = D_{57} = D_{67} = 2r$$

$$D_{11} = D_{22} = \ldots = 0.7788r$$
$$D_{14} = D_{25} = D_{36} = 4r$$
$$D_{13} = D_{24} = D_{35} = D_{46} = 2 \times 2r \times \sin(60°) = (2\sqrt{3})r$$

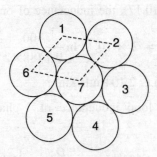

FIGURE 10.17 Example 10.1.

Self-GMD of strand-1,

$$D_{s1} = \sqrt[7]{D_{11}D_{12}D_{13}D_{14}D_{15}D_{16}D_{17}} = \sqrt[7]{0.7788r \times 2r \times (2\sqrt{3})r \times 4r \times (2\sqrt{3})r \times 2r \times 2r} = 2.2578r$$

Since strands 2, 3, 4, 5 and 6 are on the periphery of the conductor, they are in symmetrical and the self-GMD of these strands will be similar to strand-1. However, the self-GMD of strand-7 will be

$$D_{s7} = \sqrt[7]{D_{71}D_{72}D_{73}D_{74}D_{75}D_{76}D_{77}} = \sqrt[7]{2r \times 2r \times 2r \times 2r \times 2r \times 2r \times 0.7788r} = 1.7479r$$

Therefore

$$D_s = \sqrt[7]{D_{s1}D_{s2}D_{s3}D_{s4}D_{s5}D_{s6}D_{s7}} = \left[(2.2578)^6 \times (1.7479)\right]^{1/7} r = 2.176r$$

Example 10.2 If the equivalent radius of each conductor is r. Find the equivalent radius or self-GMD of four bundled conductor separated by distance d from their centres.

Solution In Figure 10.18, as the conductors are symmetrically placed, the self-GMD of one will be equal to the others. Self-GMD of conductor-1 will be

$$D_{s1} = \sqrt[4]{0.7788r \times d \times \sqrt{2}d \times d} = 1.024 \, r^{1/4} \, d^{3/4}$$

Therefore

$$D_s = 1.024r^{1/4} \, d^{3/4}$$

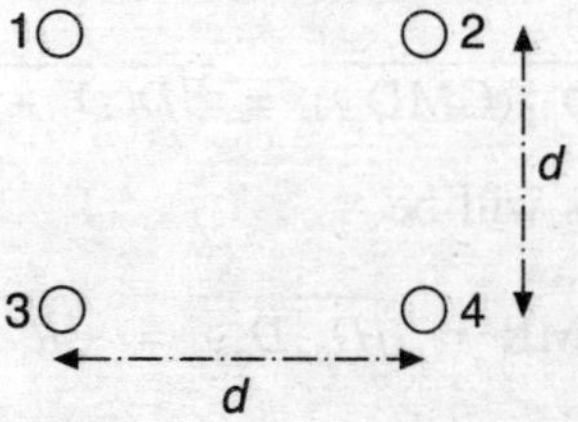

$$1 \bigcirc \qquad \bigcirc 2$$
$$\Big\updownarrow d$$
$$3 \bigcirc \xleftarrow{\qquad d \qquad} \bigcirc 4$$

FIGURE 10.18 Example 9.2.

Example 10.3   Two wires of single-phase transmission line are separated by 3 m. The radius of each conductor is 0.02 m. Find the loop inductance of the line. What will be the inductance of each conductor?

Solution   Using Equation (10.17), the inductance of one conductor will be

$$L_1 = 2 \times 10^{-7} \left(\ln \frac{D}{R'} \right) = 2 \times 10^{-7} \left(\ln \frac{300}{0.7788 \times 2} \right) = 1.052 \times 10^{-6} \text{ H/m}$$

Loop inductance will be $2 \times L_1$, i.e. 2.104 mH/km.

Example 10.4   Show that the loop inductance of 1-phase line arranged, as shown in Figure 10.19, will be

$$4 \times 10^{-7} \left(\ln \frac{D}{\sqrt{0.7788Rd}} \right) \text{H/m}$$

if $d \ll D$, where R is the radius of each conductor.

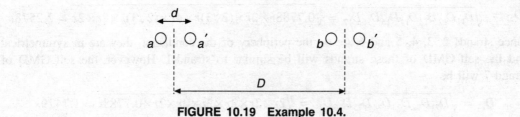

FIGURE 10.19   Example 10.4.

Solution   Using GMD and GMR, loop inductance, as in Equation (10.22), will be

$$4 \times 10^{-7} \left(\ln \frac{D_m}{D_s} \right) \text{ H/m}$$

where D_m is mutual GMD and D_s is self-GMD or GMR. Mutual GMD of conductor a and a' will be

$$\text{GMD}_a = \sqrt{D_{ab}D_{ab'}} = \sqrt{D(D + d)}$$

and

$$\text{GMD}_{a'} = \sqrt{D_{a'b}D_{a'b'}} = \sqrt{(D-d)D}$$

Since the return wire conductors b and b' are in the same configuration as "go" conductors a and a', the GMDs will also be the same. Therefore, mutual GMD will be

$$D_m = \sqrt{(\text{GMD}_a)(\text{GMD}_{a'})} = \sqrt[4]{D(D + d)D(D - d)}$$

Similarly GMR of "go" conductors will be

$$\text{GMR} = \sqrt{D_{aa}D_{aa'}} = \sqrt{R'd}$$

If $D \gg d$, $D_m = D$, thus loop inductance will be

$$4 \times 10^{-7} \left(\ln \frac{D}{\sqrt{0.7788Rd}} \right) \text{ H/m}$$

Example 10.5 Determine the inductance of 3-phase line arranged, as shown in Figure 10.20. The radius of each conductor is 0.03 m. The spacing between phase conductors is 35 cm and distance between the phases (D) is equal to 4 m.

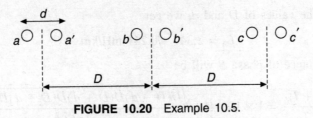

FIGURE 10.20 Example 10.5.

Solution Flux linkage of conductor a,

$$\lambda_a = 2 \times 10^{-7} \left[I_a \left(\ln \frac{1}{R'} + \ln \frac{1}{d} \right) + I_b \left(\ln \frac{1}{D} + \ln \frac{1}{D+d} \right) + I_c \left(\ln \frac{1}{2D} + \ln \frac{1}{2D+d} \right) \right]$$

Inductance of conductor a will be

$$L_a = \frac{\lambda_a}{I_a} = 2 \times 10^{-7} \left[\left(\ln \frac{1}{R'd} \right) + \frac{I_b}{I_a} \left(\ln \frac{1}{D(D+d)} \right) + \frac{I_c}{I_a} \left(\ln \frac{1}{2D(2D+d)} \right) \right]$$

If the supply is balanced, we can represent currents I_b and I_c in terms of I_a as

$$I_b = (-0.5 - j0.866)I_a \quad \text{and} \quad I_c = (-0.5 + j0.866)I_a$$

Putting these values in above equation we get

$$L_a = 2 \times 10^{-7} \left\{ \left(\ln \frac{1}{R'd} \right) + (-0.5 - j0.866) \left[\ln \frac{1}{D(D+d)} \right] + (-0.5 + j0.866) \left[\ln \frac{1}{2D(2D+d)} \right] \right\}$$

$$= 2 \times 10^{-7} \left\{ \ln \frac{\sqrt{D(D+d)2D(2D+d)}}{R'd} + j0.866 \left[\ln \frac{D(D+d)}{2D(2D+d)} \right] \right\}$$

Inductance of conductor a' will be

$$L_{a'} = 2 \times 10^{-7} \left\{ \left(\ln \frac{1}{R'd} \right) + \frac{I_b}{I_a} \left[\ln \frac{1}{D(D-d)} \right] + \frac{I_c}{I_a} \left[\ln \frac{1}{2D(2D-d)} \right] \right\}$$

$$= 2 \times 10^{-7} \left\{ \ln \frac{\sqrt{D(D-d)2D(2D-d)}}{R'd} + j0.866 \left[\ln \frac{D(D-d)}{2D(2D-d)} \right] \right\}$$

Since conductors a and a' are in parallel, the inductance of phase A will be

$$L_A = \frac{L_a + L_{a'}}{2} = 1 \times 10^{-7} \left\{ \ln \frac{\sqrt{D(D + d)2D(2D + d)D(D - d)2D(2D - d)}}{(R'd)^2} \right.$$

$$\left. + j0.866 \ln \left[\frac{D(D + d)}{2D(2D + d)} \frac{D(D - d)}{2D(2D - d)} \right] \right\} \text{ H/m}$$

Therefore, putting the values of D and d, we get

$$L_A = 2.347 - j0.241 \text{ mH/km}$$

Similarly, the inductance of phase B will be

$$L_B = \frac{L_b + L_{b'}}{2} = 1 \times 10^{-7} \left\{ \ln \frac{\sqrt{D(D - d)D(D + d)D(D + d)D(D - d)}}{(R'd)^2} \right.$$

$$\left. + j0.866 \ln \left[\frac{D(D + d)}{D(D - d)} \frac{D(D - d)}{D(D + d)} \right] \right\} \text{ H/m}$$

Therefore, $L_B = 2.069$ mH/km. Since the position of C phase is same as phase A, the inductance of phase C will be, $L_C = 2.347 - j0.241$ mH/km.
Average inductance $L_{avg} = 2.254$ mH/km

Example 10.6 Find the inductance per kilometre of a double circuit, 3-phase system, as shown in Figure 10.21. The conductor radius is 2.5 cm.

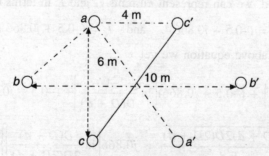

FIGURE 10.21   Example 10.6.

Solution From the figure, we can calculate the various distances as

$$D_{ab} = D_{bc} = D_{b'c'} = D_{a'b'} = \sqrt{3^2 + 3^2} = 4.243 \text{ m}$$

$$D_{aa'} = D_{cc'} = \sqrt{4^2 + 6^2} = 7.211 \text{ m}$$

$$D_{bc'} = D_{ba'} = D_{cb'} = D_{ab'} = \sqrt{3^2 + 7^2} = 7.616 \text{ m}$$

Mutual GMD of phase a in position-1

$$\text{GMD}_1 = \sqrt[4]{D_{ab}D_{ac}D_{ab'}D_{ac'}} = \sqrt[4]{4.243 \times 6 \times 7.616 \times 4} = 5.277$$

Self-GMD (or GMR) of phase a in position-1

$$\text{GMR}_1 = \sqrt{R'D_{aa'}} = \sqrt{0.7788 \times 0.025 \times 7.211} = 0.375\,\text{m}$$

Since the conductors of phase a will occupy the position of phase b conductor in next position, Mutual GMD of phase a in position-2 is

$$\text{GMD}_2 = \sqrt[4]{D_{ba}D_{bc}D_{bc'}D_{ba'}} = \sqrt[4]{4.243 \times 4.243 \times 7.616 \times 7.616} = 5.685\,\text{m}$$

Self-GMD (or GMR) of phase a in position-2 is

$$\text{GMR}_2 = \sqrt{R'D_{bb'}} = \sqrt{0.7788 \times 0.025 \times 10} = 0.441\,\text{m}$$

Similarly, the mutual-GMD of phase a in position-3 is

$$\text{GMD}_3 = 5.277\,\text{m}$$

Self-GMD (or GMR) of phase a in position-3 is

$$\text{GMR}_3 = 0.375\,\text{m}$$

Therefore, mutual GMD will be

$$D_m = \sqrt[3]{(\text{GMD}_1)(\text{GMD}_2)(\text{GMD}_3)} = 5.410\,\text{m}$$

and self-GMR will be

$$D_s = \sqrt[3]{(\text{GMR}_1)(\text{GMR}_2)(\text{GMR}_3)} = 0.396\,\text{m}$$

Inductance of phase a will be

$$L_A = 2 \times 10^{-7}\left(\ln\frac{D_m}{D_{sA}}\right) = 0.523\,\text{mH/km}$$

10.16 ELECTRIC FIELD INTENSITY DUE TO INFINITE LINE CHARGE

Consider a long wire having the charge q coulomb per metre as shown in Figure 10.22. Using Gauss's law, the flux intensity (E) at point P, which is r metre from the conductor, can be calculated as follows:

$$\oint \mathbf{D} \cdot d\mathbf{s} = Q$$

where $\mathbf{D}$ = electric flux density, $d\mathbf{s}$ = differential area $d\mathbf{s}$ with direction normal to the surface and Q = total charge enclosed by the surface area $d\mathbf{s}$.

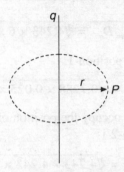

FIGURE 10.22   Electric field intensity.

The flux density at point P, considering the cylindrical shell of radius r and of length l, will be calculated using Gauss' law. The enclosed area will be $2\pi r l$ and total charge enclosed will be ql. Thus

$$D \times 2\pi r \times l = ql \quad \text{or} \quad D = \frac{q}{2\pi r} \text{ coulomb/m}^2$$

The field intensity $\mathbf{E}$ is related to field density as $\mathbf{D} = \varepsilon \mathbf{E}$. If medium is air, ε will be equal to ε_0. Therefore

$$E = \frac{q}{2\pi \varepsilon_0 r} \text{ V/m} \qquad (10.28)$$

10.17   Potential Difference between Two Points Due to Line Charge

Potential at any point is defined as the work done in moving unit positive charge from infinity to that point. If two points P_1 and P_2 are at distances r_1 and r_2 from the charge, the potential (voltage) difference between these points can be calculated by integrating field intensity (E) along any path joining two points as

$$V = -\int_{r_2}^{r_1} E\,dr = -\int_{r_2}^{r_1} \frac{q}{2\pi \varepsilon_0 r}\,dr = \frac{q}{2\pi \varepsilon_0} \ln \frac{r_1}{r_2} \text{ V} \qquad (10.29)$$

Negative sign used as unit charge is moved against the field.

10.18   Capacitance of Single-Phase Line

Capacitor is an electrical device, which consists of two conductors (plates) separated by a dielectric medium and used for storing electrostatic energy. *Capacitance* is defined as the ratio of charge on one conductor to the potential difference between the conductors.

To derive the capacitance formula for 1-phase line, following assumptions are made:

1. Charge is uniformly distributed over the surface of conductor so that flux is radial. (But the presence of other charge near to the conductor it is not uniform.)

2. Effect of earth is neglected.

With these assumptions, let us consider the two conductors are arranged, as shown in Figure 10.23, separated by distance D. If the charge density at conductor A is q coulomb/m and radius of each conductor is R, the electricity field intensity at point P situated at x metre from the centre of first conductor A, will be

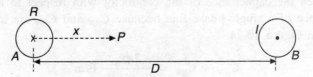

FIGURE 10.23 Single-phase two-wire system.

$$E = \frac{q}{2\pi\varepsilon_0 x}$$

However, the electricity field intensity at point P from the centre of conductor B having charge density $-q$ coulomb/m (return path of current I), will be

$$E = \frac{-q}{2\pi\varepsilon_0 (D - x)}$$

Since both the fields are in the same direction, the total electricity field intensity at point P will be

$$E_x = \frac{q}{2\pi\varepsilon_0 x} + \frac{q}{2\pi\varepsilon_0 (D - x)} \tag{10.30}$$

The potential difference between the conductors will be

$$V_{AB} = -\int_{D-R}^{R} E_x \, dx$$

$$= \frac{q}{2\pi\varepsilon_0} \left[\ln x - \ln (D - x)\right]_{R}^{D-R}$$

$$= \frac{q}{2\pi\varepsilon_0} \left[\ln (D - R) - \ln R - \ln R + \ln (D - R)\right]$$

$$= \frac{q}{\pi\varepsilon_0} \ln \frac{D - R}{R} \text{ V}$$

If $D \gg R$, $D - R \cong D$, therefore potential difference will be

$$V_{AB} = \frac{q}{\pi\varepsilon_0} \ln \frac{D}{R} \text{ V} \tag{10.31}$$

and capacitance between the conductors will be

$$C_{AB} = \frac{q}{V} = \frac{\pi\varepsilon_0}{\ln (D/R)} \text{ F/m} \tag{10.32}$$

It should be noted that in the calculation of capacitance, actual radius is used instead of R' (=0.7788R), which is used in the inductance calculations. Sometimes, it is also required to calculate the capacitance of the conductor with respect to neutral. The capacitance between the conductors, which are having the charges with opposite polarity at a time, is C_{AB}. Then the capacitance of the conductor with respect to neutral will be two times the capacitance of a single-phase line because C_{AN} and C_{BN} are in series. These can be understood from Figure 10.24.

$$C_{AN} = C_{BN} = \frac{2\pi\varepsilon_0}{\ln (D/R)} \text{ F/m} \tag{10.33}$$

FIGURE 10.24 Capacitance between conductors.

Alternate method. Using Equation (10.29), we can write the potential difference between two conductors due to the charge on conductor A as

$$V_{AB} = \frac{q_A}{2\pi\varepsilon_0} \ln \frac{D}{R} \text{ V}$$

and the potential difference between two conductors due to the charge on conductor B will be

$$V_{AB} = \frac{q_B}{2\pi\varepsilon_0} \ln \frac{R}{D} \text{ V}$$

Since the charge on conductor A will be equal and opposite to the charge on conductor B, the total potential difference due charges on both the conductors is

$$V_{AB} = \frac{q_A}{2\pi\varepsilon_0} \ln \frac{D}{R} + \frac{q_B}{2\pi\varepsilon_0} \ln \frac{R}{D} = \frac{q_A}{2\pi\varepsilon_0} \left(\ln \frac{D}{R} - \ln \frac{R}{D} \right) = \frac{q_A}{\pi\varepsilon_0} \ln \frac{D}{R} \text{ V}$$

Thus the capacitance will be calculated as in Equation (10.32).

10.19 POTENTIAL DIFFERENCE BETWEEN TWO CONDUCTORS IN A GROUP OF CONDUCTORS

Figure 10.25 represents a group of n parallel conductors. Let us assume that the sum of their charges is zero. It is also assumed that distances between the conductors are large compared to the radius of the conductors, and the effect of ground is negligible. The charges are also uniformly distributed on the surface and the length. The potential difference between conductors 1 and 2 due to the charge q_1 on conductor-1 is

$$V_{12} = \frac{q_1}{2\pi\varepsilon_0} \ln \frac{D_{12}}{R_1} \text{ V}$$

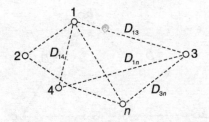

FIGURE 10.25 Group of conductors.

where D_{12} is the distance between conductor-1 and conductor-2 and R_1 is the radius of conductor-1. The potential difference between conductors 1 and 2 due to the charge q_2 on conductor-2 is

$$V_{12} = \frac{q_2}{2\pi\varepsilon_0} \ln \frac{R_2}{D_{12}} \text{ V}$$

If the distance between conductor-3 and conductor-1 is D_{13} and between conductor-3 and conductor-2 it is D_{23}, the potential difference between conductors 1 and 2 due to the charge q_3 on conductor-3 is

$$V_{12} = \frac{q_3}{2\pi\varepsilon_0} \ln \frac{D_{23}}{D_{13}} \text{ V}$$

Similarly the voltage drop between conductors 1 and 2 due to charge on other conductors can be calculated. The total potential difference between conductors 1 and 2 due to charges on all the conductors is

$$V_{12} = \frac{q_1}{2\pi\varepsilon_0} \ln \frac{D_{12}}{R_1} + \frac{q_2}{2\pi\varepsilon_0} \ln \frac{R_2}{D_{12}} + \frac{q_3}{2\pi\varepsilon_0} \ln \frac{D_{23}}{D_{13}} + \cdots + \frac{q_n}{2\pi\varepsilon_0} \ln \frac{D_{2n}}{D_{1n}} \text{ V} \quad (10.34)$$

In similar ways, the potential difference between other conductors due to charges of all the conductors can also be calculated.

10.20 CAPACITANCE OF UNSYMMETRICALLY SPACED THREE-PHASE LINES

Figure 10.26 represents a 3-phase, unsymmetrically spaced line configuration. The sequence of transposition is shown in Figure 9.10. If the line is not transposed the capacitance between the line and neutral will not be equal. The capacitance of each phase to neutral of an untransposed line will be almost the same. The error is negligible and the calculation becomes simpler.

If there are no charges in the vicinity of the phases, the sum of the charges in phases will be zero. Radius of each conductor is assumed to be R. Let us calculate the potential difference between phases a and b, V_{ab1}, in position-1 as shown in Figure 10.26 due to charges on the conductors using Equation (10.34).

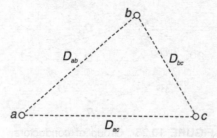

FIGURE 10.26 Three-phase transmission line with unsymmetrical spacing.

$$V_{ab1} = \frac{q_a}{2\pi\varepsilon_0} \ln \frac{D_{ab}}{R} + \frac{q_b}{2\pi\varepsilon_0} \ln \frac{R}{D_{ab}} + \frac{q_c}{2\pi\varepsilon_0} \ln \frac{D_{bc}}{D_{ac}} \tag{10.35}$$

In postion-2, conductor a will take the position of conductor b and conductor b will take the position of conductor c and so on. The potential difference between phases a and b, V_{ab2}, in position-2 will be

$$V_{ab2} = \frac{q_a}{2\pi\varepsilon_0} \ln \frac{D_{bc}}{R} + \frac{q_b}{2\pi\varepsilon_0} \ln \frac{R}{D_{bc}} + \frac{q_c}{2\pi\varepsilon_0} \ln \frac{D_{ac}}{D_{ab}}$$

Similarly, the potential difference between phases a and b, V_{ab3}, in position-3 will be

$$V_{ab3} = \frac{q_a}{2\pi\varepsilon_0} \ln \frac{D_{ac}}{R} + \frac{q_b}{2\pi\varepsilon_0} \ln \frac{R}{D_{ac}} + \frac{q_c}{2\pi\varepsilon_0} \ln \frac{D_{ab}}{D_{bc}}$$

The average potential difference between phase a and b will be

$$
\begin{aligned}
V_{ab} &= \frac{V_{ab1} + V_{ab2} + V_{ab3}}{3} \\[2mm]
&= \frac{1/3}{2\pi\varepsilon_0} \left(q_a \ln \frac{D_{ab}D_{bc}D_{ac}}{R^3} + q_b \ln \frac{R^3}{D_{ab}D_{bc}D_{ac}} + q_c \ln \frac{D_{ab}D_{bc}D_{ac}}{D_{ab}D_{bc}D_{ac}} \right) \\[2mm]
&= \frac{1}{2\pi\varepsilon_0} \left(q_a \ln \frac{D_{eq}}{R} + q_b \ln \frac{R}{D_{eq}} \right)
\end{aligned}
\tag{10.36}
$$

where $D_{eq} = (D_{ab}D_{bc}D_{ac})^{1/3}$. Similarly

$$V_{ac} = \frac{1}{2\pi\varepsilon_0} \left(q_a \ln \frac{D_{eq}}{R} + q_c \ln \frac{R}{D_{eq}} \right) \tag{10.37}$$

From the phasor diagram, as shown in Figure 10.27, it is clear that $V_{ab} + V_{ac} = 3V_{an}$. Phasor voltages are shown in Figure 10.27. The sum of phasor voltages V_{ac} and V_{ab} are represented by vector sum of BA and AD. The resultant sum will be BD in direction of V_{an}. If the magnitude of V_{an} is V, which is same for all the phases, the magnitude of V_{ac} and V_{ab} will be $V\sqrt{3}$.

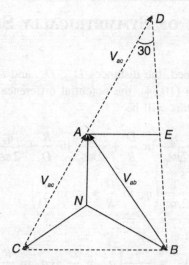

FIGURE 10.27 Phasor diagram.

$$BD = 2DE = 2 \times AD \cos (30°) = 2\sqrt{3}V \; \frac{\sqrt{3}}{2} = 3V$$

Since BD is in phase with V_{an}, therefore,

$$V_{ab} + V_{ac} = 3V_{an} \tag{10.38}$$

Using Equations (10.36) and (10.37),

$$V_{ab} + V_{ac} = \frac{1}{2\pi\varepsilon_0}\left(q_a \ln \frac{D_{eq}}{R} + q_b \ln \frac{R}{D_{eq}}\right) + \frac{1}{2\pi\varepsilon_0}\left(q_a \ln \frac{D_{eq}}{R} + q_c \ln \frac{R}{D_{eq}}\right)$$

$$= \frac{1}{2\pi\varepsilon_0}\left(2q_a \ln \frac{D_{eq}}{R} + (q_b + q_c) \ln \frac{R}{D_{eq}}\right)$$

Since $q_b + q_c = -q_a$, we can write

$$V_{ab} + V_{ac} = \frac{1}{2\pi\varepsilon_0}\left(2q_a \ln \frac{D_{eq}}{R} + (-q_a) \ln \frac{R}{D_{eq}}\right) = \frac{1}{2\pi\varepsilon_0}\left(3q_a \ln \frac{D_{eq}}{R}\right) \tag{10.39}$$

Using Equations (10.38) and (10.39), we get

$$3V_{an} = \frac{1}{2\pi\varepsilon_0}\left(3q_a \ln \frac{D_{eq}}{R}\right) \quad \text{or} \quad V_{an} = \frac{1}{2\pi\varepsilon_0}\left(q_a \ln \frac{D_{eq}}{R}\right)$$

Thus capacitance of phase conductor a to neutral plane will be

$$C_{an} = \frac{q_a}{V_{an}} = \frac{2\pi\varepsilon_0}{\ln (D_{eq}/R)} \; \text{F/m} \tag{10.40}$$

It can be seen that C_{bn} and C_{cn} will be equal to C_{an}.

10.21   CAPACITANCE OF SYMMETRICALLY SPACED THREE-PHASE LINES

If a line is symmetrically spaced, the distances D_{ab}, D_{bc} and D_{ca} in Figure 10.26 will be the same (say D). Using Equation (10.34), the potential difference between phases a and b (V_{ab}) due to charges on the conductors will be

$$V_{ab} = \frac{q_a}{2\pi\varepsilon_0} \ln \frac{D}{R} + \frac{q_b}{2\pi\varepsilon_0} \ln \frac{R}{D} + \frac{q_c}{2\pi\varepsilon_0} \ln \frac{D}{D}$$

$$= \frac{1}{2\pi\varepsilon_0} \left(q_a \ln \frac{D}{R} + q_b \ln \frac{R}{D} \right) \tag{10.41}$$

Similarly

$$V_{ac} = \frac{1}{2\pi\varepsilon_0} \left(q_a \ln \frac{D}{R} + q_c \ln \frac{R}{D} \right) \tag{10.42}$$

Solving Equations (10.41) and (10.42) similar to Equation (10.39), we get

$$V_{an} = \frac{1}{2\pi\varepsilon_0} \left(q_a \ln \frac{D}{R} \right)$$

and therefore

$$C_{an} = \frac{q_a}{V_{an}} = \frac{2\pi\varepsilon_0}{\ln (D/R)} \ \text{F/m}$$

The value of $2\pi\varepsilon_0$ is equal to 0.0555 μF/km or $\varepsilon_0 = \dfrac{10^{-9}}{36\pi}$.

10.22   CAPACITANCE OF SYMMETRICALLY SPACED DOUBLE-CIRCUIT, THREE-PHASE LINES

For symmetrical spacing, the conductors must be placed at the vertices of a regular hexagonal as shown in Figure 10.12. Conductors a, b and c belong to one circuit and a', b' and c' to the second circuit. The letters a, b and c denote the respective phases of the system. From Figure 10.12,

$$D_{ab} = D_{bc} = D_{ac'} = D_{c'b'} = D_{ca} = D_{b'a'} = D$$
$$D_{ac} = D_{b'c} = D_{c'a'} = D_{bc'} = D_{ba'} = D_{ab'} = \sqrt{3}D$$
$$D_{aa'} = D_{bb'} = D_{cc'} = 2D$$

Let us assume that there are no other charges in the vicinity, i.e. $q_a + q_b + q_c = 0$ and radius of each conductor is R. Using Equation (10.35), the potential difference between phases a and b

(V_{ab1}) due to charges on the conductors of the first circuit, i.e. *a*, *b* and *c*, will be

$$V_{ab1} = \frac{q_a}{2\pi\varepsilon_0} \ln \frac{D}{R} + \frac{q_b}{2\pi\varepsilon_0} \ln \frac{R}{D} + \frac{q_c}{2\pi\varepsilon_0} \ln \frac{D}{\sqrt{3}D}$$

$$= \frac{1}{2\pi\varepsilon_0} \left(q_a \ln \frac{D}{R} + q_b \ln \frac{R}{D} + q_c \ln \frac{D}{\sqrt{3}D} \right) \tag{10.43}$$

The potential difference between phases *a* and *b* (V_{ab2}) due to charges on the conductors of the second circuit, i.e. *a'*, *b'* and *c'* will be

$$V_{ab2} = \frac{q_a}{2\pi\varepsilon_0} \ln \frac{\sqrt{3}D}{2D} + \frac{q_b}{2\pi\varepsilon_0} \ln \frac{2D}{\sqrt{3}D} + \frac{q_c}{2\pi\varepsilon_0} \ln \frac{\sqrt{3}D}{D}$$

$$= \frac{1}{2\pi\varepsilon_0} \left(q_a \ln \frac{\sqrt{3}D}{2D} + q_b \ln \frac{2D}{\sqrt{3}D} + q_c \ln \frac{\sqrt{3}D}{D} \right) \tag{10.44}$$

Using Equations (10.43) and (10.44), the total potential difference between phases *a* and *b* (V_{ab}) due to charges on the conductors of both circuits, will be

$$V_{ab} = V_{ab1} + V_{ab2}$$

$$= \frac{1}{2\pi\varepsilon_0} \left(q_a \ln \frac{D}{R} + q_b \ln \frac{R}{D} + q_c \ln \frac{D}{\sqrt{3}D} \right)$$

$$+ \frac{1}{2\pi\varepsilon_0} \left(q_a \ln \frac{\sqrt{3}D}{2D} + q_b \ln \frac{2D}{\sqrt{3}D} + q_c \ln \frac{\sqrt{3}D}{D} \right)$$

$$= \frac{1}{2\pi\varepsilon_0} \left(q_a \ln \frac{\sqrt{3}D}{2R} + q_b \ln \frac{2R}{\sqrt{3}D} + q_c \ln 1 \right)$$

$$= \frac{1}{2\pi\varepsilon_0} \left(q_a \ln \frac{\sqrt{3}D}{2R} + q_b \ln \frac{2R}{\sqrt{3}D} \right)$$

Similarly

$$V_{ac} = \frac{1}{2\pi\varepsilon_0} \left(q_a \ln \frac{D}{R} + q_b \ln \frac{\sqrt{3}D}{D} + q_c \ln \frac{R}{2D} + q_a \ln \frac{\sqrt{3}D}{2D} + q_b \ln \frac{D}{\sqrt{3}D} + q_c \ln \frac{2D}{\sqrt{3}D} \right)$$

$$= \frac{1}{2\pi\varepsilon_0} \left(q_a \ln \frac{\sqrt{3}D}{2R} + q_c \ln \frac{2R}{\sqrt{3}D} \right)$$

Since $V_{ab} + V_{ac} = 3V_{an}$, from above equations, we can have

$$V_{ab} + V_{ac} = 3V_{an} = \frac{1}{2\pi\varepsilon_0}\left(q_a \ln \frac{\sqrt{3}D}{2R} + q_b \ln \frac{2R}{\sqrt{3}D}\right) + \frac{1}{2\pi\varepsilon_0}\left(q_a \ln \frac{\sqrt{3}D}{2R} + q_c \ln \frac{2R}{\sqrt{3}D}\right)$$

$$= \frac{1}{2\pi\varepsilon_0}\left[2q_a \ln \frac{\sqrt{3}D}{2R} + (q_b + q_c) \ln \frac{2R}{\sqrt{3}D}\right] \qquad (10.45)$$

Thus

$$V_{an} = \frac{1}{2\pi\varepsilon_0}\left(q_a \ln \frac{\sqrt{3}D}{2R}\right)$$

The capacitance of conductor *a* with respect to neutral plane will be

$$C_{an} = \frac{q_a}{V_{an}} = \frac{2\pi\varepsilon_0}{\ln[\sqrt{3}D/(2R)]} \text{ F/m/conductor} \qquad (10.46)$$

The capacitance per phase (C_n) will be $2C_{an}$, because each phase has two conductors and they are in parallel.

$$C_n = \frac{4\pi\varepsilon_0}{\ln[\sqrt{3}D/(2R)]} \text{ F/m/phase} \qquad (10.47)$$

Using GMD and GMR concept

Calculation of capacitance can also be done based on the GMD and GMR, if lines are transposed. Since there is no electric field inside the conductors as they are assumed to be perfect conductors, in GMR calculation, radius R is taken instead of R' in the case of inductance calculations. Then

$$\text{Mutual GMD of phase } a = \sqrt[8]{D_{ab}D_{ac}D_{ab'}D_{ac'}D_{a'b}D_{a'c}D_{a'b'}D_{a'c'}}$$

$$= \sqrt[8]{D(\sqrt{3}D)D(\sqrt{3}D)(\sqrt{3}D)DD(\sqrt{3}D)}$$

$$= \sqrt[4]{3}D$$

and

$$\text{Self-GMD (or GMR) of phase } a = \sqrt[4]{(R)(D_{aa'})(D_{aa'})(R)} = \sqrt[4]{(R)(2D)(2D)(R)} = \sqrt{2DR}$$

The capacitance per phase (C_n) will be

$$C_n = \frac{2\pi\varepsilon_0}{\ln[(\text{GMD})/(\text{GMR})]} \text{ F/m/phase}$$

Thus

$$C_n = \frac{2\pi\varepsilon_0}{\ln(\sqrt[4]{3D^4}/\sqrt{2RD})} = \frac{2\pi\varepsilon_0}{(1/2)\ln[(\sqrt{3}D)/(2R)]} = \frac{4\pi\varepsilon_0}{\ln[(\sqrt{3}D)/(2R)]} \text{ F/m/phase} \quad (10.48)$$

Equation (10.48) is equal to Equation (10.47).

10.23 CAPACITANCE OF UNSYMMETRICALLY SPACED DOUBLE CIRCUIT, THREE-PHASE LINE (TRANSPOSED)

Figure 10.13 shows the arrangement of a three-phase double circuit line. The capacitance can be calculated using the potential difference concept or GMD/GMR concept. Here, GMD and GMR concept is used to calculate capacitances. GMD of conductor a will be the same as GMD of conductor a'. Then

Mutual GMD of phase a in position-1, $\text{GMD}_1 = \sqrt[4]{D_{ab}D_{ac}D_{ab'}D_{ac'}} = \sqrt[4]{d(2d)gh}$

Similarly mutual-GMD of phase a in position-2 and position-3 can be written as

$$\text{GMD}_2 = \sqrt[4]{D_{ab}D_{ac}D_{ab'}D_{ac'}} = \sqrt[4]{ddgg}$$

and

$$\text{GMD}_3 = \sqrt[4]{D_{ab}D_{ac}D_{ab'}D_{ac'}} = \sqrt[4]{2ddhg}$$

Self-GMD (or GMR) of phase a in position-1,

$$\text{GMR}_1 = \sqrt{RD_{aa'}} = \sqrt{Rf}$$

Similarly self-GMR of phase a in position-2 and position-3 can be written as

$$\text{GMR}_2 = \sqrt{RD_{aa'}} = \sqrt{Rh} \quad \text{and} \quad \text{GMR}_3 = \sqrt{RD_{aa'}} = \sqrt{Rf}$$

The equivalent GMD (D_m) and GMR (D_s) of the system will be

$$D_m = \sqrt[3]{(\text{GMD}_1)(\text{GMD}_2)(\text{GMD}_3)}$$

$$= \sqrt[3]{[d(2d)gh]^{1/4}(ddgg)^{1/4}(2ddhg)^{1/4}}$$

$$= 2^{1/6}d^{1/2}g^{1/3}h^{1/6}$$

$$D_s = \sqrt[3]{(\text{GMR}_1)(\text{GMR}_2)(\text{GMR}_3)}$$

$$= \sqrt[3]{\left(Rf\right)^{1/2}\left(Rh\right)^{1/2}\left(Rf\right)^{1/2}}$$

$$= R^{1/2}f^{1/3}h^{1/6}$$

Capacitance of phase a, using Equation (10.48) will be

$$C_n = \frac{2\pi\varepsilon_0}{\ln\dfrac{2^{1/6}d^{1/2}g^{1/3}h^{1/6}}{R^{1/2}f^{1/3}h^{1/6}}} = \frac{4\pi\varepsilon_0}{\ln\dfrac{2^{1/3}dg^{2/3}}{Rf^{2/3}}} \quad \text{F/m/phase} \quad (10.49)$$

10.24   EFFECT OF EARTH ON CAPACITANCE

Figure 10.28(a) represents the flux lines and equipotential surface of an isolated charge (neglecting the earth effect). The flux lines are terminating to an imaginary charge placed at infinity. Earth can be assumed as perfectly conducting horizontal sheet with infinite extent and it will behave as equipotential surface. Any charge or charged conductor is placed near the earth surface, the fluxes emanate from them will be perpendicular to the earth as shown in Figure 10.28(b). This can be visualized by an imaginary charge of opposite polarity placed inside the earth at the same distance h, where h is the height of the charge from the earth surface. This concept is known as *image charge*. The method used to calculate the capacitance in the presence of earth is known as *method of images*. While calculating the effect of earth on the capacitor, effect of imaginary charge will also be considered.

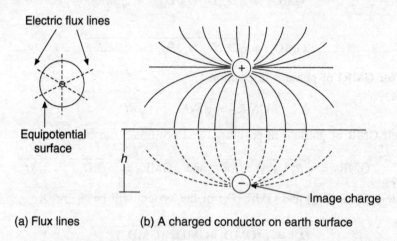

(a) Flux lines   (b) A charged conductor on earth surface

FIGURE 10.28   Earth effect on capacitance.

Capacitance of single conductor charge

Let us consider a conductor at a height h from the earth surface, as shown in Figure 10.28(b). Using the concept of images, an image charge of equal and opposite polarity will be considered. This arrangement is similar to 1-phase line separated with distance $2h$. The capacitance with reference to ground, using Equation (10.33), will be

$$C = \frac{2\pi\varepsilon_0}{\ln\,(2h/R)} \text{ F/m} \tag{10.50}$$

Earth effect on the capacitance of single-phase line

Figure 10.29 shows the one-phase conductors a and b and their image conductors a' and b' respectively. If the conductor a is having positive charge density q coulomb/m at any time t, then the charges on conductors b, a' and b' will be $-q$, $-q$ and $+q$ coulomb/m respectively.

Using Equation (10.34), the potential difference between conductor a and b (V_{ab}) due to charges on the conductors a, b, a', b' will be

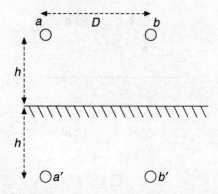

FIGURE 10.29 Single-phase line and its images.

$$V_{ab} = \left(\frac{q_a}{2\pi\varepsilon_0} \ln \frac{D_{ab}}{R} + \frac{q_b}{2\pi\varepsilon_0} \ln \frac{R}{D_{ab}} + \frac{q_{a'}}{2\pi\varepsilon_0} \ln \frac{D_{ba'}}{D_{aa'}} + \frac{q_{b'}}{2\pi\varepsilon_0} \ln \frac{D_{bb'}}{D_{ab}} \right) \text{V}$$

Since

$$D_{ab'} = D_{b'a} = \sqrt{D^2 + (2h)^2}$$

Then

$$V_{ab} = \frac{1}{2\pi\varepsilon_0} \left(q \ln \frac{D}{R} - q \ln \frac{R}{D} - q \ln \frac{\sqrt{D^2 + 4h^2}}{2h} + q \ln \frac{2h}{\sqrt{D^2 + 4h^2}} \right)$$

$$= \frac{1}{2\pi\varepsilon_0} \, 2q \ln \frac{2Dh}{R\sqrt{D^2 + 4h^2}}$$

$$= \frac{1}{\pi\varepsilon_0} q \ln \left\{ \frac{D}{R} \frac{1}{\sqrt{1 + [D^2/(2h)^2]}} \right\}$$

Thus capacitance between conductor a and b will be

$$C_{ab} = \frac{q}{V_{ab}} = \frac{\pi\varepsilon_0}{\ln \left\{ \dfrac{D}{R} \dfrac{1}{\sqrt{1 + [D^2/(2h)^2]}} \right\}} \text{ F/m} \tag{10.51}$$

It can be seen from Equation (10.51) that denominator value is decreased and therefore the effect of earth increases the capacitance. If $h \gg D$, the under-root term will be unity and this is true for all practical purposes.

Earth effect on the capacitance of three-phase line

Figure 10.30 shows the 3-phase line conductors with their image conductors. Using GMD and GMR concepts, the capacitance can not be calculated.

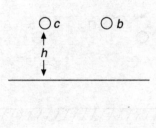

FIGURE 10.30

Using Equation (10.34), the potential difference between conductor a and b due to charges on conductors a, b, c, a', b' and c' will be

$$V_{ab} = \frac{1}{2\pi\varepsilon_0}\left[q_a \ln\frac{D_{ab}}{R} + q_b \ln\frac{R}{D_{ab}} + q_c\frac{D_{bc}}{D_{ac}} + q_{a'}\ln\frac{D_{ba'}}{D_{aa'}} + \right.$$

$$\left. qb'\ln\frac{D_{bb'}}{D_{ab'}} + q_{c'}\ln\frac{D_{bc'}}{D_{ac'}}\right]$$

$$= \frac{1}{2\pi\varepsilon_0}\left[q_a \ln\frac{D_{ab}\cdot D_{aa'}}{R\cdot D_{ba'}} + q_b \ln\frac{R\cdot D_{ab'}}{D_{ab}\cdot D_{bb'}} + q_c \ln\frac{D_{bc}\cdot D_{ac'}}{D_{ac}\,D_{bc'}}\right]$$

Similarly

$$V_{ac} = \frac{1}{2\pi\varepsilon_0}\left[q_a \ln\frac{D_{ac}\cdot D_{aa'}}{R\cdot D_{ca'}} + q_b \ln\frac{D_{cb}\cdot D_{ab'}}{D_{ab}\cdot D_{cb'}} + q_c \ln\frac{R\cdot D_{ac'}}{D_{ac}\cdot D_{cc'}}\right]$$

Thus

$$V_{ab} + V_{ac} = 3V_{an} = \frac{1}{2\pi\varepsilon_0}\left[q_a \ln\frac{D_{ab}\cdot D_{aa'}{}^2\,D_{ac}}{R^2\,D_{ca'}\cdot D_{ba'}} + q_b \ln\frac{R\cdot D_{ab'}\cdot D_{cb}\cdot D_{ab'}}{D_{ab}\cdot D_{bb'}\cdot D_{cb'}\cdot D_{ab}} + \right.$$

$$\left. q_c \ln\frac{R\cdot D_{ac'}\cdot D_{bc}\cdot D_{ac'}}{D_{a^2c}\cdot D_{cc'}\cdot D_{bc'}}\right]$$

Let

$$D_{ab} = D_{bc} = D_{ca} = D$$

$$D_{cc'} = D_{bb'} = 2h, \qquad D_{cb'} = D_{bc'} = g = \sqrt{D^2 + 4h^2}$$

$$D_{aa'} = f$$

$$D_{ac'} = D_{ab'} = l$$

Hence

$$V_{an} = \frac{1}{6\pi\varepsilon_0} \left[q_a \ln \frac{D^2 \cdot f^2}{R^2 l^2} + q_b \ln \frac{R \cdot l^2 \cdot D}{2D^2 \cdot h \cdot g} + q_c \ln \frac{R \cdot D \cdot l^2}{2D^2 \cdot h \cdot g} \right]$$

$$= \frac{1}{6\pi\varepsilon_0} q_a \left[\ln \frac{D^2 \cdot f^2}{R^2 \cdot l^2} \frac{2D^2 \cdot h \cdot g}{R \cdot l^2} \right]$$

$$\Rightarrow \qquad = \frac{q_a}{2\pi\varepsilon_0} \left[\ln \frac{D}{R} \left(\frac{2f^2 \cdot g \cdot h}{\sqrt{l^4}} \right)^{1/3} \right]$$

$$\therefore \qquad C_{an} = \frac{2\pi\varepsilon_0}{\ln \left[\frac{D}{R} \left(\frac{2f^2 \cdot g \cdot h}{l^4} \right)^{1/3} \right]} \text{ F/m /phase}$$

Example 10.7   A single-phase 10-km line is 8 m above the ground. The diameter of the conductors is 2 cm and is separated by 4 m horizontally. Find:

(a) Capacitance between conductors
(b) Capacitance between phase and neutral plane
(c) Capacitance when effect of ground is neglected
(d) Charging current when the line is charged at 33-kV, 50-Hz supply.

Solution   (a) Using Equation (10.51), the capacitance between the conductors will be

$$C_{ab} = \frac{\pi\varepsilon_0}{\ln \left\{ \frac{D}{R} \sqrt{1 + [D^2/(2h)^2]}} \right\}} = \frac{\pi \times 10^{-9}/(36\pi)}{\ln \frac{4.0}{0.01} \frac{1}{\sqrt{1 + [4^2/(2 \times 8)^2]}}} = 4.78 \text{ pF/m}$$

(b) The capacitance between phase and neutral plane will be twice of capacitance between conductors. Therefore $C_{an} = C_{bn} = 9.56$ pF/m.

(c) The capacitance between the conductors when effect of earth is ignored will be

$$C_{ab} = \frac{\pi\varepsilon_0}{\ln (D/R)} = \frac{\pi \times 10^{-9}/(36\pi)}{\ln (4.0/0.01)} = 4.64 \text{ pF/m}$$

(d) Charging current (I_c) will be $\omega C_{ab} V$. Therefore,

$$I_c = \omega C_{ab} V = 2\pi \times 50 \times 4.78 \times 10^{-12} \times 10 \times 10^3 \times 33 \times 10^3 = 0.496 \text{ A}$$

It should be noted that the charging current for single-phase line is the multiplication of capacitive reactance contributed by capacitance between the conductors and voltage between the conductors. Whereas in the case of 3-phase lines, the charging current per phase will be the multiplication of capacitive reactance contributed by capacitance between the phase and neutral, and phase voltage.

Example 10.8   Determine the capacitance per phase of a 3-phase transmission line shown in Figure 10.31. Diameter of conductors is 2.5 cm. Assume the line is transposed.

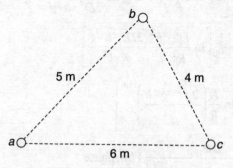

FIGURE 10.31   Example 10.8.

Solution   Using Equation (10.40), the capacitance of phase a to neutral plane will be

$$C_{an} = \frac{2\pi\varepsilon_0}{\ln (D_{eq}/R)} \text{ F/m}$$

where

$$D_{eq} = \sqrt[3]{D_{ab}D_{bc}D_{ac}} = \sqrt[3]{5 \times 4 \times 6} = 4.93 \text{ m}$$

Thus

$$C_{an} = \frac{2\pi \times 10^{-9}/(36\pi)}{\ln 4.93/0.0125} = 9.29 \text{ pF/m}$$

Example 10.9   A 50-Hz 3ϕ line (transposed) composed of one ACSR Moose conductor (overall Dia. = 31.8 mm) per phase has flat horizontal spacing of 10 m between adjacent conductors. Compare the inductive and capacitive reactances in ohms per kilometre per phase of this line with that of a line (transposed) using a three-conductor bundle of ASCR lynx conductor (each having overall Dia. = 19.6 mm) having 10 m spacing measured from the centre of the bundles. The bundle conductors in each phase are arranged in an equilateral triangle formation with spacing between conductors in the bundle as 40 m.

Solution   **Case–I**   Unbundled (single) Moose conductor

Radius of conductor $(r_1) = \dfrac{31.8}{2} \times 10^{-3} = 15.9 \times 10^{-3}$ m

G.M.D. $= D_m = \sqrt[3]{10 \times 10 \times 20} = 12.6$ m

GMR for ind. calculation $D_S^L = 0.7788 \times r_1 = 12.383 \times 10^{-3}$ m

GMR for cap. calculation $D_S^C = r_1 = 15.9 \times 10^{-3}$

Inductance $(L) = 2 \times 10^{-7} \ln \dfrac{D_m}{D_S^L}$ H/m and capacitance $(C) = \dfrac{2\pi\varepsilon_0}{\ln\dfrac{D_m}{D_S^C}}$ F/m

Inductive Reactance $(X_L) = 2\pi f \times L$ ohm/m/phase

$$= 2 \times \pi \times 50 \times 2 \times 10^{-4} \ln\left(\frac{12.6}{12.383 \times 10^{-3}}\right) \ \Omega/\text{km/ph}$$

$$= 0.435 \ \Omega/\text{km/phase}$$

Capacitive Reactance $(X_c) = \dfrac{1}{2\pi fc} = \dfrac{\ln(12.6/15.9 \times 10^{-3})}{(2\pi)^2 \times 50 \times 8.85 \times 10^{-12}} \ \Omega \, \text{km/ph}$

$$= 3.821 \times 10^5 \ \Omega \, \text{km/ph}$$

Case–II   **Bundled conductor**

$$r_2 = \frac{19.6}{2} \times 10^{-3} = 9.8 \times 10^{-13} \, \text{m}$$

$$\text{GMD} = D_m = 12.6 \text{ m (as above case–I)}$$

GMR for Inductive calculation, $D_s^{'L} = \sqrt[3]{0.7788 \, r_2 \times D_b^2}$

$$= \sqrt[3]{0.7788 \times 9.8 \times 10^{-13} \times (0.4)^2} = 0.10689 \text{ m}$$

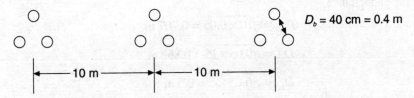

$D_b = 40 \text{ cm} = 0.4 \text{ m}$

GMR for cap. calculation $D_S^{'C} = \sqrt[3]{r_2 \times (D_b)^2} = \sqrt[3]{9.8 \times 10^{-3} \times (10.4)^2} = 0.1162 \text{ m}$

$\therefore$ Inductive Reactance $(X_L') = 2\pi f \times L' = 2\pi \times 50 \times 2 \times 10^{-4} \ln\left(\dfrac{12.6}{0.10689}\right)$

$$= 0.2997 \ \Omega/\text{km/phase}$$

Capacitive Reactance $(X_C') = \dfrac{1}{2\pi fc} = \dfrac{\ln\left(\dfrac{12.6}{0.1162}\right) \times 10^{-3}}{(2\pi)^2 \times 50 \times 8.85 \times 10^{-12}}$

$$= 2.6825 \times 10^5 \ \Omega\text{-km/phase}$$

$\therefore$ with bundle conductor, both X_L and X_C decreases.

Example 10.10   Three-phase double circuit line as shown given below has conductor radius 5 cm. Find the inductance and capacitances per/km/phase.

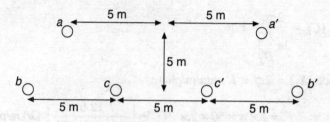

Solution

$$D_{as} = \sqrt[4]{as \times as' \times a'b \times a'b'} = \sqrt[4]{5.6 \times 13.46 \times 13.46 \times 5.6} = 8.68 \text{ m}$$

$$D_{bc} = \sqrt[4]{bc \times bc' \times b'c \times b'c'} = \sqrt[4]{5 \times 10 \times 10 \times 5} = 7.07 \text{ m}$$

$$D_{ca} = \sqrt[4]{ac \times ac' \times a'c' \times a'c} = \sqrt[4]{5.6 \times 9 \times 5.6 \times 9} = 7.1 \text{ m}$$

$$D_{eq} = \sqrt[3]{D_{ab} D_{bc} D_{ca}} = 7.58 \text{ m}$$

$$D_{sa} = \sqrt[4]{aa' \times a'a \times l' \times l'} = \sqrt{10 \times 0.788 \times 0.05} = 0.624 \text{ m}$$

$$D_{sb} = \sqrt[4]{bb' \times b'b \times r' \times r'} = \sqrt{15 \times 0.7788 \times 0.05} = 0.764 \text{ m}$$

$$D_{sc} = \sqrt[4]{cc' \times c'c \times l' \times l'} = \sqrt{5 \times 0.7788 \times 0.05} = 0.44 \text{ m}$$

$$D_s = \sqrt[3]{D_{sa} \times D_{sb} \times D_{sc}} = 0.594 \text{ m}$$

$$L = 2 \times 10^{-r}/n \frac{D_m}{Ds} = 2'10^{-r}/n \frac{7.58}{0.594} = 0.509 \text{ mH/km/phase}$$

GMR for capacitance

$$D_{sa} = \sqrt{10 \times 0.05} = 0.707 \text{ m}$$

$$D_{sb} = \sqrt{0.05 \times 15} = 0.866 \text{ m}$$

$$D_{sc} = \sqrt{0.05 \times 5} = 0.5 \text{ m}$$

$$D_s = 3\sqrt{D_{sa} D_{sb} D_{sc}} = 0.553 \text{ m}$$

$$\text{Capacitance} = \frac{2\pi\varepsilon_0}{\ln D_m / D_s} = 21.23 \text{ nF/km/phase}$$

Transmission line parameters

Table 10.2 shows the transmission line parameters (at 100 MVA base) of different voltage lines used in India.

Table 10.2 Parameters of transmission lines

S.No.	Voltage class	Type of conductor	R pu/100 km	X pu/100 km	B pu/100 km
1.	800 kV	Quad ACSR 'BERSIMIS'	0.00019	0.00474	2.40644
2.	400 kV	Twin ACSR 'MOOSE'	0.00186	0.02075	0.5550
3.	220 kV	Single ACSR 'ZEBRA'	0.0176	0.0886	0.1350
4.	132 kV	Panther ACSR			

PROBLEMS

10.1 Determine the self-GMD of the following types of conductors (Figure 10.32) in terms of radius R of an individual strand

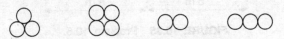

FIGURE 10.32 Problem 10.1.

10.2 Determine the inductance of single-phase transmission line having arrangement of conductor as shown in Figure 10.33. One circuit consists of three wires of 1-cm diameter each and the other circuit two wires of 2-cm diameter each.

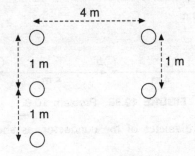

FIGURE 10.33 Problem 10.2.

10.3 Derive the expression, staring from flux linkage, for inductance per phase of three-phase double-circuit line with unsymmetrical spacing (all the three phases are in the same vertical plane). Also calculate the capacitance per phase. The line is transposed.

10.4 In the arrangement of conductors for the single-phase transmission line having arrangement of conductors, as shown in Figure 10.34. Diameter of each conductor is 2 cm. Assuming the current of equally distributed in the conductors, calculate the inductance per kilometre length of line.

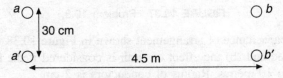

FIGURE 10.34 Problem 10.4.

10.5 Determine the inductance per kilometre of a 3-phase transmission line having two conductors per phase, as shown in Figure 10.35. Diameter of each conductor is 25 mm and carries 50% of the phase current.

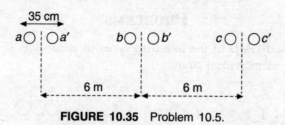

FIGURE 10.35   Problem 10.5.

10.6   Determine the inductance per kilometre per phase of a double-circuit three-phase transmission line, as shown in Figure 10.36. The radius of each conductor is 2 cm.

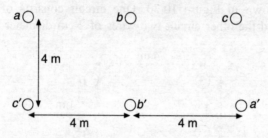

FIGURE 10.36   Problem 10.6.

10.7   Calculate the effective diameter of the conductor, as shown in Problem 10.1, using Guy's theorem.

10.8   Determine the capacitance and inductance per kilometre length of a double-circuit three-phase line, as shown in Figure 10.37. The transmission line is transposed. The diameter of each conductor is 25 mm.

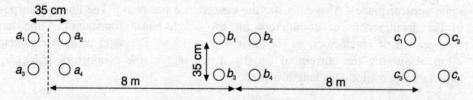

FIGURE 10.37   Problem 10.8.

10.9   Determine the capacitance of arrangement shown in Figure 10.38 when (a) the effect of earth is neglected and (b) the effect of earth is considered if the heights of conductors from ground are 10 metres. Radius of conductors is 2 cm.

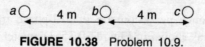

FIGURE 10.38   Problem 10.9.

10.10 A 3-phase line has inductance 1.2 mH/km. The radius of each phase conductor is 2 cm. Find the capacitance of phase to neutral. Assume that conductors are equilaterally spaced.

10.11 A 3-phase line has flat, horizontal spacing of 2 m between adjacent conductors. The radius of each conductor is 0.25 cm. At a certain instant, the charges on the centre conductor and one of the outer conductors are identical and voltage drop between these identically charged conductors is 775 kV. Neglect the effect of ground and find the value of the identical charge in coulomb/km at the instant specified.

10.12 Determine the capacitance and charging current per kilometre length as in Problem 10.2, if the line is operating at 20 kV, 50 Hz.

10.13 Determine the capacitance and charging current per kilometre length as in Problem 10.4, if the line is operating at 11 kV, 50 Hz.

10.14 Determine the capacitance and charging current per kilometre length as in Problem 10.5, if the line is operating at 220 kV, 50 Hz.

10.15 Determine the capacitance and charging current per kilometre length as in Problem 10.6, if the line is operating at 400 kV, 50 Hz.

10.16 A 50-Hz 3ϕ line composed of one ASCR Bluejay conductor per phase has flat horizontal spacing of 11 m between adjacent conductor. Compare the inductive reactance in ohms per kilometre per phase of this line with that of a line using a two conductor bundle conductors each having the same distance as the single conductor and 11 m spacing measured from the centre of the bundles. The spacing between conductors in the bundle is 40 cm.

10.17 For the data given in Problem 10.16, compare the capacitive reactances in ohm-kilometres per phase of the two line configurations.

10.18 Six conductors of ACSR Drake constitute a 50-Hz double circuit three-phase line arranged as shown in Figure 10.39. The vertical spacing however is 5 m; the longer horizontal distance is 10 m; and shorter horizontal distances are 8 m. Find

(a) The inductance per phase (in H/km) and the inductive (in Ω/km).

(b) The capacitive reactance to neutral (in Ω/km) and the charging current in A/km per phase and per conductor at 132 kV.

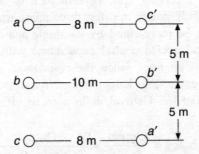

FIGURE 10.39 Typical arrangement of conductors of a parallel circuit 3-phase line.

Chapter 11

Analysis of Transmission Lines

11.1 INTRODUCTION

The technical analysis of transmission line is done to know its performance to transfer power from the sending end to the receiving end. Performance of a transmission line includes efficiency and regulation. For bulk power transfer, three-phase transmission lines are used but for analysis purposes, line can be represented by its single-phase equivalent using the phase resistance, phase inductance and line to neutral capacitance with assumption that supply and load are balanced in transmission line. Since the resistance, inductance, capacitance and conductance are distributed over the line length, the performance of the line depends on the manner how these are accounted for. General definitions of efficiency and regulation in per unit are:

$$\text{Efficiency} = \frac{\text{Output}}{\text{Input}} = \frac{\text{Output}}{\text{Output} + \text{Losses}}$$

and

$$\text{Regulation} = \frac{\text{Change in output voltage}}{\text{Rated voltage}}$$

For the transmission lines, *efficiency* is defined as the ratio of power delivered at the receiving end to the power sent at sending end. Mathematically, it is defined as

$$\text{Efficiency} = \frac{\text{Power delivered at the receiving end}}{\text{Power sent from the sending end}}$$

$$= \frac{\text{Power delivered at the receiving end}}{\text{Power delivered at the receiving end + Losses}}$$

The end where load is connected is called as *receiving end* while the end that supplies power is known as *sending end*. To calculate the efficiency in percentage, 100 is multiplied to the value of 'efficiency'.

   Regulation of transmission line is defined as the ratio of change in voltage at the receiving end, from no load to full load keeping the sending-end voltage and frequency constant, to the full load voltage. Mathematically, percentage regulation is defined as

$$\%\text{Regulation} = \frac{\text{No-load voltage} - \text{Full-load voltage}}{\text{Full-load voltage}} \times 100 = \frac{V_r' - V_r}{V_r} \times 100$$

where V_r' is the receiving end voltage magnitude at no load and V_r is the full-load voltage magnitude at receiving end.

11.2 CLASSIFICATION OF LINES

Transmission lines are represented into three categories: short lines, medium lines and long lines. A line having length less than 80 km is called a *short line*. The charging of capacitance (shunt) can be ignored in the analysis and series resistance and inductance can be treated as lumped parameter, as shown in Figure 11.1. If the transmission line is between 80 km and 200 km, the charging capacitance of the line cannot be ignored however the series impedance can be taken as lumped parameters. Charging capacitance is also considered as lumped parameters and can be represented as nominal-T and nominal-π, which are shown in Figure 11.2. These are called so because line parameters are considered as lumped parameter that is not accurate. The line more than 200 km mile is called *long lines,* whose exact representation is required. The line can also be represented as T or π but since line parameters are taken as distributed parameters, they are known as *equivalent-T* and *equivalent-π* representations.

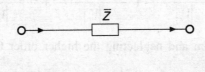

FIGURE 11.1 Short transmission line.

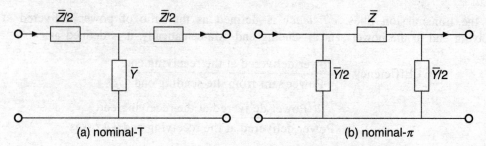

FIGURE 11.2   Medium transmission line representation.

11.3   SHORT TRANSMISSION LINES

Short line and its phasor diagram are shown in Figure 11.3.

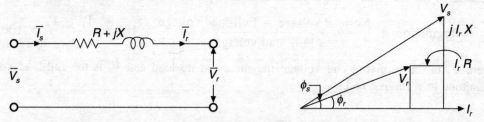

FIGURE 11.3   Short transmission line and its phasor representation.

Receiving-end current ($\overline{I}_r$) is taken as reference. R and X are per-phase resistance and inductance, respectively, of the transmission line. From the phasor diagram, we get

$$\left|\overline{V}_s\right|\cos\phi_3 = \left|\overline{V}_r\right|\cos\phi_r + \left|\overline{I}_r\right|R \tag{11.1}$$

and

$$\left|\overline{V}_s\right|\sin\phi_s = \left|\overline{V}_r\right|\sin\phi_r + \left|\overline{I}_r\right|X \tag{11.2}$$

Squaring and adding, Equations (11.1) and (11.2), we get

$$\left|\overline{V}_s^2\right| = \left|\overline{V}_r^2\right| + 2\left|\overline{I}_r\right|R\left|\overline{V}_r\right|\cos\phi_r + 2\left|\overline{I}_r\right|X\left|\overline{V}_r\right|\sin\phi_r + \left|\overline{I}_r^2\right|(X^2 + R)$$

$$= \left|\overline{V}_r\right|\left(1 + \frac{2\left|\overline{I}_r\right|R\cos\phi_r}{\left|\overline{V}_r\right|} + \frac{2\left|\overline{I}_r\right|X\sin\phi_r}{\left|\overline{V}_r\right|} + \frac{\left|\overline{I}_r^2\right|(X^2 + R^2)}{\left|\overline{V}_r^2\right|}\right)^{1/2}$$

Using Taylor series expansion and neglecting the higher order terms, we obtain

$$\left|\overline{V}_s\right| \approx \left|\overline{V}_r\right|\left(1 + \frac{\left|\overline{I}_r\right|R\cos\phi_r}{\left|\overline{V}_r\right|} + \frac{\left|\overline{I}_r\right|X\sin\phi_r}{\left|\overline{V}_r\right|}\right)$$

$$\approx \left|\overline{V}_r\right| + \left|\overline{I}_r\right|R\cos\phi_r + \left|\overline{I}_r\right|X\sin\phi_r \tag{11.3}$$

Since there is no shunt part,

$$\text{Sending-end current } (|\bar{I}_s|) = \text{Receiving-end current } (|\bar{I}_r|)$$

and

$$\text{Sending-end voltage } (V_s) = \text{Receiving-end voltage } (V_r)$$

at no load. Therefore,

$$\text{Per cent regulation} = \frac{|\bar{V}_s| - |\bar{V}_r|}{|\bar{V}_r|} \times 100$$

$$= \frac{|\bar{I}_r| R \cos \phi_r}{|\bar{V}_r|} \times 100 + \frac{|\bar{I}_r| X \sin \phi_r}{|\bar{V}_r|} \times 100 \tag{11.4}$$

and

$$\text{Regulation in per unit} = \frac{|\bar{I}_r| R \cos \phi_r}{|\bar{V}_r|} + \frac{|\bar{I}_r| X \sin \phi_r}{|\bar{V}_r|}$$

$$= v_r \cos \phi_r + v_x \sin \phi_r \tag{11.5}$$

Taking receiving-end voltage and current as base values, v_r and v_x represent per unit resistance and reactance of the line respectively. From Equation (11.5), we obtain the following relationship for zero regulation.

$$0 = v_r \cos \phi_r + v_x \sin \phi_r$$

or

$$\tan \phi_r = -\frac{R}{X}$$

or

$$\tan \left(\phi_r + \frac{\pi}{2} \right) = \frac{X}{R}$$

or

$$\phi_r = -\frac{\pi}{2} + \tan^{-1} \frac{X}{R} \tag{11.6}$$

Equation (11.6) shows that for zero regulation the power factor of load must be leading. If the power delivered at the receiving-end is P, the efficiency in percentage of the line is written as

$$\%\eta = \frac{P}{P + 3I_r^2 R} \times 100 \tag{11.7}$$

Example 11.1 Find the power factor for short transmission lines for maximum regulation.

Solution For maximum regulation,

$$\frac{d(\text{regulation})}{d\phi_r} = 0$$

Using Equation (11.5), we get

$$\frac{d(\text{regulation})}{d\phi_r} = 0 = -\frac{|\bar{I}_r| R}{|\bar{V}_r|} \sin \phi_r + \frac{|\bar{I}_r| X}{|\bar{V}_r|} \cos \phi_r$$

or

$$\tan \phi_r = \frac{X}{R} \tag{11.8}$$

Thus the power factor angle of the load should be

$$\phi_r = \tan^{-1} \frac{X}{R} \text{ lagging}$$

11.4 GENERALIZED CIRCUIT CONSTANTS

It is important to represent the transmission line in terms of the sending- and receiving-end voltages and currents. A transmission line can be represented as four-terminal (2-port) network, as shown in Figure 11.4. This terminal pair circuit is passive (no energy source), linear (where impedances are independent of the amount of current flowing through the element) and bilateral (where impedances are independent of direction of current flow). Following relationships can be established,

$$\bar{V}_s = A\bar{V}_r + B\bar{I}_r \tag{11.9}$$

$$\bar{I}_s = C\bar{V}_r + D\bar{I}_r \tag{11.10}$$

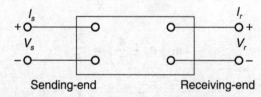

FIGURE 11.4   2-port network representation.

In matrix form, it will be

$$\begin{bmatrix} \bar{V}_s \\ \bar{I}_s \end{bmatrix} = \begin{bmatrix} A & B \\ C & D \end{bmatrix} \begin{bmatrix} \bar{V}_r \\ \bar{I}_r \end{bmatrix} \tag{11.11}$$

where A, B, C and D are *generalized circuit constants* and hold the following properties:

1. These are complex constants.
2. They hold, $AD - BC = 1$.
3. If symmetrical network, $A = D$.
4. A, D are dimensionless.
5. B is impedance, C admittance.

Proof of $AD - BC = 1$

Consider Figure 11.5(a), where an ideal voltage source (with zero internal impedance) is connected to sending-end, and receiving-end is short-circuited with zero impedance. Thus $V_r = 0$ and following relations can be obtained using Equations (11.9) and (11.10):

$$\overline{V}_s = \overline{B}\overline{I}_r = \overline{s} \text{ (say)} \quad \text{and} \quad \overline{I}_s = D\overline{I}_r$$

or

$$\overline{I}_r = \frac{\overline{V}_s}{B} = \frac{E}{B} \tag{11.12}$$

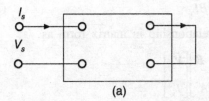 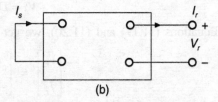

FIGURE 11.5 2-port network.

Suppose the sending-end is short-circuited and the same ideal voltage (E) is applied at the receiving-end. From Equation (11.9), we get

$$0 = AE + BI_r \quad \text{or} \quad \overline{I}_r = \frac{A\overline{E}}{B} \tag{11.13}$$

Using reciprocating theorem, $\overline{I}_s = -\overline{I}_r$ (Figure 11.5b). From Equation (11.10),

$$\overline{I}_s = -\overline{I}_r = C\overline{E} + D\overline{I}_r$$

Using Equations (11.13) and (11.12),

$$-\overline{I}_r = C\overline{E} - \frac{DA\overline{E}}{B} = -\frac{\overline{E}}{B}$$

Thus

$$AD - BC = 1 \tag{11.14}$$

This relation is very useful for checking the constants A, B, C and D which are calculated independently.

A, B, C and D quantities in terms of $\overline{V}_r$ and $\overline{I}_r$

Sometimes it is also important to represent the receiving-end voltage and current in terms of sending-end voltage and current with the help of A, B, C and D parameters. Pre-multiplying Equations (11.9) and (11.10) by C and A respectively, we get

$$C\,(\overline{V}_s = A\overline{V}_r + B\overline{I}_r) \tag{11.15}$$

$$A(\overline{I}_s = C\overline{V}_r + D\overline{I}_r) \tag{11.16}$$

Subtracting Equation (11.16) from Equation (11.15) and using relationship $AD - BC = 1$, we get

$$\bar{I}_r = -C\bar{V}_s + A\bar{I}_s \tag{11.17}$$

Pre-multiplying Equations (11.9) and (11.10) by D and B respectively, we get

$$D(\bar{V}_s = A\bar{V}_r + B\bar{I}_r) \tag{11.18}$$

$$B(\bar{I}_s = C\bar{V}_r + D\bar{I}_r) \tag{11.19}$$

Subtracting Equation (11.19) from Equation (11.18) and using relationship $AD - BC = 1$, we get

$$\bar{V}_r = D\bar{V}_s - B\bar{I}_s \tag{11.20}$$

Using Equations (11.17) and (11.20), we get the relationship in matrix form as

$$\begin{bmatrix} \bar{V}_r \\ \bar{I}_r \end{bmatrix} = \begin{bmatrix} D & -B \\ -C & A \end{bmatrix} \begin{bmatrix} \bar{V}_s \\ \bar{I}_s \end{bmatrix}$$

Constants for two networks in tandem

Let two 2-port networks having constants A_1, B_1, C_1, D_1 and A_2, B_2, C_2, D_2, respectively be connected in tandem, as shown in Figure 11.6. If the receiving-end voltage and current of first network are V and I which are also sending-end voltage and current for the second network, the resultant constants A, B, C, D can be calculated as follows:

Using Equations (11.9) and (11.10), we have

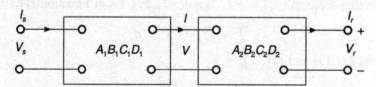

FIGURE 11.6 Two 2-port networks in tandem.

$$\bar{V}_s = A_1\bar{V} + B_1\bar{I}, \quad \bar{V} = A_2\bar{V}_r + B_2\bar{I}_r$$

and

$$\bar{I}_s = C_1\bar{V} + D_1\bar{I}, \quad \bar{I} = C_2\bar{V}_r + D_2\bar{I}_r$$

or

$$\begin{bmatrix} \bar{V}_s \\ \bar{I}_s \end{bmatrix} = \begin{bmatrix} A_1 & B_1 \\ C_1 & D_1 \end{bmatrix} \begin{bmatrix} A_2 & B_2 \\ C_2 & D_2 \end{bmatrix} \begin{bmatrix} \bar{V}_r \\ \bar{I}_r \end{bmatrix} = \begin{bmatrix} A & B \\ C & D \end{bmatrix} \begin{bmatrix} \bar{V}_r \\ \bar{I}_r \end{bmatrix}$$

Constants for two networks connected in parallel

Let two 2-port networks having constants A_1, B_1, C_1, D_1 and A_2, B_2, C_2, D_2, respectively be connected in parallel as shown in Figure 11.7. If the sending-end and receiving-end currents are $\bar{I}_{s1}$ and $\bar{I}_{r1}$ in the first network and $\bar{I}_{s2}$ and $\bar{I}_{r2}$ are the sending-end and receiving-end currents in the second network, the resultant constants A, B, C, D can be calculated as follows:

For the first and second network, following relations can be written

$$\bar{V}_s = A_1 \bar{V}_r + B_1 \bar{I}_{r1} \tag{11.21}$$

$$\bar{I}_{s1} = C_1 \bar{V}_r + D_1 \bar{I}_{r1} \tag{11.22}$$

$$\bar{V}_s = A_2 \bar{V}_r + B_2 \bar{I}_{r2} \tag{11.23}$$

$$\bar{I}_{s2} = C_2 \bar{V}_r + D_2 \bar{I}_{r2} \tag{11.24}$$

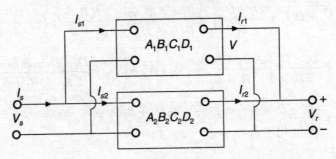

FIGURE 11.7 Two 2-port networks in parallel.

Since

$$\bar{I}_s = \bar{I}_{s1} + \bar{I}_{s2} \quad \text{and} \quad \bar{I}_r = \bar{I}_{r1} + \bar{I}_{r2}$$

Pre-multiplying Equation (11.21) by B_2 and Equation (11.23) by B_1 and adding, we get

$$(B_2 + B_1)\bar{V}_s = (A_1 B_2 + A_2 B_1)\bar{V}_r + B_1 B_2 (\bar{I}_{r1} + \bar{I}_{r2})$$

or

$$\bar{V}_s = \frac{A_1 B_2 + A_2 B_1}{B_2 + B_1} \bar{V}_r + \frac{B_1 B_2}{B_2 + B_1} \bar{I}_r$$

Since transmission line is symmetrical, hence $A = D$, where

$$A = D = \frac{A_1 B_2 + A_2 B_1}{B_2 + B_1} \tag{11.25}$$

and

$$B = \frac{B_1 B_2}{B_1 + B_2} \tag{11.26}$$

C can be determined using A, B and D from Equations (11.25) and (11.26) and putting in $AD - BC = 1$, we can have

$$\frac{(A_1 B_2 + A_2 B_1)^2}{(B_2 + B_1)^2} - C \frac{B_1 B_2}{B_1 + B_2} = 1$$

Thus

$$C = \frac{(A_1 B_2 + A_2 B_1 + B_2 + B_1)(A_1 B_2 + A_2 B_1 - B_2 - B_1)}{(B_2 + B_1)B_1 B_2} \tag{11.27}$$

Adding Equations (11.22) and (11.24), we get

$$\bar{I}_s = (C_1 + C_2)\bar{V}_r + D_2\bar{I}_{r2} + D_1\bar{I}_{r1} = (C_1 + C_2)\bar{V}_r + D_2\bar{I}_r + (D_1 - D_2)\bar{I}_{r1}$$

Putting the value of $\bar{I}_{r1}$ from Equation (11.21) in above equation, we have

$$\bar{I}_s = (C_1 + C_2)\bar{V}_r + D_2\bar{I}_r + \frac{D_1 - D_2}{B_1}(\bar{V}_s - A_1\bar{V}_r)$$

$$= (C_1 + C_2)\bar{V}_r + D_2\bar{I}_r + \frac{D_1 - D_2}{B_1}\left(\frac{A_1B_2 + A_2B_1}{B_2 + B_1}\bar{V}_r + \frac{B_1B_2}{B_2 + B_1}\bar{I}_r\right) - \frac{(D_1 - D_2)A_1}{B_1}\bar{V}_r$$

$$= \left[C_1 + C_2 + \frac{D_1 - D_2}{B_1}\left(\frac{A_1B_2 + A_2B_1}{B_2 + B_1} - A_1\right)\right]\bar{V}_r + \left(D_2 + \frac{D_1 - D_2}{B_1}\frac{B_1B_2}{B_2 + B_1}\right)\bar{I}_r$$

$$= \left[C_1 + C_2 + \frac{(D_1 - D_2)(A_2 - A_1)}{B_2 + B_1}\right]\bar{V}_r + \frac{B_1D_2 + B_2D_1}{B_2 + B_1}\bar{I}_r \qquad (11.28)$$

$$= C\bar{V}_r + D\bar{I}_r$$

Regulation of short lines in *ABCD* constants

Generally, quantities P, I_r (or V_r) and $\cos \phi_r$ are given and so A, B, C, D constants. Using equation $\bar{V}_s = A\bar{V}_r + I_r\bar{B}$, the no load ($I_r = 0$) voltage at the receiving-end will be V_s/A
Thus

$$\text{Per cent regulation} = \frac{\left|(\bar{V}_s/A)\right| - |\bar{V}_r|}{|\bar{V}_r|} \times 100$$

Example 11.2 A 3-phase, 5-km long transmission line, having resistance of 0.50 ohm/km and inductance of 1.76 mH/km, is delivering power at 0.8-p.f. lagging. The receiving-end (RE) voltage is 32 kV. If the supply-end (SE) voltage is 33 kV, 50 Hz, find (a) line current, (b) regulation and (c) efficiency of the transmission line.

Solution Sending-end (SE) line-to-line voltage = 33 kV. Therefore,

$$\text{SE phase voltage, } |\bar{V}_s| = \frac{33}{\sqrt{3}} = 19.052 \text{ kV}$$

and

$$\text{RE phase voltage } |\bar{V}_r| = \frac{32}{\sqrt{3}} = 18.48 \text{ kV}$$

We also have

$$\text{Total resistance of line } R = 0.5 \times 5 = 2.5 \text{ ohm}$$

and

$$\text{Total reactance of line } X = 2\pi fL = 2.765 \text{ ohm}$$

Since $\cos \phi_r = 0.8$, then $\sin \phi_r = 0.6$.

(a) Using Equations (11.1) and (11.2), we can write

$$\left|\overline{V}_s^2\right| = \left|\overline{V}_r^2\right| + 2\left|\overline{I}_r\right| R \left|\overline{V}_r\right| \cos\phi_r + 2\left|\overline{I}_r\right| X \left|\overline{V}_r\right| \sin\phi_r + \left|\overline{I}_r^2\right|(X^2 + R^2)$$

Putting the values of $\left|\overline{V}_s\right|$, $\left|\overline{V}_r\right|$, R, X and ϕ_r, we get, assuming $\left|\overline{I}_r\right|$ in kA,

$$362.98 = 341.33 + I_r^2(6.25 + 7.645) + I_r(135.24)$$

or

$$\left|\overline{I}_r^2\right| + 9.733\,\overline{I}_r - 1.558 = 0$$

Solving this equation, ignoring the negative value of current, we get,

$$\text{Line current } \left|\overline{I}_r\right| = 0.157 \text{ kA}$$

(b) At no load, receiving-end voltage will be equal to the sending-end voltage, thus

$$\% \text{ Regulation} = \frac{\left|\overline{V}_s\right| - \left|\overline{V}\right|_r}{\left|\overline{V}_r\right|} \times 100 = \frac{19.052 - 18.48}{18.48} \times 100 = 3.125\%$$

(c) Power output, $P = 3$ (Phase voltage) × (Phase current) × (Power factor)

Therefore

$$P = 3 \times 18.48 \times 0.157 \times 0.8 = 6.96 \text{ MW}$$

and

$$\text{Losses in the line} = 3I_r^2 R = 0.185 \text{ MW}$$

Thus the efficiency will be

$$\% \text{ Efficiency } \eta = \frac{P}{P + 3I_r^2 R} \times 100 = \frac{6.96}{6.96 + 0.185} \times 100 = 97.41\%$$

11.5 MEDIUM LINES

When the length of transmission line is more than 80 km, the line-charging capacitance is significant and cannot be ignored. Since capacitance is distributed over the line, but for analysis purposes, this can be assumed as lumped parameter either at the centre of line (nominal-T) or at both the ends of a transmission line (nominal-π). These are called *nominal-T* or *nominal-π* because, it is approximate representation due consideration of distributed parameters as lumped parameters. The detail performance analysis of both representations is given below.

11.5.1 Nominal-T Representation

Figure 11.8 shows the nominal-T representation of a transmission line. For analysis, it is preferable to take the receiving-end current as reference. Phasor diagram is represented in Figure 11.9.

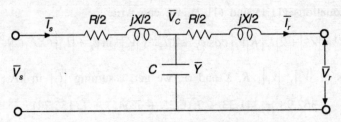

FIGURE 11.8 Nominal-T representation of a line.

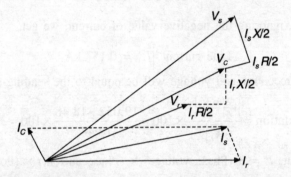

FIGURE 11.9 Phasor diagram of nominal-T representation.

Let us calculate the sending-end voltage. The voltage at point C will be

$$\bar{V}_C = \bar{V}_r (\cos \phi_r + j \sin \phi_r) + \bar{I}_r \left(\frac{R}{2} + \frac{jX}{2} \right) \tag{11.29}$$

If the current in the shunt branch is $\bar{I}_C$, it can be calculated as

$$\bar{I}_C = j\omega C V_C \quad \text{and} \quad \bar{I}_s = \bar{I}_C + \bar{I}_r \tag{11.30}$$

Thus

$$\bar{V}_s = \bar{V}_C + I_s \left(\frac{R}{2} + \frac{jX}{2} \right)$$

$$= \bar{V}_r (\cos \phi_r + j \sin \phi_s) + \bar{I}_r \left(\frac{R}{2} + \frac{jX}{2} \right) + I_s \left(\frac{R}{2} + jX \right) \tag{11.31}$$

Receiving-end voltage with no-load ($I_r = 0$, $I_s = I_C$) will be $V_r' = V_C$. The current in shunt branch will be

$$\bar{I}_C' = \frac{\bar{V}_s}{\{(R/2) + (jX/2) - [j/(\omega C)]\}}$$

Thus

$$\bar{V}_C = \frac{\bar{V}_s}{j\omega C \{(R/2) + (jX/2) - [j/(\omega C)]\}}$$

$$\% \text{ Regulation} = \frac{|\bar{V}_r'| - |\bar{V}_r|}{|\bar{V}_r|} \times 100$$

$$\% \text{ Efficiency } \eta = \frac{P}{P + 3[(I_r^2 R/2) + (I_s^2 R/2)]} \times 100\%$$

Determination of A, B, C, D constants

Taking any reference, the voltage equations can be written as

$$\bar{V}_C = \bar{V}_r + \bar{I}_r \frac{\bar{Z}}{2}, \quad \bar{I}_C = \bar{V}_C \bar{Y}$$

and

$$\begin{aligned} \bar{V}_s &= \bar{V}_C + (\bar{I}_C + \bar{I}_r) \frac{\bar{Z}}{2} \\ &= \bar{V}_r + \bar{I}_r \frac{\bar{Z}}{2} + \bar{Y} \left(\bar{V}_r + \bar{I}_r \frac{\bar{Z}}{2} \right) \frac{\bar{Z}}{2} + I_r \frac{\bar{Z}}{2} \\ &= \bar{V}_r \left(1 + \frac{\bar{Y}\bar{Z}}{2} \right) + \bar{I}_r \left(1 + \frac{\bar{Y}\bar{Z}}{4} \right) \bar{Z} \end{aligned} \tag{11.32}$$

The current equation becomes

$$\bar{I}_s = \bar{I}_r + \bar{I}_C = \bar{I}_r + \bar{Y} \left(\bar{V}_r + \frac{\bar{I}_r \bar{Z}}{2} \right) = \bar{Y}\bar{V}_r + \left(1 + \frac{\bar{Y}\bar{Z}}{2} \right) I_r \tag{11.33}$$

Comparing Equations (11.9) and (11.10) with Equations (11.32) and (11.33), respectively, we get

$$A = 1 + \frac{\bar{Y}\bar{Z}}{2}, \quad B = \bar{Z} \left(1 + \frac{\bar{Y}\bar{Z}}{4} \right), \quad C = Y, \quad D = 1 + \frac{\bar{Y}\bar{Z}}{2}$$

It can be seen that following relations are valid for the transmission lines. These relations are used to check the accuracy of the parameters calculated.

$$A = D \quad \text{and} \quad AD - BC = 1$$

11.5.2 Nominal-π Representation

Figure 11.10 shows the nominal-π representation of a transmission line. For analysis, it is convenient to take voltage as reference. The vector diagram is shown in Figure 11.11.

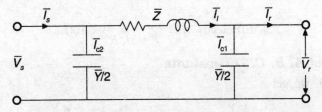

FIGURE 11.10 Nominal-π representation of a line.

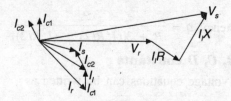

FIGURE 11.11 Phasor diagram of nominal-π.

Let us calculate the sending-end voltage $(\overline{V}_s)$ and current $(\overline{I}_s)$, taking receiving-end voltage as reference:

$$\overline{I}_{c1} = \frac{jV_r\omega C}{2}$$

$$\overline{I}_1 = \overline{I}_r\,(\cos\phi_r - j\sin\phi_r) + \frac{j\overline{V}_r\omega C}{2}$$

Thus

$$\overline{V}_s = \overline{V}_r + \overline{I}_l\overline{Z} = \overline{V}_r + (R + jX)\left[\overline{I}_r\,(\cos\phi_r - j\sin\phi_r) + \frac{j\overline{V}_r\omega C}{2}\right]$$

Sending end current will be

$$\overline{I}_s = \overline{I}_l + \overline{I}_{c2} \quad \text{and} \quad I_{c2} = \frac{j\overline{V}_s\omega C}{2} \tag{11.34}$$

Thus

$$\overline{I}_s = \overline{I}_r\,(\cos\phi_r - j\sin\phi_r) + \frac{j\overline{V}_r\omega C}{2} + \frac{j\omega C}{2}\left\{\overline{V}_r + (R + jX)\left[\overline{I}_r(\cos\phi_r - j\sin\phi_r) + \frac{j\overline{V}_r\omega C}{2}\right]\right\}$$

For calculation of regulation, receiving-end voltage at no-load can be calculated as

$$\overline{V}_r' = \frac{\overline{V}_s}{\{R + jX - [2j/(\omega C)]\}}\left(-\frac{2j}{\omega C}\right) \tag{11.35}$$

Using Equation (11.35), we can calculate regulation as

$$\% \text{ Regulation} = \frac{\left|\overline{V}'\right|_r - \left|\overline{V}_r\right|}{\left|\overline{V}_r\right|} \times 100\%$$

$$\% \text{ Efficiency } \eta = \frac{P}{P + 3I_l^2 R} \times 100\%$$

Determination of A, B, C, D constants

From Figure 11.10, we get

$$\overline{I}_{c1} = \frac{\overline{V}_r\overline{Y}}{2} \quad \text{and} \quad \overline{I}_l = \overline{I}_{c1} + \overline{I}_r = \overline{I}_r + \frac{\overline{V}_r\overline{Y}}{2}$$

Thus

$$\bar{V}_s = \bar{V}_r + \bar{I}_l\bar{Z} = \bar{V}_r + \left(\bar{I}_r + \frac{\bar{V}_r\bar{Y}}{2}\right)Z = \left(1 + \frac{\bar{Y}\bar{Z}}{2}\right)\bar{V}_r + \bar{I}_r\bar{Z} \qquad (11.36)$$

Sending-end current will be

$$\bar{I}_s = \bar{I}_l + \bar{I}_{c2} = I_l + \frac{\bar{V}_s\bar{Y}}{2}$$

$$= \bar{I}_r + \frac{\bar{V}_r\bar{Y}}{2} + \left[\left(1 + \frac{\bar{Y}\bar{Z}}{2}\right)\bar{V}_r + \bar{Z}\bar{I}_r\right]\frac{\bar{Y}}{2} = \bar{Y}\left(1 + \frac{\bar{Y}\bar{Z}}{4}\right)\bar{V}_r + \left(1 + \frac{\bar{Y}\bar{Z}}{2}\right)\bar{I}_r \qquad (11.37)$$

Comparing Equations (11.36) and (11.37) with Equations (11.9) and (11.10), respectively, we get

$$A = 1 + \frac{\bar{Y}\bar{Z}}{2}, \quad B = \bar{Z}, \quad C = \bar{Y}\left(1 + \frac{\bar{Y}\bar{Z}}{4}\right), \quad D = 1 + \frac{\bar{Y}\bar{Z}}{2}$$

From these relations, we obtain

$$A = D \quad \text{and} \quad AD - BC = 1$$

Example 11.3 A 3-phase, 100-km, transmission line is delivering 50 MW, 0.8-p.f. lagging at 132 kV. Each conductor is having resistance 0.1 ohm/km, reactance 0.3 ohm/km, and admittance 3×10^{-6} mho/km. If the load is balanced and leakage is neglected, calculate the sending-end voltage, sending-end power factor, efficiency and regulation of the line using (a) nominal-T and (b) nominal-π representations.

Solution We have

Receiving-end phase to neutral voltage $|\bar{V}_r| = \dfrac{132}{\sqrt{3}} = 76.21 \, \text{kV}$

Series impedance $\bar{Z} = (0.1 + j0.3) \times 100 = 10 + j30 \, \text{ohm}$

Shunt admittance $\bar{Y} = (0.0 + j3 \times 10^{-6}) \times 100 = j3 \times 10^{-4} \, \text{mho}$

Current in each phase $= \dfrac{P}{3V_r \cos\phi_r} = \dfrac{50 \times 10^3}{3 \times 76.21 \times 0.8} = 273.36 \, \text{A}$

(a) *Using nominal-T representation:* Refer to Figure 11.9. Taking receiving-end current as reference, the voltage at point *C*,

$$\bar{V}_C = \bar{V}_r (\cos\phi_r + j\sin\phi_r) + \frac{\bar{I}_r\bar{Z}}{2}$$

$$= 76.21(0.8 + j0.6) + 273.36(10 + j30) \times 0.5 \times 10^{-3}$$

$$= 62.334 + j49.827 \, \text{kV}$$

The current in the shunt branch

$$\bar{I}_C = \bar{Y}\bar{V}_C = j3 \times 10^{-4} \times (62.334 + j49.827) \times 10^3 = -14.9 + j18.7 \, \text{A}$$

and

$$\bar{I}_s = \bar{I}_C + \bar{I}_r = -14.9 + j18.7 + 273.36 = 258.46 + j18.7 = 259.14 \angle 4.14° \text{ A}$$

Thus

$$\bar{V}_s = \bar{V}_C + \frac{\bar{I}_s \bar{Z}}{2}$$

$$= 62.334 + j49.827 + (258.46 + j18.7)\frac{(10 + j30) \times 10^{-3}}{2}$$

$$= 63.346 + j53.797$$

$$= 83.11 \angle 40.34° \text{ kV}$$

Therefore, the sending-end voltage (line–line) is 143.95 kV.

From the phasor diagram (Figure 11.9), power factor angle is (40.34 − 4.14 = 36.2). The power factor is 0.807 (=cos 36.2) lagging. Now, the receiving-end voltage at no-load

$$\left|\bar{V}_r'\right| = \left|\frac{\bar{V}_s(1/\bar{Y})}{(\bar{Z}/2) + (1/\bar{Y})}\right| = \left|\frac{\bar{V}_s}{1 + (\bar{Z}\bar{Y}/2)}\right| = \frac{83.11}{\left|1 + [(10 + j30) \times j3 \times 10^{-4}/2]\right|} = 83.49 \text{ kV}$$

and

$$\% \text{ Regulation} = \frac{83.49 - 76.21}{76.21} \times 100 = 9.55\%$$

$$\% \text{ Efficiency } \eta = \frac{P}{P + 3[(I_s^2 R/2) + (I_r^2 R/2)]}$$

$$= \frac{50 \times 10^6}{50 \times 10^6 + 3 \times (273.36)^2 \times 5 + 3 \times (259.14)^2 \times 5}$$

$$= 95.92\%$$

(b) *Using nominal-π representation:* Taking receiving-end voltage as reference, we get from (Figure 11.10),

$$\bar{I}_{c1} = \frac{\bar{Y}}{2}\bar{V}_r = j11.43 \text{ A}$$

$$\bar{I}_l = \bar{I}_r + \bar{I}_{c1}$$

$$= 273.36(0.8 - j0.6) + j11.43 = 218.688 - j152.586$$

$$= 266.65 \angle -34.90°$$

$$\bar{V}_s = \bar{V}_r + \bar{I}_l \bar{Z}$$

$$= 76.21 + (218.688 - j152.586) \times (10 + j30) \times 10^{-3}$$

$$= 82.97 + j5.034 \text{ kV}$$

$$= 83.13 \angle 3.472° \text{ kV}$$

Sending-end voltage (line–line) will be 143.98 kV (= 83.13 $\sqrt{3}$). Now,

$$\bar{I}_{c2} = \frac{\bar{Y}}{2}\bar{V}_s = j1.5 \times 10^{-4} \times (82.97 + j5.034) \times 10^3 = 0.755 + j12.446 \text{ A}$$

and

$$\bar{I}_s = \bar{I}_l + \bar{I}_{c2} = 218.688 - j152.586 + 0.755 + j12.446 = 260.37\angle-32.56° \text{ A}$$

Power factor = cos (32.56 + 3.472) = 0.809 lagging. Receiving-end voltage at no-load will be

$$|\bar{V}'| = \left| \frac{\bar{V}_s(2/\bar{Y})}{\bar{Z} + [1/(\bar{Y}/2)]} \right| = \left| \frac{\bar{V}_s}{1 + (\bar{Z}\bar{Y}/2)} \right| = \frac{83.13}{\left| 1 + [(10 + j30) \times j3 \times 10^{-4}/2] \right|} = 83.51 \text{ kV}$$

and

$$\% \text{ Regulation} = \frac{83.13 - 76.21}{76.21} \times 100 = 9.58\%$$

$$\% \text{ Efficiency } \eta = \frac{P}{P + 3I_l^2 R} = \frac{50 \times 10^6}{50 \times 10^6 + 3(266.65)^2 \times 10} = 95.91\%$$

Alternate method (using *A*, *B*, *C*, *D* constants and nominal-T representation). Taking V_r as reference, we get

$$\bar{V}_s = A\bar{V}_r + B\bar{I}_r \quad \text{and} \quad \bar{I}_s = C\bar{V}_r + D\bar{I}_r$$

where

$$A = 1 + \frac{\bar{Y}\bar{Z}}{2} = 0.9955 + j1.5 \times 10^{-3} = 0.9955 \angle 0.086°$$

$$B = \bar{Z}\left(1 + \frac{\bar{Y}\bar{Z}}{2}\right) = 9.955 + j29.94 = 31.552 \angle 71.608°$$

$$C = \bar{Y} = 3 \times 10^{-4} \angle 90°$$

$$D = A$$

Therefore

$$\bar{V}_s = (0.9955\angle0.086) \times 76.21 + (31.552\angle71.608)(273.36\angle-36.87) \times 10^{-3}$$

$$= 82.954 + j5.029$$

$$= 83.11\angle3.469° \text{ kV}$$

Sending-end voltage (line–line) will be 143.95 kV (=83.11√3). We also have

$$\bar{I}_s = (3 \times 10^{-4}\angle90) \times (76.21 \times 10^3) + (0.9955\angle0.086) \times (273.36\angle-36.87)$$

$$= 217.95 - j140.687$$

$$= 259.41\angle-32.84° \text{ A}$$

and the sending-end power factor = cos (32.84 + 3.47) = 0.806. Similarly, other quantities can be calculated.

11.6 LONG TRANSMISSION LINE

For the transmission line less than 200 km, the transmission parameters: resistance, reactance and admittance, can be taken as lumped. But for lines more than 200 km, distributed parameters are considered for accuracy of analysis where voltage and current vary at each point in the transmission line. Figure 11.12 shows the representation of a long line. Receiving end is taken as reference for measuring the distances. For analysis, an incremental length Δx is considered, as shown in Figure 11.13.

Let

z = Series impedance per unit length
y = Shunt admittance per unit length
l = Length of line
$Z = zl$ = Total series impedance
$Y = yl$ = Total shunt admittance

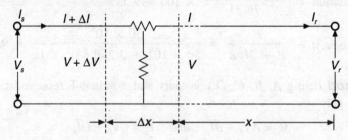

FIGURE 11.12 Long transmission line.

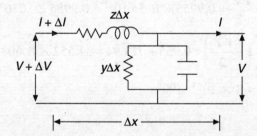

FIGURE 11.13 Representation of length Δx.

If the voltage and current at distance x is V and I respectively, these will be $V + \Delta V$ and $I + \Delta I$ at distance $x + \Delta x$ respectively, as shown in Figure 11.13. We also obtain

$$\Delta I = Vy\Delta x \quad \text{and} \quad \Delta V = (I + \Delta I)\, z\Delta x \cong Iz\Delta x \qquad (11.38)$$

Equation (11.38) can be written as

$$\frac{\Delta I}{\Delta x} = Vy \quad \text{and} \quad \frac{\Delta V}{\Delta x} = Iz \qquad (11.39)$$

If considered section Δx is very small, $(\Delta x \to 0)$. From Equation (11.39), we obtain

$$\frac{dI}{dx} = Vy \qquad (11.40)$$

and

$$\frac{dV}{dx} = Iz \tag{11.41}$$

Differentiating Equation (11.41) with respect to x and simplifying using Equation (11.40), we get

$$\frac{d^2V}{dx^2} = \frac{dI}{dx}z = Vyz \tag{11.42}$$

Equation (11.42) gives

$$\bar{V} = A \exp\left(\sqrt{yz}x\right) + B \exp\left(-\sqrt{yz}x\right) = Ae^{\gamma x} + Be^{-\gamma x} \tag{11.43}$$

where $\sqrt{(yz)} = \gamma = \alpha + j\beta$ is called the *propagation constant* which is a complex quantity. Here, α is called *attenuation constant* and β is called *phase constant* and has unit of radian/unit length. Now, differentiating Equation (11.43), we get

$$\frac{dV}{dx} = A\gamma e^{\gamma x} - B\gamma e^{-\gamma x} = \bar{I}z$$

or

$$\bar{I} = \frac{1}{\bar{Z}_c}(Ae^{\gamma x} + Be^{-\gamma x}) \tag{11.44}$$

where $\bar{Z}_c = \sqrt{(z/y)}$, which is known as *characteristic impedance*.

Using the limiting conditions, i.e. at $x = 0$, $V = V_r$ and $I = I_r$ and putting these values in Equations (11.43) and (11.44), we have

$$\bar{V}_r = A + B \quad \text{and} \quad \bar{I}_r = \frac{A - B}{Z_c}$$

Thus

$$A = \frac{V_r + I_r Z_c}{2} \quad \text{and} \quad B = \frac{V_r - I_r Z_c}{2}$$

Now Equations (11.43) and (11.44) can be written as

$$\bar{V} = \frac{\bar{V}_r + \bar{I}_r \bar{Z}_c}{2}e^{\gamma x} + \frac{\bar{V}_r - \bar{I}_r \bar{Z}_c}{2}e^{-\gamma x} = \bar{V}_r\frac{e^{\gamma x} + e^{-\gamma x}}{2} + \bar{I}_r\bar{Z}_c\frac{e^{\gamma x} - e^{-\gamma x}}{2}$$

or

$$\bar{V} = \bar{V}_r \cosh(\gamma x) + \bar{Z}_c\bar{I}_r \sinh(\gamma x) \tag{11.45}$$

Similarly, we can also simplify current Equation (11.44) in the following form

$$\bar{I} = \frac{\bar{V}_r}{\bar{Z}_c}\sinh(\gamma x) + \bar{I}_r \cosh(\gamma x) \tag{11.46}$$

Sending-end voltage and current equations can be obtained by putting $x = l$ in Equations (11.45) and (11.46)

$$\bar{V}_s = \bar{V}_r \cosh(\gamma l) + \bar{Z}_c \bar{I}_r \sinh(\gamma l) \tag{11.47}$$

$$\bar{I}_s = \frac{\bar{V}_r}{\bar{Z}_c} \sinh(\gamma l) + \bar{I}_r \cosh(\gamma l) \tag{11.48}$$

Comparing Equations (11.47) and (11.48) with Equations (11.9) and (11.10) respectively, we get

$$A = D = \cosh(\gamma l), \qquad B = Z_c \sinh(\gamma l), \qquad C = \frac{\sinh(\gamma l)}{Z_c} \tag{11.49}$$

From these relations, we obtain

$$A = D \quad \text{and} \quad AD - BC = 1$$

Surge impedance and surge impedance loading

Characteristic impedance is defined as the square root of the ratio of series impedance to shunt admittance which is a complex quantity. The phase angle of transmission line is usually less than 15°. Mathematically, characteristic impedance can be written as

$$\bar{Z}_c = \sqrt{\frac{z}{y}} = \sqrt{\frac{r + (j\omega L)}{g + (j\omega C)}}$$

If the line is lossless ($r = 0$ and $g = 0$), the characteristic impedance is known as *surge impedance,* that is a pure resistance and can be written as

$$\bar{Z}_c = \sqrt{\frac{j\omega L}{j\omega C}} = \sqrt{\frac{L}{C}}$$

Normally, surges are of high frequencies and therefore losses are neglected. Thus in case of lossless line, the term 'surge impedance' is used instead of 'characteristic impedance'. It should be noted that surge impedance or characteristic impedance is independent of the length of lines. Surge impedance of overhead lines and cables depends on the configuration of conductors and their placing. The approximate value of surge impedance for overhead lines is 400 ohm and for cables it is 40 ohm. Since distances between cable conductors are small, the value of inductance is smaller and capacitance is relatively higher compared to overhead lines, thus low surge impedance.

Surge impedance loading (SIL) of a line is the power transmitted when a lossless line operating at its nominal voltage, is terminated with a resistance equal to surge impedance of the line. It can be written as

$$P_{\text{SIL}} = \frac{|\bar{V}|^2}{Z_0} \tag{11.50}$$

If the voltage in Equation (11.50) is phase voltage, the P_{SIL} will be per phase surge impedance loading and for getting the 3-phase surge impedance loading, three must be multiplied. If voltage is a line–line voltage, the P_{SIL} will be three-phase surge impedance loading. Surge impedance loading is also known as *natural loading* of the line, which indicates that it is the maximum power that can be delivered and is useful in transmission line design. Surge impedance loading of AC lines are given in Table 11.1.

Table 11.1 Surge Impedance Loading (SIL) of AC Lines

S.no.	Line voltage (kV)	Conductor configuration	SIL (MW)
1	765	Quad Bersimis	2250
2	400	Quad Bersimis	691
3	400	Twin Moose	515
4	400	Twin AAAC	425
5	400	Quad Zebra	647
6	400	Quad AAAC	646
7	400	Tripple Snowbird	605
8	400	Twin ACAR	557
9	220	Twin Zebra	175
10	220	Single Zebra	132
11	132	Single Panther	50
12	66	Single Dog	10

To increase the power transmitted through a long transmission line, the operating voltage of the line can be increased or Z_0 can be reduced. Z_0 can be reduced either by using double circuit line which is very expensive or by increasing the value of capacitance or by decreasing the value of inductance.

Waves on transmission lines

Looking at Equation (11.43), two terms $Ae^{\gamma x}$ and $Be^{-\gamma x}$ represent the two waves of the voltage evaluated at x metre from the right-hand side of the line. The total voltage at any point is the sum of these two components. If x increases (wave is moving from right-hand side to left-hand side), the value of $Ae^{\gamma x}$ increases. It has the highest value at left-hand side and the lowest value at right-hand side. Since left-hand side is the sending-end and left-hand side is the receiving-end, term $Ae^{\gamma x}$ is incident wave voltage. Similarly, we can give argument for second term, which is reflected wave voltage.

Now, Equation (11.45) can be written as

$$\bar{V} = \bar{V}_s^+ e^{\gamma x} + \bar{V}_s^- e^{-\gamma x}$$

where

$$\bar{V}_s^+ = \frac{\bar{V}_r + (\bar{I}_r \bar{Z}_c)}{2} \qquad \text{(incident voltage)}$$

$$\bar{V}_s^- = \frac{\bar{V}_r - (\bar{I}_r \bar{Z}_c)}{2} \qquad \text{(reflected voltage)}$$

A line terminated with characteristic impedance is called *flat* or *infinite line* (no reflection). It can be seen that driving point impedance of the line will be Z_c.

If the line is terminated with $\bar{Z}_c$, we have

$$\bar{V}_r = \bar{I}_r \bar{Z}_c$$

and Equations (11.47) and (11.48) become

$$\overline{V}_s = \overline{V}_r \left[\cosh(\gamma l) + \sinh(\gamma l) \right] \quad \text{and} \quad \overline{I}_s = \overline{I}_r \left[\sinh(\gamma l) + \cosh(\gamma l) \right]$$

Thus

$$\frac{\overline{V}_s}{\overline{I}_s} = \frac{\overline{V}_r}{\overline{I}_r} = \overline{Z}_c$$

11.7 LUMPED-CIRCUIT EQUIVALENT REPRESENTATION

In nominal-π or nominal-T representations, we take the lumped parameters instead of distributed parameters, which is not accurate. After deriving the *ABCD* constants of the line in terms of distributed parameters, they can also be represented as lumped-circuit equivalent-T or equivalent-π (also known as *equivalent-T* or *equivalent-π*).

11.7.1 Equivalent-π Representation

Figure 11.14 shows the lumped circuit equivalent-π of a long line, where $\overline{Z}'$ and $\overline{Y}'$ are circuit parameters. These can be calculated using *ABCD* parameters approach.

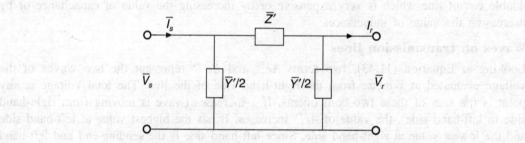

FIGURE 11.14 Equivalent-π representation.

For the network given as in Figure 11.14, we can write the following relationship:

$$\overline{V}_s = \overline{V}_r + \overline{Z}'\left(I_r + \overline{V}_r \frac{\overline{Y}'}{2} \right)$$

or

$$\overline{V}_s = \left(1 + \frac{\overline{Z}'\overline{Y}'}{2} \right)\overline{V}_r + \overline{Z}'\overline{I}_r \tag{11.51}$$

and

$$\overline{I}_s = \overline{V}_s \frac{\overline{Y}'}{2} + \overline{I}_r + \overline{V}_r \frac{\overline{Y}'}{2}$$

$$= \left[\left(1 + \frac{\overline{Z}'\overline{Y}'}{2} \right)\overline{V}_r + \overline{Z}'\overline{I}_r \right]\frac{\overline{Y}'}{2} + \overline{I}_r + \overline{V}_r \frac{\overline{Y}'}{2}$$

$$= \overline{Y}'\left(1 + \frac{\overline{Z}'\overline{Y}'}{4} \right)V_r + \left(1 + \frac{\overline{Z}'\overline{Y}'}{2} \right)I_r \tag{11.52}$$

Comparing Equations (11.51) and (11.52) with Equations (11.9) and (11.10), we get

$$A = 1 + \frac{\bar{Y}'\bar{Z}'}{2}, \quad B = \bar{Z}', \quad C = \bar{Y}'\left(1 + \frac{\bar{Y}'\bar{Z}'}{4}\right), \quad D = 1 + \frac{\bar{Y}'\bar{Z}'}{2} \tag{11.53}$$

Equating the B parameter in Equations (11.53) and (11.49), we get

$$\bar{Z}' = \bar{Z}_c \sinh(\gamma l) = \sqrt{\frac{z}{y}}\,\sinh(\gamma l) = \sqrt{\frac{z}{y}}\,\frac{\sqrt{zy}\,l\,\sinh(\gamma l)}{\gamma l} = \bar{Z}\,\frac{\sinh(\gamma l)}{\gamma l} \tag{11.54}$$

where $\bar{Z}(= zl)$ is the total series impedance of the line. Equating parameter A in Equations (11.53) and (11.47), we have

$$1 + \frac{\bar{Y}'\bar{Z}'}{2} = \cosh(\gamma l) \tag{11.55}$$

Eliminating the value of Z' from Equation (11.54), we have

$$\frac{\bar{Y}'}{2} = \frac{\cosh(\gamma l) - 1}{\bar{Z}'} = \frac{\cosh(\gamma l) - 1}{\bar{Z}_c \sinh(\gamma l)}$$

$$= \frac{\left[\left(\cosh^2\dfrac{\gamma l}{2}\right) + \left(\sinh^2\dfrac{\gamma l}{2}\right)\right] - \left[\left(\cosh^2\dfrac{\gamma l}{2}\right) - \left(\sinh^2\dfrac{\gamma l}{2}\right)\right]}{2\bar{Z}_c \sinh\dfrac{\gamma l}{2}\cosh\dfrac{\gamma l}{2}} \tag{11.56}$$

$$= \frac{1}{\bar{Z}_c}\tanh\frac{\gamma l}{2} = \sqrt{\frac{y}{z}}\,\frac{\tanh(\gamma l/2) \times \sqrt{zy}\,l}{\sqrt{zy}\,l} = \frac{\bar{Y}}{2}\,\frac{\tanh(\gamma l/2)}{\gamma l/2}$$

If the line is not long, the term

$$\frac{\tanh(\gamma l/2)}{\gamma l/2}$$

will be equal to unity.

11.7.2 Equivalent-T Representation

Figure 11.15 shows the equivalent-T representation of the line. The values of Z' and Y' are to be determined in terms of distributed parameters.

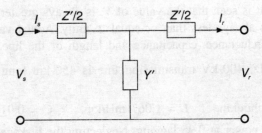

FIGURE 11.15 Equivalent-*T* representation.

From the figure, we get

$$\bar{V}_s = \bar{V}_r + \bar{I}_r \frac{\bar{Z}'}{2} + \left[\left(\bar{V}_r + \bar{I}_r \frac{\bar{Z}'}{2} \right) \bar{Y}' + \bar{I}_r \right] \frac{\bar{Z}'}{2} = \left(1 + \frac{\bar{Y}'\bar{Z}'}{2} \right) \bar{V}_r + \bar{Z}' \left(1 + \frac{\bar{Y}'\bar{Z}'}{4} \right) \bar{I}_r \quad (11.57)$$

and

$$\bar{I}_s = \left[\left(V_r + \bar{I}_r \frac{\bar{Z}'}{2} \right) \bar{Y}' + \bar{I}_r \right] = \bar{Y}'\bar{V}_r + \left(1 + \frac{\bar{Y}'\bar{Z}'}{2} \right) \bar{I}_r \quad (11.58)$$

Comparing Equations (11.57) and (11.58) with Equations (11.47) and (11.48), we get

$$Y' = \frac{\sinh(\gamma l)}{Z_c} \quad (11.59)$$

and

$$1 + \frac{\bar{Y}'\bar{Z}'}{2} = \cosh(\gamma l) \quad (11.60)$$

Putting the value of Y' from Equation (11.59) in Equation (11.60), we have

$$\frac{\bar{Z}'}{2} = \bar{Z}_c \frac{\cosh(\gamma l) - 1}{\sinh(\gamma l)} = \bar{Z}_c \tanh \frac{\gamma l}{2} = \sqrt{\frac{z}{y}} \frac{[\tanh(\gamma l/2)](\gamma l/2)}{\gamma l/2} = \frac{\bar{Z}}{2} \frac{\tanh(\gamma l/2)}{\gamma l/2} \quad (11.61)$$

Equation (11.59) can further be simplified as

$$\bar{Y}' = \frac{\sinh(\gamma l)}{Z_c} = \sqrt{\frac{y}{z}} \frac{\sinh(\gamma l)}{\gamma l} \gamma l = \bar{Y} \frac{\sinh(\gamma l)}{\gamma l} \quad (11.62)$$

11.8   FERRANTI EFFECT

In long transmission lines and cables, receiving-end voltage is greater than sending-end voltage during light-load or no-load operation. This occurs due to high-charging current. This effect is known as *ferranti effect*. When an open-circuited line (no-load) is charged, it draws significant amount of current due to capacitive effect of the line. This is more in high-voltage long-transmission lines. Ferranti effect can be understood as follows.

Under no-load ($I_r = 0$), we can write Equation (11.47) as

$$\bar{V}_s = \bar{V}_r \cosh(\gamma l) \quad \text{or} \quad \bar{V}_r = \frac{\bar{V}_s}{\cosh(\gamma l)} \quad (11.63)$$

From Equation (11.63), it is seen that the value of V_r is always greater or equal to V_s because the value of $\cosh(\gamma l)$ is always less than or equal to unity. Actual value depends on the γl, which is a function of inductance, capacitance and length of the line.

Example 11.4   A 50-Hz, 400-kV transmission line is 450-km long and having following distributed parameters:

$$r = 0.033 \text{ ohm/km}, \qquad L = 1.067 \text{ mH/km}, \qquad C = 0.0109 \text{ μF/km}$$

It is delivering 420-MW power at 0.95 lagging. Neglecting the leakage conductance, calculate

(a) Voltage at sending end
(b) Current at sending end
(c) Sending-end power factor and load angle
(d) *ABCD* parameters
(e) Regulation of line
(f) Efficiency.

Solution Let us calculate the impedance and admittance as

$$z = r + jx = 0.033 + j2\pi fL = (0.033 + j0.335) \text{ ohm/km}$$

and

$$y = j\omega C = j3.425 \times 10^{-6} \text{ mho/km}$$

Then the characteristic impedance

$$\bar{Z}_c = \sqrt{\frac{z}{y}} = \sqrt{\frac{0.3366}{3.425 \times 10^{-6}}} \angle -5.626 = 313.49 \angle -2.813° \text{ ohm/km}$$

and

$$\text{Propagation constant } \gamma = \sqrt{zy} = 1.074 \times 10^{-3} \angle 87.19°$$

Therefore

$$\gamma l = \alpha l + j\beta l = 0.4833\angle 87.19° = 0.0237 + j0.4827$$

Let us calculate $\sinh(\gamma l)$ and $\cosh(\gamma l)$:

$$\sinh(\gamma l) = \frac{e^{\gamma l} - e^{-\gamma l}}{2} = \frac{e^{\alpha l}e^{j\beta l}}{2} - \frac{e^{-\alpha l}e^{-j\beta l}}{2}$$

$$= \frac{1}{2}(1.024\angle 0.4827\text{rad} - 0.9766\angle -0.4827\text{rad})$$

$$= 0.021 + j0.4643$$

$$= 0.4648\angle 87.41°$$

$$\cosh(\gamma l) = \frac{e^{\gamma l} + e^{-\gamma l}}{2} = \frac{e^{\alpha l}e^{j\beta l}}{2} + \frac{e^{-\alpha l}e^{-j\beta l}}{2}$$

$$= \frac{1}{2}(1.024\angle 0.4827\text{rad} + 0.9766\angle -0.4827\text{rad})$$

$$= 0.886 + j0.11$$

$$= 0.886\angle 0.71°$$

Now, the receiving-end current

$$I_r = \frac{420 \times 10^6}{\sqrt{3} \times 400 \times 10^3 \times 0.95} = 638.12 \text{ A}$$

and the receiving-end phase voltage

$$V_r = \frac{400}{\sqrt{3}} = 230.94 \text{ kV}$$

(a) Taking receiving-end voltage at reference, using Equation (11.47), sending-end voltage can be calculated as

$$\bar{V}_s = \bar{V}_r \cosh(\gamma l) + \bar{Z}_c \bar{I}_r \sinh(\gamma l)$$

$$= 230.94 \times 0.886\angle 0.71° + 313.49\angle -5.626° \times 0.63812\angle -18.19° \times 0.4648\angle 87.41°$$

$$= 260.48\angle 19.23° \text{ kV}$$

Line–line voltage will be 451.16 kV ($=260.48\sqrt{3}$).

(b) Using Equation (11.48), sending-end current will be

$$\bar{I}_s = \frac{\bar{V}_r}{\bar{Z}_c} \sinh(\gamma l) + \bar{I}_r \cosh(\gamma l)$$

$$= \frac{230.94 \times 10^3}{313.49\angle -5.626°} \times 0.4648\angle 87.41° + 0.63812\angle -18.19° \times 0.886\angle 0.71°$$

$$= 548.78\angle 18.28° \text{ A}$$

(c) Sending power factor $pf_s = \cos(19.23 - 18.28) = 0.9998$ lagging and load angle $\delta = 19.23°$.

(d) Using Equation (11.49), A, B, C, D parameters will be calculated as

$$A = D = \cosh(\gamma l) = 0.886\angle 0.71°$$

$$B = Z_c \sinh(\gamma l) = 313.49\angle -5.626° \times 0.4648\angle 87.41° = 145.71\angle 81.78° \text{ ohm}$$

$$C = \frac{\sinh(\gamma l)}{Z_c} = \frac{0.4648\angle 87.41°}{313.49\angle -5.626°} = 1.483 \times 10^{-3}\angle 93.04° \text{ mho}$$

(e) Regulation (percentage) $= \dfrac{|\bar{V}_s/A| - |\bar{V}_r|}{|\bar{V}_r|} \times 100 = 27.3\%$

(f) We also get

$$\text{Input power} = 3|V_s||I_s|pf_s = 428.84 \text{ MW}$$

and

$$\text{Efficiency } \eta = \frac{420}{428.84} \times 100 = 97.94\%$$

11.9 POWER FLOW THROUGH A TRANSMISSION LINE

Figure 11.16 shows the transmission line connected with load. At sending end, a power source is supplying the power to the load. Receiving end is assumed as reference. The sending-end angle δ should be positive because real power flows from higher angle to lower angle. It is also true that reactive power always flows from higher voltage to lower voltage, which varies throughout the line. The direction of real power flow is same throughout the line, however, reactive power depends on the voltage profile of the line.

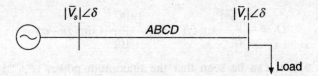

FIGURE 11.16 A transmission line with load and power source.

The sending quantities can be represented in terms of constants A, B, C, D of the line as

$$\bar{V}_s = A\bar{V}_r + B\bar{I}_r \quad \text{and} \quad \bar{I}_s = C\bar{V}_r + D\bar{I}_r$$

We can derive the current equations as

$$\bar{I}_r = \frac{\bar{V}_s}{B} - \frac{\bar{V}_r A}{B} \tag{11.64}$$

$$\bar{I}_s = C\bar{V}_r + \bar{V}_s \frac{D}{B} - \bar{V}_r \frac{AD}{B}$$

$$= \bar{V}_s \frac{D}{B} + \frac{\bar{V}_r(BC - AD)}{B}$$

$$= \bar{V}_s \frac{D}{B} - \frac{\bar{V}_r}{B} \tag{11.65}$$

Let

$$A = |A|\angle\alpha, \quad B = |B|\angle\beta, \quad D = |D|\angle\alpha \quad (\text{as } D = A)$$

Receiving-end power

Receiving-end complex power

$$\bar{S}_r = \bar{V}_r \bar{I}_r^*$$

$$= \bar{V}_r \left(\frac{\bar{V}_s^*}{B^*} - \frac{A^*\bar{V}_r^*}{B^*} \right)$$

$$= \frac{|\bar{V}_s||\bar{V}_r|}{|B|} \angle(\beta - \delta) - \frac{|A||\bar{V}_r|^2}{|B|} \angle(\beta - \alpha) \tag{11.66}$$

If V_s, V_r are in kV and are line voltages, the complex power will be a three-phase power in MVA. From Equation (11.66), real power (P_r) and reactive power (Q_r) at receiving end can be written as

$$P_r = \frac{|\bar{V}_s||\bar{V}_r|}{|B|} \cos(\beta - \delta) - \frac{|A||\bar{V}_r|^2}{|B|} \cos(\beta - \alpha) \tag{11.67}$$

and

$$Q_r = \frac{|\bar{V}_s||\bar{V}_r|}{|B|} \sin(\beta - \delta) - \frac{|A||\bar{V}_r|^2}{|B|} \sin(\beta - \alpha) \tag{11.68}$$

From Equation (11.67), it can be seen that the maximum power (P_r^{max}) (keeping voltages constant) received by the load will be at $\beta = \delta$, because α and β are constants and depend on the line configuration and design. Therefore, we get

$$P_r^{max} = \frac{|\bar{V}_s||\bar{V}_r|}{|B|} - \frac{|A||\bar{V}_r|^2}{|B|} \cos(\beta - \alpha) \tag{11.69}$$

and

$$Q_r = -\frac{|A||\bar{V}_r|^2}{|B|} \sin(\beta - \alpha)$$

These equations indicate that load must draw leading reactive power to receive maximum real power.

For short line, $A = D = 1\angle 0$ and $B = |\bar{Z}| \angle \theta$, where $\cos q = R/|\bar{Z}|$. Substituting these values in Equation (11.69), we get

$$P_r^{max} = \frac{|\bar{V}_s||\bar{V}_r|}{|Z|} - \frac{|\bar{V}_r|^2}{|Z|^2} R \tag{11.70}$$

If line is short and $R \ll X$, then $Z = jX$ and Equations (11.67) and (11.68) can be written as

$$P_r = \frac{|\bar{V}_s||\bar{V}_r|}{X} \sin\delta \tag{11.71}$$

and

$$Q_r = \frac{|\bar{V}_s||\bar{V}_r|}{|X|} \cos\delta - \frac{|\bar{V}_r|^2}{|X|} \tag{11.72}$$

From Equation (11.71), we can make following observations:

1. Receiving-end power will be maximum at $\delta = 90°$.
2. Receiving-end power can be increased by increasing sending-end voltage magnitude $|V_s|$ and/or receiving-end voltage magnitude $|\bar{V}_r|$.
3. Reducing reactance of the line can increase receiving-end power.

Normally, angle δ is very small; Equation (11.72) can be further simplified as

$$Q_r = \frac{|\bar{V}_r|}{|X|} \left(|\bar{V}_s| - |\bar{V}_r| \right)$$

or

$$Q_r = \frac{|\bar{V}_r|}{|X|} |\Delta V| \tag{11.73}$$

From Equation (11.73), it can be observed that the reactive power is directly proportional to the difference in the voltage magnitudes. It also indicates that the reactive power is mainly dependent on the voltage however real power is mainly dependent on the angle δ.

Sending-end power

At this point it is obvious to think why we use voltages in power calculation rather than current. The main reason is that voltages are easily obtainable and in current, direction is involved but in voltage it is not. Sending-end power (taking RE voltage as reference) can be written as

$$S_s = \bar{V}_s \bar{I}_s^* = \bar{V}_s \left(\frac{D}{B} \bar{V}_s - \frac{1}{B} \bar{V}_r \right)^*$$

or

$$\bar{S}_s = \frac{|A||\bar{V}_s|^2}{|B|} \angle (\beta - \alpha) - \frac{|\bar{V}_s||\bar{V}_r|}{|B|} \angle (\delta + \beta) \tag{11.74}$$

At the sending end, the real power can be written as

$$P_s = \frac{|A||\bar{V}_s|^2}{|B|} \cos (\beta - \alpha) - \frac{|\bar{V}_s||\bar{V}_s|}{|B|} \cos (\delta + \beta) \tag{11.75}$$

whereas the reactive power is

$$Q_s = \frac{|A||\bar{V}_s|^2}{|B|} \sin (\beta - \alpha) - \frac{|\bar{V}_s||\bar{V}_s|}{|B|} \sin (\delta + \beta) \tag{11.76}$$

From Equation (11.75), it can be seen that the sending-end power will be maximum at $\delta + \beta = \pi$. The maximum sending-end power will be

$$P_s^{max} = \frac{|A||\bar{V}_r|^2}{|B|} \cos (\beta - \alpha) + \frac{|\bar{V}_s||\bar{V}_r|}{|B|} \tag{11.77}$$

Thus the transmission real power loss, $P_L = -P_r + P_s$.

Circle diagram

Sometimes it is easier to calculate the quantities using the circle diagram. Sending-end and receiving-end circle diagrams can be drawn separately. Consider the circle diagram for receiving end. If the power factor at receiving end is θ_r, we can write Equation (11.67) as

$$\left|\overline{V}_r\right|\left|\overline{I}_r\right|\cos\theta_r = P_r = \frac{\left|\overline{V}_s\right|\left|\overline{V}_r\right|}{\left|B\right|}\cos(\delta-\beta) - \frac{\left|A\right|\left|\overline{V}_r\right|^2}{\left|B\right|}\cos(\alpha-\beta)$$

Squaring and adding Equations (11.67) and (11.68), we get

$$\left[P_r + \frac{\left|A\right|\left|\overline{V}_r\right|^2}{\left|B\right|}\cos(\beta-\alpha)\right]^2 + \left[Q_r + \frac{\left|A\right|\left|\overline{V}_r\right|^2}{\left|B\right|}\sin(\beta-\alpha)\right]^2 = \left(\frac{\left|\overline{V}_s\right|\left|\overline{V}_r\right|}{\left|B\right|}\right)^2 \qquad (11.78)$$

If P_r and Q_r are on the *x*-axis and *y*-axis respectively, Equation (11.78) shows a circle having radius of

$$\frac{\left|\overline{V}_s\right|\left|\overline{V}_r\right|}{\left|B\right|}$$

and centre at

$$\left(-\frac{\left|A\right|\left|\overline{V}_r\right|^2}{\left|B\right|}\cos(\beta-\alpha), -\frac{\left|A\right|\left|\overline{V}_r\right|^2}{\left|B\right|}\sin(\beta-\alpha)\right)$$

Figure 11.17 shows the circle diagram of receiving-end power.

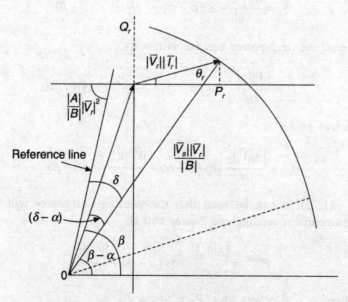

FIGURE 11.17   Receiving-end circle diagram.

For given P_r, θ_r, V_r and *ABCD* constants, sending-end voltage can be determined using the receiving-end circle diagram. Following steps must be used (Figure 11.18).

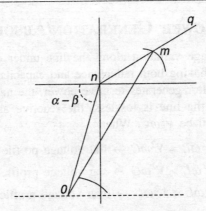

FIGURE 11.18 Circle diagram.

(a) Convert the three-phase quantities into per phase quantities, such as power and voltages.

(b) Calculate $(|A|/|B|)\left|\overline{V}_r\right|^2$.

(c) Choose a suitable scale by looking P_r and $(|A|/|B|)\left|\overline{V}_r\right|^2$.

(d) Draw a horizontal line and set a point n. Draw line nq with an angle θ_r and cut it at m with value $\left|\overline{V}_r\right|\left|\overline{I}_r\right|$.

(e) Drawn a line no of length $(|A||B|)\left|\overline{V}_r\right|^2$ with angle $\beta - \alpha$ in third quadrant.

(f) Connect o with m and measure om and convert to kVA with scale which will be equal to $|\overline{V}_s||\overline{V}_r|/|B|$.

(g) Calculate the value of $\left|\overline{V}_s\right|$.

11.10 Effect of Transformer on the Performance of a Transmission Line

There are several situations where transmission line is connected with transformer at either ends. It is important to analyze the effect of these transformers on the line performance. Equivalent circuit diagram of a transformer is shown in Figure 11.19.

This is a representation of two-port network and its *ABCD* parameters can be easily calculated. Using *ABCD* constant with transmission line constants, a final *ABCD* values can be calculated and performance of the system will be analyzed.

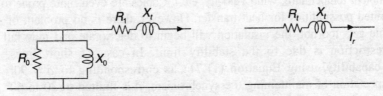

FIGURE 11.19 Transformer equivalent circuit.

11.11 REACTIVE POWER GENERATION/ABSORPTION OF A LINE

Figure 11.20 shows the voltage variation along the line under different loading conditions. Since transmission lines are having both inductance and capacitance, where inductor absorbs the reactive power and capacitor generates reactive power, the net reactive power depends on the loading of the lines. If the line is lossless, the reactive absorption will be $I^2\omega L$ and reactive power generation will be $V^2\omega C$. When

$$I^2\omega L = V^2\omega C \rightarrow \text{flat voltage profile}$$

$$I^2\omega L > V^2\omega C \rightarrow \text{sag voltage profile}$$

$$I^2\omega L < V^2\omega C \rightarrow \text{over-voltage profile}$$

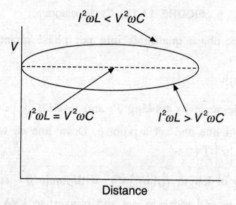

FIGURE 11.20 Voltage variation along a line.

11.12 POWER TRANSFER CAPABILITY OF TRANSMISSION LINES

Power transfer capability of transmission lines is restricted mainly due to three reasons: *thermal* limit, *voltage-drop* limit and *stability* limit. Thermal limit is due to heat generated when current flows in the conductor. Heat generated by line losses (I^2R) causes a temperature rise. Since line temperature of overhead lines must be kept within a safe limit to prevent excessive line sag between transmission towers and to prevent irreversible stretching, the ground clearance must be maintained in the case of overhead transmission lines. This imposes condition on the maximum safe current in a line. Several factors other than the current flowing in conductor are responsible for increase in the temperature such as design conditions (conductor size and geometry, spacing between towers, etc.) and operating conditions (ambient temperature, wind velocity, etc.). Cables are even more prone to thermal limit because of limited possibilities for heat transfer. However, there is no problem of sag in cables. But if the cable gets too hot, the insulation will begin to deteriorate and may fail in future.

Other restriction is due to the stability limit. In case of short lines, the ultimate transmission capability, using Equation (11.71), is corresponding to $\delta = 90°$. But to have reasonable expectation of maintaining the synchronism, δ is limited to 30 to 60°. In this case, the stability limit is 60 to 70% of the ultimate capability. In short lines, the power handling capability is set by thermal limit rather than stability limit. However it is reverse in the case of long transmission lines. For long line, power transfer can be expressed in terms of surge impedance loading of the line. If the line is lossless ($\gamma = j\beta$) and at both the side's voltages are same, we can write from Equation (11.70)

$$P_r = \frac{|\overline{V}_s||\overline{V}_r|}{|B|}\sin\delta = \frac{|\overline{V}_s||\overline{V}_r|}{|\overline{Z}_c\sinh(\gamma l)|}\sin\delta = \frac{|\overline{V}_s||\overline{V}_r|}{\overline{Z}_c\sin(\beta l)}\sin\delta = \frac{|\overline{V}|^2}{\overline{Z}_c\sin(\beta l)}\sin\delta = P_{SIL}\frac{\sin\delta}{\sin(\beta l)}$$

This shows that if the line length increased, βl increases and P_r decreases.

In medium transmission lines, the voltage drop is the main criterion for transferring maximum power over the lines. A line has current rating which provides the safe operation and above which it is not recommended for operation especially for long duration of time. Since lines are designed to operate at certain voltage level (restricted due to string insulators and clearances), sometimes rating is also given in terms of power which is multiplication of current and voltage. Extra-high voltage lines normally operate near to unity, the rating in MVA is almost the same as MW. Figure 11.21 shows the limits with length of lines.

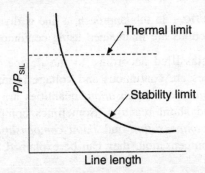

FIGURE 11.21 Capability limits of lines.

11.13 COMPENSATION OF TRANSMISSION LINES

Compensation means modification of the electrical (not physical) characteristics of transmission line in order to increase its power transfer capacity and satisfying the following fundamental requirements of transmission:

1. Major synchronous machines must remain stable in synchronism.
2. Voltage must be kept near rated values.

This first requirement is necessary to maintain the all generators and synchronous condensers to be in synchronism. This is the requirement of stability of the system. The second requirement is for a healthy operation of the system. In the system, there may be under-voltage, which may be due to high-load current or due to fault in the system. However, over-voltage may occur due to fault or switching transients. Both under-voltage and over-voltage may lead to unreliable operation of the system. The main objectives of compensation of the system are:

- To produce a substantially flat voltage profile at all the levels of power transmission
- To improve the stability of the system
- To meet the economical way for reactive power requirement of the system.

Compensation can be categorized by several ways. If compensation is done for changing the characteristic impedance of line, it is known as *surge impedance compensation* or Z_0-*compensation*. It is also possible to change the electrical length of the line, and the compensation used for this purpose is known as *line-length compensation* or θ-*compensation*. Transmission lines are compensated by using different sections and is known as *compensation-by-sectioning*.

Z_0-compensation. Ignoring the losses, the surge impedance of the line will be $\sqrt{(x_l x_c)}$, where x_l is the series reactance and x_c [$=1/(j\omega C)$] is the shunt reactance of the line. By changing x_l or x_c, Z_0 can be changed.

θ-compensation. In this compensation scheme, the effective value of θ is reduced. Since $\theta = \beta l = \sqrt{(x_l/x_c)}$, by reducing x_l, the value of θ can be reduced. Normally, the series capacitor is used. Practically it is not possible to increase x_c.

Compensation by sectioning. In this approach, a line is divided into several sections and voltages as the terminal of sections are maintained using continuous voltage control devices.

Compensation can also be classified according to the device-control operation. In *active compensation*, control variables are continuous and voltage is maintained (such as static var compensators). However in *passive compensation*, quantities are not continuously controlled such as series capacitors and shunt reactors. Sometimes compensation is categorized by devices used such as *series compensation* and *shunt compensation*. Taking an ideal case as uniformly distributed fixed compensation, they can be explained as follows:

Shunt compensation

If a uniformly distributed shunt compensating inductance is $l_{\gamma sh}$ (H/m), the effective value of the shunt capacitance C' will be related as

$$b_c' = b_c + b_{\gamma sh} \Rightarrow j\omega C' = j\omega C + \frac{1}{j\omega l_{\gamma sh}} = j\omega C(1 - k_{sh})$$

where k_{sh} is the degree shunt compensation and defined as

$$k_{sh} = \frac{x_c}{x_{\gamma sh}} = \frac{b_{\gamma sh}}{b_c} = \frac{1}{\omega^2 C l_{\gamma sh}} \qquad (11.79)$$

where b_c is the shunt capacitive susceptance per unit length and $b_{\gamma sh}$ is the shunt compensation susceptance per unit length. The value of k_{sh} is positive for inductive shunt compensation and it is negative for capacitive shunt compensation. The effective value of surge impedance (Z_0') and phase constant (β') with shunt compensation can be given by

$$Z_0' = \sqrt{\frac{x_l}{b_c'}} = \frac{Z_0}{\sqrt{1 - k_{sh}}} \qquad (11.80)$$

and

$$\beta' = \sqrt{x_l b_c'} = \beta\sqrt{1 - k_{sh}} \tag{11.81}$$

From Equations (11.80) and (11.81), it is clear that shunt inductive compensation will increase Z_0 and decrease β, whereas the shunt capacitive compensation will decrease Z_0 and increase β.

Series compensation

If uniformly distributed series capacitive compensation is C_{yse} (F/m), the effective value of series reactance x_l' will be related as

$$x_l' = x_l - x_{yse} = x_l(1 - k_{se})$$

where k_{se} is the *degree series compensation* and defined as

$$k_{se} = \frac{x_{yse}}{x_l}$$

The value of k_{se} is positive for capacitive series compensation and it is negative for inductive series compensation. The effective value of surge impedance (Z_0') and phase constant (β') with shunt compensation can be given by

$$Z_0' = \sqrt{x_l' x_c} = Z_0\sqrt{1 - k_{se}} \tag{11.82}$$

and

$$\beta' = \sqrt{\frac{x_l'}{x_c}} = \beta\sqrt{1 - k_{se}} \tag{11.83}$$

From Equations (11.82) and (11.83), it is clear that series inductive compensation will increase Z_0 and β, whereas the series capacitive compensation will decrease both Z_0 and β.

The combined effect of series and shunt compensations are as follows:

$$Z_0' = Z_0\sqrt{\frac{1 - k_{se}}{1 - k_{sh}}} \tag{11.84}$$

and

$$\beta' = \beta\sqrt{(1 - k_{sh})(1 - k_{se})} \tag{11.85}$$

The effective line length and natural load (P_0') can be given by

$$\theta' = \theta\sqrt{(1 - k_{sh})(1 - k_{se})} \tag{11.86}$$

and

$$P_0' = P_0\sqrt{\frac{1 - k_{se}}{1 - k_{sh}}} \tag{11.87}$$

The effect of power variation with different degree of compensation is shown as in Figure 11.22.

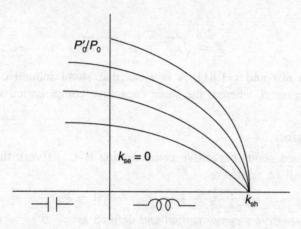

FIGURE 11.22   Effect of power transfer with degree of compensation.

Series and shunt compensations in the network

For the voltage control, normally shunt capacitors are used as a reactive power source. It is ideally suited for compensating the line if the reduction of effective characteristic impedance is primary consideration. However, shunt capacitors increase the effective line length. Shunt capacitor compensation could lead to reduction in small signal stability margin and poor voltage regulation. Shunt reactors are used in long transmission lines to reduce the electrical length of the lines.

Series capacitors are most suitable for the application when reduction of effective line angle is the primary consideration. It increases the effective natural load and improves the small signal stability and voltage regulation. However, series compensation could cause subsynchronous resonance problems. Static var compensators are used for direct and rapid control of voltage.

11.14   POWER FLOW IN A LONG TRANSMISSION LINE

If the line is lossless, the sending-end voltage can be written as

$$\overline{V}_s = \overline{V}_r \cosh(\gamma l) + \overline{I}_r \overline{Z}_c \sinh(\gamma l)$$

$$= \overline{V}_r \cos(\beta l) + j\overline{I}_r \overline{Z}_0 \sin(\beta l)$$

$$= \overline{V}_r \cos\theta + j\overline{I}_r \overline{Z}_0 \sin\theta$$

Putting the value of I_r as

$$\overline{I}_r = \frac{P - jQ}{\overline{V}_r}$$

Taking V_r as a reference and separating the real and imaginary parts, we get

$$\left|\overline{V}_s\right| \cos\delta = V_r \cos\theta + Z_0 \frac{Q}{V_r}\sin\theta$$

$$|\bar{V}_s| \sin \delta = 0 + Z_0 \frac{P}{V_r} \sin \theta$$

or

$$P = \frac{|\bar{V}_s||\bar{V}_r|}{Z_0 \sin \theta} \sin \delta \qquad (11.88)$$

If θ is very small, $\sin \theta = \theta = \beta l$. Thus,

$$Z_0 \sin \theta = Z_0 \theta = \sqrt{x_l x_c} \sqrt{\frac{x_l}{x_c}} = x_l$$

Therefore, the power will be

$$P = \frac{|\bar{V}_s||\bar{V}_r|}{x_l} \sin \delta \qquad (11.89)$$

Example 11.5 The *ABCD* constants of a loss less three-phase, 400-kV transmission line are,

$$A = D = 0.85 + j0$$
$$B = 0 + j150$$
$$C = j0.001$$

(a) Obtain the sending end quantities and the voltage regulation when line delivers a load of 750 MVA at 0.8 lagging power factor at 400 kV.

To improve the line performance, series capacitors, each having reactance $X_C = -j50$ ohms, are installed at both ends in each phase of the transmission line.

(b) Determine the compensated ABCD constants.

(c) Determine the sending end quantities and the voltage regulation when the compensated line delivers a load of 750 MVA at 0.8 lagging power factor at 400 kV.

Solution (a) For uncompensated line

$$A = D = 0.85, \ B = j150, \ C = j0.001$$

$$\bar{V}_R = \frac{400}{\sqrt{3}} \angle 0° \ \text{kV}$$

(Phase voltage) = 231 kV

Load is 750 MVA at 0.8 p.f. lag

$$\therefore \qquad \bar{I}_R = \frac{750 \times 10^3}{\sqrt{3} \times 400} \angle -36.87° = 1082.56 \angle -36.87° \ \text{Amps}$$

$$\therefore \qquad \bar{V}_S = A \cdot \bar{V}_R + B \cdot \bar{I}_R$$

$$= 0.85 \times \frac{400 \times 10^3}{\sqrt{3}} + j150 \times 1082.56 \ (0.8 - j0.6) \ \text{volts}$$

$$= (293.7804 + j129.91)\text{kV} = 321.22 \angle 23.85° \text{ per phase}$$

$$\bar{I}_S = C\bar{V}_R + D\bar{I}_R$$

$$= j0.001 \times \frac{400 \times 10^3}{\sqrt{3}} + 0.85 \times 1082.56 \,(0.8 - j0.6)$$

$$= 736.14 - j321.11 = 803.1275 \angle -23.57° \text{ Amps}$$

$$\therefore \quad \% \text{ voltage regulation} = \frac{|\bar{V}_S|/|A| - |\bar{V}_R|}{|\bar{V}_R|} \times 100$$

$$= \frac{321.22/0.85 - 231}{231} \times 100$$

$$= 63.6\%$$

(b) With series compensation, ABCD parameters of the compensated line will be

$$\begin{bmatrix} A' & B' \\ C' & D' \end{bmatrix} = \begin{bmatrix} 1.0 & -j50 \\ 0 & 1.0 \end{bmatrix} \begin{bmatrix} 0.85 & j50 \\ j0.001 & 0.85 \end{bmatrix} \begin{bmatrix} 1.0 & -j50 \\ 0 & 1.0 \end{bmatrix}$$

$$= \begin{bmatrix} 0.9 & j62.5 \\ j0.001 & 0.9 \end{bmatrix}$$

(c) For compensated line

$$\bar{V}_S' = 0.9 \times 231 + j62.5 \times \frac{1082.56}{1000}(0.8 - j0.6)\,\text{kV}$$

$$= 248.5 + j54.13 = 254.33 \angle 12.29° \text{ kV per phase}$$

$$\bar{I}_S' = j0.001 \times 231 \times 10^3 + 0.9 \times 1082.56\,(0.8 - j0.6)$$

$$= 779.44 - j353.58 = 855.9 \angle -24.4° \text{ Amps}$$

$$\therefore \quad \% \text{ Voltage regulation} = \frac{(254.33/0.9) - 231}{231} \times 100 = 22.33\%$$

Example 11.6 A 3ϕ 420 kV, 60 Hz transmission line is 463 km long and may be assumed lossless. The line is energized with 420 kV at the sending end. When the load at the receiving end is removed, the voltage at the receiving end is 700 kV, and the per phase sending end current is 646.6 $\angle 90°$ A

(a) Find the phase constant β in radians per km and the surge impedance Z_0 in Ω

(b) Ideal reactors are to be installed at the receiving end to keep $V_S = V_R = 420$ kV when load is removed. Determine the reactance per phase and the required 3ϕ kVAr.

Solution $V_s = 420$ kV, $f = 60$ Hz, $l = 463$ km, $V_r = 700$ kV.

(a) $V_s = V_{r \text{ (no load)}} \cos \beta l$

$$\beta l = \cos^{-1}\left(\frac{V_S}{V_R}\right) = \cos^{-1}\left[\frac{420}{700}\right] = 0.927 \text{ rad.}$$

$\therefore$ $$\beta = \frac{0.927}{463} = 0.002 \text{ rad/km}$$

$$\bar{I}_s = j\frac{1}{Z_0}\sin \beta l \cdot V_r$$

$$Z_0 = \frac{V_r(\sin \beta l)}{646.6} = \frac{700 \times 10^3 \sin(0.002/463)}{\sqrt{3} \times 646.6} = 500 \ \Omega$$

(b) $V_s = V_r = 420$ kV

reactance per phase of reactor

$$X_{Lsh} = \frac{\sin \beta l}{(1 - \cos \beta l)} Z = \frac{\sin 53.13}{1 - \cos 53.13} \times 500$$

$$X_{Lsh} = 1000 \Omega$$

$$3\phi \text{ shunt reactor rating} = \frac{(\text{kV rated})^2}{X_{Lsh}} = \frac{420^2}{1000} = 176.4 \text{ MVAr}$$

PROBLEMS

11.1   Calculate the performance of a 10-km long, 3-phase transmission line delivering 2500 kVA at 0.8-p.f. lagging. The voltage at the sending-end being 33 kV, 50 Hz and $R = 0.531$ ohm/km and $L = 1.76$ mH/km.

11.2   The input to a short 3-phase line of parameters $R = 0.4$ ohm and $X = 0.4$ ohm is 2000 kVA at a p.f. of 0.8 lagging. If the load voltage is 3000 V, find the load power, p.f. and the source voltage.

11.3   A three-phase, 50-Hz line has a resistance of 8 ohm and a reactance of 11 ohm. It supplies a 0.8 lagging p.f. load at a voltage of 11 kV. Find the load at which the source-end voltage equals the load-end voltage when a 25-microfarad capacitor is connected across the load in each phase.

11.4   Determine the sending end voltage, p.f., efficiency and regulation of a 3-phase, 100 km, 50-Hz transmission line delivering 50 MW at a p.f. of 0.8 lagging and 132 kV to a balance load. The conductors are of copper, each having resistance 0.1 ohm/km, 2.0-cm outside diameter, spaced equilaterally 4 m between the centres. Neglect the leakage and use (i) nominal-T, (ii) nominal-π and (iii) exact solution methods.

11.5   A three-phase, 50-Hz transmission line is 400-km long having series impedance of $(0.15 + j0.78)$ ohm/km and a shunt admittance of 5×10^{-6} mho/km.

(a) Determine the A,B,C,D constants assuming (i) the line could be represented by nominal-π or nominal-T and (ii) the exact representation.

(b) Derive equivalent π and T circuits for the line.

(c) If the load on the line is 125 MW at 400 kV and 0.8 lagging power factor, calculate the current, voltage and power factor at sending end. Also, calculate the power angle.

(d) Calculate the charging current of the line under the no-load condition.

11.6 The A,B,C,D constants of a 3-phase transmission line are $A = D = 0.936 + j0.016$, $B = 33.5 + j138$ ohm and $C = (-0.9280 + j901.223) \times 10^{-6}$ mho. The load at the receiving end is 40 MW at 220 kV with power factor of 0.86 lagging. Find the magnitude of the sending-end voltage, current, power, line efficiency and the voltage regulation. Assume the magnitude of the sending-end voltage remains constant.

11.7 A 40-MW unity power factor load is supplied by a 3-phase line having $\bar{Z} = 300\angle 78°$ and $\bar{Y} = 0.0024\angle 90°$. The receiving-end voltage is 130 kV. There is a load of 12 MW at unity p.f. at the middle of the transmission line. Find the voltage at the generator-end and at the middle of the line.

11.8 A 3-phase overhead transmission line has resistance and reactance per phase of 5 and 25 ohm, respectively. The load at the receiving end is 15 MW, 33 kV, 0.8-p.f. lagging. Find the capacity of the compensation equipment needed to deliver this load with a sending-end voltage of 33 kV. Draw the receiving-end circle diagram.

11.9 Calculate the extra load of 0.8-lagging power factor which can be delivered with the compensating equipment (of capacity as calculated in Problem 10.8) installed, if the receiving-end voltage is permitted to drop to 28 kV.

11.10 A one-phase, 50-Hz, 2-kV short transmission line may be represented by an equivalent circuit having (a) total resistance/phase = 1.0 ohm, (b) total reactance/phase = 1.0 ohm. Sending-end voltage is 2 kV while receiving-end voltage is held constant at 2 kV by means of a capacitor at receiving end. If the load at receiving end is 10 kVA at 0.8-p.f. lagging, find the value of capacitance.

11.11 Using the nominal-π method, find the sending-end voltage and voltage regulation of a 3-phase, 100 km, 50-Hz transmission line delivering 25 MVA at 0.8-lagging power factor to a balanced load at 132 kV. The line conductors spaced equilaterally is of 4.0 m. Also calculate the A, B, C and D constants of the line. The radius of conductors is 2 cm and having resistance of 0.1 Ω/km.

11.12 Find the following for a 3-phase transmission line delivering a load of 45 MVA at 132 kV and p.f. of 0.8 lagging:

(a) Sending end voltage

(b) Sending end current

(c) Sending power

(d) Efficiency of transmission line

Given $A = D = 0.99\angle 3°$; $B = 70\angle 69°$ ohm; $C = 4.0 \times 10^{-4}\angle 90°$ mho.

11.13 If a line is terminated with its characteristic impedance Z_c, find

(a) Voltage gain $|\bar{V}_r|/|\bar{V}_s|$

(b) Current gain $|\bar{I}_r|/|\bar{I}_s|$

(c) Complex power gain $\bar{S}_r/\bar{S}_s$

(d) Efficiency P_r/P_s

Also calculate above if the line is lossless.

11.14 The ABCD constants of a lossless 3-phase, 500-kV transmission line are

$$A = D = 0.86 + j0$$
$$B = 0 + j369.8$$
$$C = j0.002$$

(a) Obtain the sending end quantities and the voltage regulation when line delivers 1000 MVA at 0.8 lagging power factor at 500 kV.

To improve the line performance, series capacitors are installed at both ends in each phase of the transmission line. As a result of this, the compensated *ABCD* constants become

$$\begin{bmatrix} A' & B' \\ C' & D' \end{bmatrix} = \begin{bmatrix} 1 & \frac{1}{2}jX_C \\ 0 & 1 \end{bmatrix}\begin{bmatrix} A & B \\ C & D \end{bmatrix}\begin{bmatrix} 1 & \frac{1}{2}jX_C \\ 0 & 1 \end{bmatrix}$$

where X_C is the total reactance of the series capacitor. If $X_C = 100\ \Omega$

(b) Determine the compensated ABCD constants.

(c) Determine the sending-end quantities and the voltage regulation when line delivers 1000 MVA at 0.8 lagging power factor at 500 kV.

11.15 A 3-phase, 50 Hz line has a resistance of 8 ohm and a reactance of 11 ohm. It supplies a 0.8 lagging p.f. load at a voltage of 11 kV. Find the load at which the source-end voltage equals the load-end voltage when a 25 microfarad capacitor is connected across the load in each phase.

12

Insulators for Overhead Transmission Lines

12.1 INTRODUCTION

Overhead transmission lines are supported on the towers. Since towers are at ground potential, the lines must be insulated with the tower structure. *Insulators* are used to insulate tower from the bare conductors. Ideal insulators must have the following characteristics:

1. There should not be any pores or air spaces.
2. There should not be any impurities.
3. There should be perfectly homogeneous material.
4. Leakage current through insulators should be minimum.
5. Insulators should be able to withstand over-voltage and normal working voltage.
6. It should be mechanically strong to bear the conductor load.

First-three are physical characteristics of the insulator but the 4th and 5th are electrical characteristics. Last one is mechanical characteristic of the insulators. Porcelain and toughened glass are two main materials used for the construction of insulators for overhead transmission lines. Some other materials such as polymers and other moulded materials are also used.

Porcelain is most widely used insulator material as it is cheap. It is thoroughly verified and glazed before use. Glazing is necessary to keep the surface free from dust and moisture. Porcelain consists of 20% silica, 30% feldspar and 50% clay and having the dielectric strength of 120–280 kV/cm. Any impurity will reduce the dielectric strength of the insulator. It is difficult to manufacture a perfectly homogenous porcelain in the thickness required and therefore, it is necessary to go for different pieces and cemented together.

Toughened glass, which is normally having dielectric strength of 1200 kV/cm, is another material used for insulators. The glass is toughened to make skin more resistant to damage by chipping and arc. The main advantages of glass insulators are:

- High dielectric strength
- Longer life
- High thermal sock resistant thus reduced damage from the flashover
- Lower coefficient of thermal expansion
- Greater mechanical strength under the compression but in tension it is same as porcelain
- Fault can be easily seen from the naked eyes.

Instead of several advantages, it has some disadvantages such as:

- Moistures are readily condensed on the surface.
- It is expensive than porcelain.
- Its resistance to continuous mechanical load and temperature changes is poor compared to porcelain and toughened glass.

12.2 RATINGS

Insulators are rated by three voltages: working voltage (or rated voltage), puncture voltage and flashover voltage. The *working* voltage rating is the voltage at which an insulator is designed to bear the steady state voltage stress. If the line voltage is V_{LL}, the working voltage will be $V_{LL}/\sqrt{3}$. The *flashover* voltage is the voltage at which flashover occurs through air surrounding the insulator. The *puncture* voltage is the voltage at which the insulator breaks through between conductor and pin. It destroys the insulator. This ratings is determined by applying the voltage while insulator is emerged in oil. This is done because before the puncture, there will be flashover. Flashover voltage is less than puncture voltage and higher than working voltage of insulators. A safety factor is defined relating the flashover and working voltages. Mathematically, it is written as

$$\text{Safety factor} = \frac{\text{Flashover voltage}}{\text{Working voltage}} \tag{12.1}$$

12.3 TYPES OF INSULATORS

There are four types of insulators which are used in overhead transmission lines: sackle type, pin type, suspension type and strain type. *Sackle* type insulators are normally used in 230–440-V lines. A sackle insulator looks like a dumbly shape and is used in one unit.

For medium voltages, pin type of insulator is used. The pin type insulators are small, simple in construction and cheap. However, the cost of such insulators increases if the voltage rating is increased. Pin type insulators are uneconomical for higher voltage. As its name, the pin or bolt is used to clamp the insulator to cross arm on the pole. There should be sufficient thickness of porcelain between line conductor and the insulator pin to give a safety factor up to 10 against puncture. It is desirable to design the insulator such that flashover voltage should occur before the puncture. Figure 12.1 shows a pin type insulator. The groove at the top of insulator is used for conductor placing. The insulator and pin must have a sufficient mechanical strength to bear the weight of conductor, wind pressure and ice loading, if any. The safety factor is different under wet and dry conditions. Pin type insulator is designed in such way that it should have a sufficient spark over distance. For 11-kV and 33-kV lines, pin type of insulators are used. The maximum rating of pin insulator of single unit is 50 kV, however for larger rating, multiple units can be used.

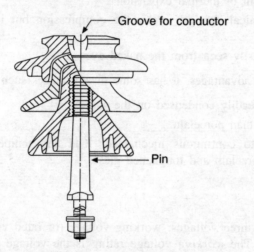

FIGURE 12.1 Pin type insulator.

For higher voltage, string type of insulators are used and can be categorized into suspension type and strain type. Suspension type of insulator, as shown in Figure 12.2, consists of one or more insulating units. It is hung from cross-arm and carrying power conductor at the lowest extremity. It is free to swing and therefore larger cross-arm is required, than the pin type insulators. The main advantages of suspension insulators are:

- Economical for voltage above 33 kV.
- Each insulator is designed for 11 kV and hence for any operating voltage, a string can be made.
- Failure of any unit can be replaced without changing the whole string.
- Since it is allowed to swing in the air, mechanical stress at a point of attachment is reduced.
- Flexible in extension of voltage rating by adding more units.
- Since the conductors lay below the cross-arm, the line outages due to lightening strokes are reduced.

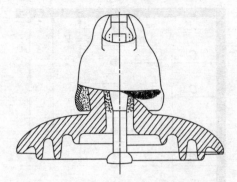

FIGURE 12.2 Suspension type insulator.

Strain insulators are similar to suspension type insulators in shape but they are used in vertical plane rather than horizontal plane as suspension type of insulators are used. Normally, strain insulators are used at dead ends or at anchor towers. When the tension in the conductor is very high, two or more insulators are used in parallel.

12.4 VOLTAGE DISTRIBUTION ACROSS SUSPENSION INSULATORS

Normally, the string units are similar in shape and size, the capacitance of each unit can be taken as the same. The capacitance between metal part and structure (at the earth potential) is formed which is not negligible because the cross-arms are not longer. If the cross-arm length is long enough, the capacitance between the metal structure and the earth (tower) can be neglected. Under this condition, the current flows in each string will be the same and the potential distribution will also be the same in each insulator. But this assumption is not true and the current in lower string (near to line conductor) is larger than the topmost string (near to earth) and this uneven distribution of current causes the different voltage across the string. Let the capacitance of each unit (also called *mutual capacitance*) is mC and defined a ratio m as

$$m = \frac{\text{Mutual capacitance}}{\text{Capacitance between each link-pin and the earth}}$$

Let us calculate the voltage across each string (unit). I_n is current through capacitance between nth pin to the earth and i_n is current through nth string. V_n is the voltage across nth string and v_n is the voltage between nth pin to the earth. From Figure 12.3, we can write for the first string near to earth as

$$i_2 = I_1 + i_1$$

and

$$V_2\, m\omega C = V_1 \omega C + V_1 m\omega C$$

Therefore,

$$V_2 = V_1\left(1 + \frac{1}{m}\right) \tag{12.2}$$

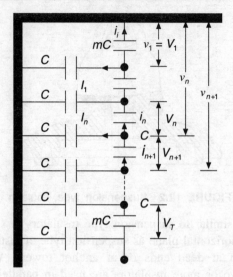

Line conductor

FIGURE 12.3   Voltage variation across suspension insulator.

Similarly,

$$i_3 = I_2 + i_2 = v_2 \omega C + V_2 m \omega C$$

and

$$V_3 m \omega C = (V_1 + V_2) \omega C + V_2 m \omega C$$

From Equation (12.2), substituting the value of V_2 we get

$$V_3 = V_1 \left(1 + \frac{3}{m} + \frac{1}{m^2} \right) \qquad (12.3)$$

In the same way, we can find the voltage across each string.

It is convenient to use the general formula for getting the same. We write

$$i_{n+1} = I_n + i_n$$

and

$$V_{n+1} m \omega C = v_n \omega C + V_n m \omega C$$

or

$$V_{n+1} = V_n + \frac{v_n}{m} \qquad (12.4)$$

If $m = 5$, the voltage across each unit in terms of voltage of top string will be

$$V_2 = 1.2V_1, \qquad V_3 = 1.64V_1, \qquad V_4 = 2.408V_1, \cdots$$

This shows that the voltage across the unit nearest to the conductor is the highest and therefore the unit near to the conductor is highly stressed and the topmost string is less utilized. It is also to note that the capacitance formed between the line conductor and the structure will not affect the voltage distribution across the disc units. Therefore, it can be ignored in the calculation.

12.5 STRING EFFICIENCY

Normally, *efficiency* is defined as a ratio of output to input. However, *string efficiency* is a measure of utilization of material in the string. If the number of units used in the string is n, the string efficiency is defined as

$$\text{String efficiency } \eta = \frac{\text{Voltage across the } n \text{ strings}}{n \times \text{Voltage across the unit near to the power conductor}}$$

$$= \frac{\text{Spark-over voltage of } n \text{ strings}}{n \times \text{Spark-over voltage of one disc}}$$

From this definition, if the voltage distribution is same across each unit, the string efficiency will be 100%.

Example 12.1 A string insulator has 4 units and each unit is having capacitance C. The pin-to-earth capacitance is $C/10$, find the voltages across each unit of the string, and the string efficiency.

Solution Given that $m = 10$. Let voltage across the topmost unit (near to earth) is V_1. From Equation (12.2), the voltage across the second unit from the top will be

$$V_2 = V_1\left(1 + \frac{1}{m}\right) = 1.1V_1$$

Voltage across the third unit from the top will be

$$V_3 = V_1\left(1 + \frac{3}{m} + \frac{1}{m^2}\right) = 1.31V_1$$

Similarly, using Equation (12.4), the voltage across the fourth unit from the top will be

$$V_4 = V_3 + \frac{v_3}{m}$$

$$= V_3 + \frac{V_1 + V_2 + V_3}{m}$$

$$= V_3\left(1 + \frac{1}{m}\right) + \frac{V_2}{m} + \frac{V_1}{m}$$

$$= (1.441 + 0.11 + 0.1)V_1$$

$$= 1.651V_1$$

Since the line is operating at 33 kV, the total voltage across the string will be $33/\sqrt{3}$ (=19.05) kV. That is

$$V_1 + V_2 + V_3 + V_4 = 19.05 \text{ kV}$$

Therefore

Voltage across the topmost unit $V_1 = 3.76$ kV

Voltage across the second unit from the top V_2 = 4.14 kV
Voltage across the third unit from the top V_3 = 4.93 kV
Voltage across the fourth unit from the top V_4 = 6.21 kV

$$\text{String efficiency} = \frac{19.05}{4 \times 6.21} = 0.7669$$

Therefore, the string efficiency is 76.69%.

12.6 Methods to Improve String Efficiency

String efficiency can be improved by the following four ways:

1. Increasing value of m
2. Grading of units
3. Static shielding
4. Conducting glazes

These are discussed now.

Increasing value of m. If the value of m is increased, which can be achieved by increasing the cross-arm length so that the capacitance between pin to earth is decreased, the voltage distribution across the unit can be improved and thus higher efficiency can be achieved. However, increasing the cross-arm length after certain value will not be economical. Mathematically, we can achieve 100% efficiency (equal voltage across each units), if the value of m is infinity. It is found that the value of m greater than 10 is not economical.

Grading of units. Since the current in each unit is different which is not possible to eliminate, voltages across each unit can be equalized using the different capacity units. As the current in the lowest string is highest, the low-impedance unit (or high-capacitance unit) near to the conductor will improve the string efficiency. This shows that if discs are arranged in decreasing order of capacitance from bottom (near to the conductor) to top, the voltage across each unit can be equalized. In other words, if the product of a capacitive reactance to the current flowing through discs is the same, the voltage across each unit will be the same. This is possible only if the capacitance of the upper unit is less than that of the lower unit.

Let us calculate the relationship for different unit capacitance for equal potential across each unit. Figure 12.4 shows the different capacitance units. If the voltage across each unit is V, we can have relation for nth unit as

$$i_{n+1} = I_n + i_n$$

and

$$V\omega C_{n+1} = v_n\omega C + V\omega C_n = nV\omega C + V\omega C_n$$

or

$$C_{n+1} = nC + C_n \tag{12.5}$$

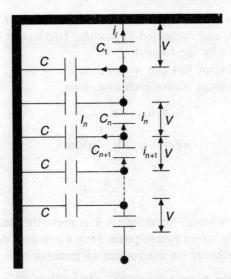

FIGURE 12.4 Grading of units.

Grading of units is also called *capacitance grading*. This method of improving the efficiency will result in the need for large stock of different sizes of units, which outweighs the advantages of string insulators. Good results can be obtained by using insulators of one size for most of the units and larger units for the one or two adjacent to the line. In practice this method is used for very high voltage lines.

Static shielding. In this method, current from pin to earth is equalized by injecting current from the line to the pin, as shown in Figure 12.5, so that equal current flows through the unit and therefore the voltage across each unit can be the same. This is achieved by the

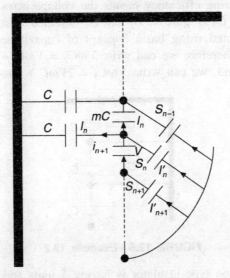

FIGURE 12.5 Static shielding.

employment of a grading or guard ring, which usually takes the form of a large metal ring surrounding the bottom unit, and connected to the line. Due to this arrangement, capacitances between line to pin of the units are formed.

If the capacitance between link-pin n and guard ring is S_n, and the number of units used are k, for the same voltage across each unit, then

$$i_n = i_{n+1} \quad \text{or} \quad I_n = I'_n$$

and

$$nV\omega C = (kV - nV)\omega S_n$$

Hence

$$S_n = \frac{n}{k - n}C \tag{12.6}$$

In practice, it is difficult to achieve. Nevertheless it is normally used and advantage is gained partially. However, grading ring solves two purposes. First, it equalizes the voltage drop across units and protects string from flashover on the surface of insulator when used with arcing horns.

Conducting glazes. Since there are uneven voltages in each unit due to unsymmetrical current, each mutual capacitance (also called self-capacitances) could be shunted by a resistor of such a magnitude that the capacitance currents were swamped by the effect of the leakage current through the resistors. Then a more uniform voltage division can be obtained. This can be achieved by coating insulators with a conducting glaze. This method is practically impossible due to difficulty of producing glaze for long time.

Example 12.2 A suspension type insulator is having 3 units and the value of pin-to-earth capacitance is C. If the capacitance of top unit is $5C$, find the capacitances of each unit to make the string efficiency 100%.

Solution A 100% string efficiency means the voltage across each disc unit is same. The values of C_1, C_2 and C_3 (Figure 12.6) can be obtained using Equation (12.5). These values can also be calculated using basic concept of capacitance grading. Since voltage across C_2 is same as C_1, therefore we can write $V\omega C_2 = V\omega C + V\omega C_1$. Thus $C_2 = 6C$.

Similarly for lower unit, we can write $V\omega C_3 = 2V\omega C + V\omega C_2$. Thus $C_3 = 8C$.

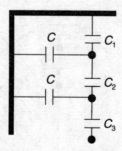

FIGURE 12.6 Example 12.2.

Example 12.3 A suspension type insulator is having 5 units and the value of pin-to-earth capacitance is C. Find the line-to-pin capacitances to equalize the voltage across each unit.

Solution The line-to-pin capacitances S_1, S_2, S_3 and S_4 as shown in Figure 12.7, can be obtained by using Equation (12.6). However, here the same is calculated with basic principle. Let potential across each disc is V. The line voltage will be 5 V. Potential of point A will be V. For equal voltages across each unit, the current through each disc having same capacitance will be same. Therefore, the current through S_1 will be same as current through pin-to earth capacitance. Hence

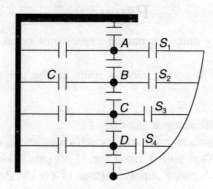

FIGURE 12.7 Example 12.3.

$$V\omega C = (5V - V)\omega S_1 \quad \text{or} \quad S_1 = \frac{C}{4}$$

Similarly at point B

$$2V\omega C = (5V - 2V)\omega S_2 \quad \text{or} \quad S_2 = \frac{2C}{3}$$

At point C

$$3V\omega C = (5V - 3V)\omega S_3 \quad \text{or} \quad S_3 = \frac{3C}{2}$$

At point D

$$4V\omega C = (5V - 4V)\omega S_4 \quad \text{or} \quad S_4 = 4C$$

Example 12.4 A string insulator has 4 units and each unit is rated for 12 kV. Find the maximum line voltage on which it can be operated safely. The mutual capacitance of unit is 10 times the capacitance between the pin to earth. Find the string efficiency.

Solution Here $m = 10$; if rating of each insulator is 12 kV.

So, $V_2 = 1.1\ V_1$; $V_3 = 1.31\ V_1$, $V_4 = 1.651\ V$

$$12 = 1.651\ V_1$$

$$V_1 = 7.268 \text{ kV}$$

So

$$V_2 = 7.995 \text{ kV}$$

$$V_3 = 9.521 \text{ kV}$$

Total voltage across line string $= V_1 + V_2 + V_3 + V_4 = 36.78$ kV

$\therefore$ Safe operating maximum line voltage $= \sqrt{3} \times 36.78$

$$= 63.71 \text{ kV}$$

String efficiency $= \dfrac{36.78}{4 \times 12} \times 100 = 76.62\%$

PROBLEMS

12.1 A string of 5 insulator units has mutual capacitance equal to 10 times the pin-to-earth capacitance. Find:
   (a) Voltage distribution across various units as the per cent of total voltage across string.
   (b) String efficiency.
   (c) Find the string efficiency if $m = 5$.

12.2 A string has a few insulator units and its self-capacitance is equal to 10 times the pin-to-earth capacitance. One unit is rated for 11 kV(rms). Find the minimum number of insulator units for each phase supply voltage of 66 kV, 3ϕ line.

12.3 A string of 6 suspension insulators is to be graded for obtaining uniform voltage distribution across string. If the pin-to-earth capacitances are equal to C and mutual capacitance of the top insulator is $10C$. Find the mutual capacitances of each unit in terms of C.

12.4 In a string of 4 suspension insulators, capacitances may be represented as shown in Figure 12.8 (capacitances S_1 being due to guard ring). Find the voltage (as a percentage of total voltage) across each disc and string efficiency. Given $C' = 0.10C$ and $S_1 = 0.05C$.

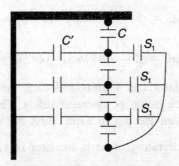

FIGURE 12.8 Problem 12.4.

12.5 A string insulator has 5 units and each unit is rated for 11 kV. Find the maximum voltage on which it can be operated safely. The mutual capacitance of unit is 10 times the capacitance between the pin-to-earth.

Chapter 13

Design of Transmission Lines

13.1 INTRODUCTION

The main objective of designing a high-voltage transmission line is to transmit electrical energy at the lowest cost and with required reliability. Both electrical and mechanical design considerations are studied properly to see its performance. The main electrical considerations are:

(a) Choice of voltage, size of conductors and spacing between conductors

(b) Calculation of line constants for determination of voltage regulation and efficiency of the line at full load

(c) Calculation of corona loss

(d) Choice of the method of grounding

(e) Calculation of radio interference

(f) Stability consideration

(g) Electrostatic and electromagnetic effects

(h) Insulation coordination

(i) Protective system

(j) Choosing number and type of insulators

Since transmission lines are supported on the towers, their conductors form the catenary. The factors affecting a mechanical design of overhead transmission lines are:

1. Selection of line route
2. Types of towers/poles
3. Right-of-way
4. Ground and conductor clearance
5. Tower spacing, span length
6. Mechanical loading

Basically four types of supporting structures are used:

(a) Wood poles
(b) Concrete poles
(c) Steel poles
(d) Aluminium poles

In order to specify the tension to be used in stringing the line conductors, the values of sag and tension for different conditions must be known. The factors affecting the sag of a conductor strung between supports are:

1. Weight of conductor per unit length
2. Load due to ice, snow, wind, etc.
3. Distance between the supports (span length)
4. Temperature
5. Conductor tension.

13.2 CALCULATION OF SAG AND TENSION

Supports at the same level

Figure 13.1 shows a wire *AOB* of length *l* supported at two towers *A* and *B* and are spaced *L* unit apart. Let *O* is the lowest point of the wire. Consider a length *OP* of the curve length *s*.

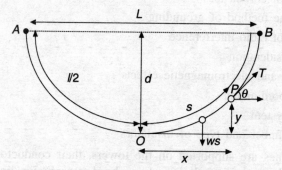

FIGURE 13.1 Conductors supported at same level.

If w = weight/unit length, H = tension at point O and T = tension at point P, the tension T can be resolved into horizontal and vertical components as

$$T \sin\theta = ws \quad \text{and} \quad T \cos\theta = H$$

Then

$$\tan\theta = \frac{ws}{H}$$

In triangle shown in Figure 13.2, ds represents very small section and therefore we have

$$(ds)^2 = (dx)^2 + (dy)^2$$

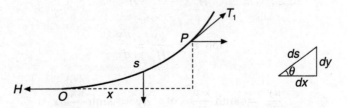

FIGURE 13.2 A small section of catenary.

or

$$\left(\frac{ds}{dx}\right)^2 = 1 + \left(\frac{dy}{dx}\right)^2$$

or

$$\frac{dy}{dx} = \tan\theta$$

Substituting the value of $\tan\theta$, we get

$$\frac{ds}{dx} = \sqrt{1 + \left(\frac{ws}{H}\right)^2}$$

and

$$dx = \frac{ds}{\sqrt{1 + (ws/H)^2}}$$

Integrating both sides, we have

$$x = \frac{H}{w}\sinh^{-1}\frac{ws}{H} + A \tag{13.1}$$

where A is the integration constant. With initial condition at $x = 0$, $s = 0$ we find $A = 0$. Therefore,

$$x = \frac{H}{w}\sinh^{-1}\frac{ws}{H} \tag{13.2}$$

and

$$s = \frac{H}{w}\sinh\frac{wx}{H} \tag{13.3}$$

At $x = L/2$, $s = l/2$, we obtain

$$l = \frac{2H}{w} \sinh \frac{wL}{2H} \qquad (13.4)$$

Expanding the sinh $[wL/(2H)]$ and ignoring higher order terms, we get

$$l = L\left(1 + \frac{w^2 L^2}{24H^2}\right) \qquad (13.5)$$

Equation (13.3) can be rewritten as

$$\frac{ws}{H} = \sinh \frac{wx}{H}$$

Since

$$\tan \theta = \frac{ws}{H} = \frac{dy}{dx}$$

We get

$$\frac{dy}{dx} = \sinh \frac{wx}{H} \quad \text{or} \quad dy = \sinh \frac{wx}{H} dx$$

Integrating both sides, we obtain

$$y = \frac{H}{w} \cosh \frac{wx}{H} + B \qquad (13.6)$$

where B is the integration constant and can be obtained with initial condition at $x = 0$, $y = 0$. Thus, we get $B = -H/w$. Therefore, Equation (13.6) gives

$$y = \frac{H}{w}\left[\cosh\left(\frac{wx}{H}\right) - 1\right] \qquad (13.7)$$

It is equation of the *sag* that is called a *catenary*. Expanding the equation, we get

$$y = \frac{H}{w}\left[1 + \frac{1}{2!}\left(\frac{wx}{H}\right)^2 + \cdots - 1\right]$$

or

$$y \cong \frac{wx^2}{2H} \qquad (13.8)$$

This is a parabola. For the short span this equation is valid. Tension (T) at point P will be

$$T^2 = (T \sin \theta)^2 + (T \cos \theta)^2 = H^2 + (ws)^2$$

Substituting the value of s from Equation (13.3) and simplifying, we have

$$T = H\left[1 + \sinh^2 \frac{wx}{H}\right]^{1/2} = H \cosh \frac{wx}{H} \qquad (13.9)$$

For short span and short sags, the difference between the maximum tension T and the horizontal tension H is small. The tension will be the highest at the conductor supports and will be minimum at the lowest point of catenary. Thus

$$T = \begin{cases} H & \text{at the lowest point } (x = 0) \\ H \cosh \dfrac{wL}{2H} & \text{at the supports} \end{cases}$$

When $x = L/2$, y is equal to the sag or deflection d. Therefore, using Equation (13.7), the sag (d), is

$$d = \frac{H}{w}\left[\cosh\left(\frac{wL}{2H}\right) - 1\right] \tag{13.10}$$

or

$$d \cong \frac{wL^2}{8H} \tag{13.11}$$

Using Equations (13.5) and (13.11), the length of wire (perimeter of conductor) between span in terms of the span length and sag can be calculated as

$$l = L\left(1 + \frac{8d^2}{3L^2}\right) \tag{13.12}$$

Supports at different levels (unsymmetrical span)

Let P_1 and P_2 are two points at heights h_1 and h_2 from the ground respectively, as shown in Figure 13.3. If the point O is the lowest point, by using Equation (13.11), we can write sags in two sections as

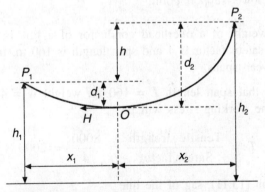

FIGURE 13.3 Supports at different levels.

$$d_1 = \frac{wx_1^2}{2H} \quad \text{and} \quad d_2 = \frac{wx_2^2}{2H}$$

Therefore,

$$d_2 - d_1 = h = \frac{w}{2H}\left(x_2^2 - x_1^2\right)$$

where h is difference between the elevations of two supports. If the span length is L, $x_1 + x_2 = L$. Therefore

$$h = \frac{w}{2H}(x_1 + x_2)(x_2 - x_1) = \frac{wL}{2H}(x_2 - x_1)$$

or

$$x_2 - x_1 = \frac{2Hh}{wL} \qquad\qquad (13.13)$$

Using relation $x_1 + x_2 = L$ and Equation (13.13), we get

$$x_1 = \frac{L}{2} - \frac{Hh}{wL} \qquad\qquad (13.14)$$

and

$$x_2 = \frac{L}{2} + \frac{Hh}{wL} \qquad\qquad (13.15)$$

From Equation (13.14), x_1 can be

$$x_1 > 0 \quad \text{or} \quad \frac{L}{2} > \frac{Hh}{wL}$$

$$x_1 < 0 \quad \text{or} \quad \frac{L}{2} < \frac{Hh}{wL}$$

$$x_1 = 0 \quad \text{or} \quad \frac{L}{2} = \frac{Hh}{wL}$$

If x_1 is negative, the lowest point of the curve lies outside the actual span. It must be noted that the lowest point is always be at a lower support side. If x_1 is zero, the lowest point of the curve will be at a lower-support point.

Example 13.1 The weight of a overhead conductor of a line is 4.0 N/m. The ultimate strength is 8000 N. If safety factor is 4 and span length is 160 m, find (a) sag and (b) total length of the line between spans.

Solution Given that span length $L = 160$ m, weight $w = 4.0$ N/m and the tensile strength is 8000 N. The working stress will be

$$T = \frac{\text{Tensile strength}}{\text{Safety factor}} = \frac{8000}{4} = 2000 \text{ N}$$

(a) Using Equation (13.11), sag of the line

$$d = \frac{wL^2}{8T} = \frac{4 \times 160^2}{8 \times 2000} = 6.4 \text{ m}$$

(b) Using Equation (13.5), total length of conductor in spans

$$l = L\left(1 + \frac{w^2 L^2}{24T^2}\right) = L + \frac{w^2 L^3}{24T^2} = 160 + \frac{4^2 \times 160^3}{24 \times 2000^2} = 160.73 \text{ m}$$

Example 13.2   An overhead transmission line conductor has the following data:

Weight = 0.35 kg/m;
Maximum allowable strength = 800 kg;
Safety factor = 2;
Span length = 160 m.

Supports are at different levels where one support is at 70 m from the ground. Find the minimum clearance from the ground and the minimum point of the catenary from the supports when the second support is at (a) 40 m and (b) 65 m.

Solution   The working stress

$$T = \frac{\text{Tensile strength}}{\text{Safety factor}} = \frac{800}{2} = 400 \text{ kg}$$

(a) The difference in supports is $h = 70 - 40 = 30$ m. Using Equation (13.13), the distance of minimum point from the lower support is

$$x_1 = \frac{L}{2} - \frac{Th}{wL} = \frac{160}{2} - \frac{400 \times 30}{0.35 \times 160} = -134.29 \text{ m}$$

This shows that the minimum point lies outside of the span is 134.29 m from the lower span. Therefore, the minimum ground clearance is 40 m that is the height of lower support.

(b) When the lower support is at 65 m, the level difference (h) is $70 - 65 = 5$ m. Using Equation (13.13), the distance of minimum point from the lower support is

$$x_1 = \frac{L}{2} - \frac{Th}{wL} = \frac{160}{2} - \frac{400 \times 5}{0.35 \times 160} = 44.29 \text{ m}$$

Thus the minimum point lies inside the span that is 44.29 m from lower span. The sag from lower support

$$d_1 = \frac{wx_1^2}{2T} = \frac{0.35 \times 44.29^2}{2 \times 400} = 0.86 \text{ m}$$

The minimum ground clearance will be $65 - 0.86 = 64.14$ m.

13.3   EQUIVALENT SPAN LENGTH AND SAG

There are several situations where the span length between the supports is not same and therefore the tension in each span will be different. However, it is not possible with suspension insulators since the insulator strings would swing so as to equalize the tension in each span. It is impractical to dead end and to erect each span separately. It is possible to assume a uniform tension between dead-end supports by defining an equivalent span called *ruling span* and make the calculations based on it. If the length L_i is the *i*th span length, the equivalent span or ruling span length

$$L = \sqrt{\frac{\sum_{i=1}^{n} L_i^3}{\sum_{i=1}^{n} L_i}} = \sqrt{\frac{L_1^3 + L_2^3 + \cdots + L_n^3}{L_1 + L_2 + \cdots + L_n}} \tag{13.16}$$

where n is the number of span of the line.

Sometimes it is not necessary to get the exact value of the ruling span. An approximate equivalent span can be calculated as

$$L = L_{av} + \frac{2}{3}(L_{max} - L_{av}) \tag{13.17}$$

where L_{av} is the average span length and L_{max} is the maximum span length in line. The line tension T can be estimated using the ruling span length and then the sag for each span can be calculated.

13.4 EFFECT OF ICE- AND WIND-LOADING

The sag and tension of lines are different in normal weather conditions. Since lines are designed for all the conditions, it is important to calculate the sag and tension during the ice- and wind-loading conditions.

Effect of ice

In snowy areas, ice is deposited on conductors. Sometimes, thickness of ice is more than the conductor's diameter and its accumulation on the conductor affects the design of the line:

(a) by increasing the weight per metre and

(b) by increasing the projected surface area subject to wind pressure.

Ice deposition may not be uniform but it can be assumed to be uniformly distributed around the conductor, as shown in Figure 13.4. Due to ice, the sag and tension of the conductor increase and therefore the line should be suitably designed to take care of this effect.

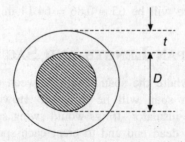

FIGURE 13.4 Cross-sectional view of uniform ice around the conductor.

Let the diameter of a conductor is D and the thickness of ice is t, the cross-sectional area of ice (A_i) will be the cross-sectional area of the ice along with the conductor minus cross-sectional area of the conductor. The cross-sectional area of ice

$$A_i = \frac{\pi}{4}[(D + 2t)^2 - D^2] = \pi(D + t)t \tag{13.18}$$

If the density of ice is ρ_i (normally 915) kg/m³, the weight of ice acting downward (assuming the ice is spread through out the span) will be

$$w_i = \pi[(D + t)t]\rho_i \text{ kg/m} \tag{13.19}$$

where diameter and thickness are in metres. If the weight per unit length of the conductor is w and of ice is w_i, the total weight per unit length $w_T = w + w_i$.

Effect of wind

The effect of wind is taken horizontally across the projected area of the conductor covered with ice, if present, as shown in Figure 13.5. Therefore, it affects only to increase the transverse loading on the conductor. If D is diameter of bare conductor in metre, t is thickness of ice in metre, projected area for l-metre length will be $(D + 2t)l$. If the wind pressure is p kg/m², the wind loading will be

$$w_w = (D + 2t)p \text{ kg/m} \tag{13.20}$$

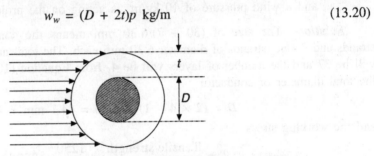

FIGURE 13.5 Wind pressure on a conductor covered with ice.

The wind pressure depends on the shape of conductors. It is assumed to act on (2/3)rd of the projected area for cylindrical surfaces while it acts on full-face area in the square conductors. The wind pressure also depends on the velocity of the wind, which can be calculated by using $p = 0.006v^2$ kg/m², where v is the velocity of wind in km/hr. The effective load acting on the conductor will be

$$w_e = \sqrt{w_w^2 + (w + w_i)^2} \tag{13.21}$$

where w and w_i are per unit weight of conductor and ice respectively. The loading is acting at an angle

$$\theta = \tan^{-1}\frac{w_w}{w + w_i}$$

to the vertical plane, as shown in Figure 13.6. The total sag and tension must be calculated with an effective weight in case of ice- and wind-loaded lines.

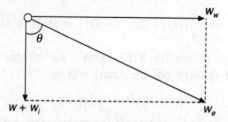

FIGURE 13.6 Vertical plan of wind pressure on a conductor.

Example 13.3 An ACSR conductor has the following data: normal copper area = 120 mm^2; size = (30 + 7)/6.30 mm; weight = 0.4 kg/m, tensile strength = 1250 kg, safety factor = 5. If span length is 200 m, find

(a) Sag in still air

(b) Sag, if the conductor is covered with 0.5-cm thick ice (ice density of 915 kg/m^3)

(c) Sag (total and vertical), if the conductor is covered with ice of 0.5-cm thickness and a wind pressure of 10 kg/m^2 is acting on the projected area.

Solution   The size of (30 + 7)/6.30 mm means the conductor has 30 aluminium strands and 7 steel strands of diameter 6.30 mm each. The total number of equal size strands will be 37 and the number of layers will be 4, from Equation (10.1). From Equation (10.2), the total diameter of conductor

$$D = (2 \times 4 - 1) \times 6.30 = 44.1 \text{ mm} = 4.41 \text{ cm}$$

and the working stress

$$T = \frac{\text{Tensile strength}}{\text{Safety factor}} = \frac{1250}{5} = 250 \text{ kg}$$

(a) Sag (d) in still air

$$d = \frac{wL^2}{8T} = \frac{0.4 \times 200^2}{8 \times 250} = 8.0 \text{ m}$$

(b) Using Equation (13.19), the weight of ice

$$w_i = \pi[(D + t)t]\rho_i = \pi[(4.41 + 0.5) \times 10^{-2} \times 0.5 \times 10^{-2}] \times 915 = 0.706 \text{ kg/m}$$

The total weight = 0.4 + 0.706 = 1.106 kg/m. Thus the sag

$$d = \frac{wL^2}{8T} = \frac{1.106 \times 200^2}{8 \times 250} = 22.11 \text{ m}$$

(c) The wind loading

$$w_w = (D + 2t)p = (4.41 + 1) \times 10^{-2} \times 10 = 0.541 \text{ kg/m}$$

The effective loading will be

$$w_e = \sqrt{w_w^2 + (w + w_i)^2} = \sqrt{0.541^2 + (0.4 + 0.706)^2} = 1.231 \text{ kg/m}$$

The total sag will be

$$d = \frac{wL^2}{8T} = \frac{1.231 \times 200^2}{8 \times 250} = 24.62 \text{ m}$$

This sag will be acting at an angle

$$\theta = \tan^{-1}\frac{w_w}{w + w_i} = 26.07°$$

to the vertical. Thus the vertical sag will be 24.62 cos 26.07° = 22.11 m. This is the same as in (b), because the wind pressure is acting in transverse direction.

13.5 STRINGING CHART

Stringing chart is helpful in providing sag and tension at any temperature, if the sag and tension is known for a particular temperature. The curves of sag and tension with temperature variation are called the 'stringing' charts and are useful in erecting the transmission line conductors at specified temperatures and loading conditions.

At high temperature, sag in still air is more and tension is less. However in case of low temperature, sag is less and tension is more. Let w, f, l, d and t represent the load per unit length, the stress, the conductor length in span, the sag and the temperature, respectively. The suffix 1 represents the quantities at wind and ice loading (at low temperature, usually –5.0°C) and suffix 2 denotes the quantities in still air at high temperature (normally temperature at erection, no ice). Let A is the area of conductor, α the coefficient of linear expansion, L the span length and E is the Young's modulus. The problem now is to calculate maximum working stress in the conductor during fair weather and still air conditions.

For short span, we have derived

$$T = H; \quad y = \frac{wx^2}{2H} = \frac{wx^2}{2T}$$

Therefore

$$d = \frac{wL^2}{8T} \quad \text{and} \quad l = L\left(1 + \frac{w^2L^2}{24T^2}\right)$$

Since stress $f = T/A$, the length of conductor between the span at temperature t_1 is

$$l_1 = L\left(1 + \frac{w_1^2L^2}{24f_1^2A^2}\right)$$

Due to increase in temperature from t_1 to t_2, the increase in length is equal to

$$\alpha(t_2 - t_1)l_1 \cong \alpha(t_2 - t_1)L$$

At the same time, another effect of the increase in temperature is a reduction in stress, which causes decrease in length. Young modulus is defined as

$$E = \frac{\text{Change in stress}}{\text{Change in strain}} = \frac{\Delta f}{(\Delta l)/l}$$

Thus decrease in length due to reduction in stress is

$$\frac{f_1 - f_2}{E} l_1 \cong \frac{f_1 - f_2}{E} L$$

Therefore, length of conductor between spans at temperature t_2 is

$$l_2 = l_1 + \alpha(t_2 - t_1)L - \frac{f_1 - f_2}{E} L \qquad (13.22)$$

Substituting the values of l_1 and l_2 in Equation (13.22), we get

$$L + \frac{w_2^2 L^3}{24 f_2^2 A^2} = L + \frac{w_1^2 L^3}{24 f_1^2 A^2} + \alpha(t_2 - t_1)L - \frac{f_1 - f_2}{E} L \qquad (13.23)$$

Simplifying Equation (13.23), we have

$$\frac{w_2^2 L^2 E}{24 A^2} = \left[\frac{w_1^2 L^2 E}{24 f_1^2 A^2} + \alpha(t_2 - t_1)E - f_1 + f_2 \right] f_2^2 \qquad (13.24)$$

Equation (13.24) is a cubic equation of f_2 and can be solved by using any mathematical algorithm. After getting the value of f_2, sag at temperature t_2 can be calculated as

$$d_2 = \frac{w_2 L^2}{8 f_2 A} \qquad (13.25)$$

Thus the variation of sag with temperature can be plotted. Figure 13.7 shows the plots of sag and tension with temperature variation that is known as stringing chart.

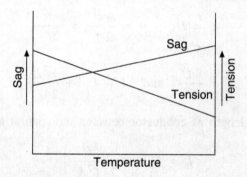

FIGURE 13.7 Variations of sag and tension versus temperature.

13.6 SAG TEMPLATE

It is a plot of curves on transparent paper which is used for locating the tower positions. In order to locate the position of towers, a suitable value of tower support must be known, however there are no clear-cut guidelines for the same and several alternatives may be tried. The ground clearance is maintained which varies with a specific voltage level. Table 13.1 shows the typical span length, ground clearance and clearance between phases.

Table 13.1 Span Length, Ground Clearance and Clearance between Phases

Voltage level	Span length (in metre)	Minimum ground clearance (in metre)	Clearance between phases (in metre)
400 V	80	4.6	0.2
11 kV	100	4.6	1.2
132 kV	350–365	6.1	3.9
220 kV	365–380	7.0	5.13
400 kV	400	8.8	7.0

The following empirical formula is used for determining the spacing of aluminium conductor lines: where d is sag in metres and V is line voltage in kV:

$$\text{Spacing} = \left(\sqrt{d} + \frac{V}{150} \right) \text{m} \qquad (13.26)$$

13.7 CONDUCTOR VIBRATIONS AND VIBRATION DAMPERS

In addition to the horizontal swing due to wind pressure, overhead conductors experience vibrations in the vertical plane. These vibrations can be broadly classified as: resonant vibration or aeolian vibration and galloping (or dancing).

Aeolian vibrations

Aeolian or *resonant* vibration is of low magnitude (up to 5 cm) and high frequency (5–40 Hz) with a loop length of 1–10 m. It is caused by a vortex phenomenon in light winds (6–30 km/hr). The frequency f is empirically given by $50 \times (v/D)$ where v is wind velocity (km/hr) and D is conductor diameter (in mm). The length of a loop (half wave length) depends on tension T (N) and conductor weight w (kg/m) and is given by

$$\frac{\sqrt{T/w}}{2f}$$

These vibrations are common to all conductors and are more or less always present. Since these vibrations are small in magnitude, these are less harmful. However they may give rise to troubles at heavy anchor clamps and may cause conductor failure. Two devices are used to solve these vibrations: *Armour rods* or *reinforcement* and *dampers*. In Armour rods scheme, a spiral layer of small round rods, preferably tapered at each end and larger in diameter compared to conductor, surrounds the conductors. Armour rods also provide the best protection against flashover. To minimize the effect of resonant vibrations, dampers are used which absorb vibrational energy of the conductor by hysteresis and inter-strand friction in the flexible damper cable. There are several designs but stock-bridge damper, as shown in Figure 13.8, is extensively used, which is simple too. It comprises of two hollow weights fixed at both the ends of a short length of stranded steel cable suspended from the conductor around midway between two nodes of vibrations, i.e. where the amplitude of the vibration is maximum. There may be required additional dampers to be installed in the lines.

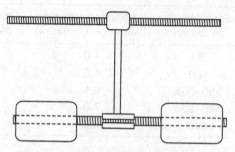

FIGURE 13.8 Stock-bridge damper.

Galloping (or dancing) of conductors

These vibrations are of low frequency (0.25–2 Hz) and high amplitude (up to 6 m) and are generally caused by asymmetrical layer of ice formation. It is a self-excited type vibration. When an ice coated conductor is acted upon by a light drift wind particularly where ground slopes at right angles to the line, the wind travels up the slope and appears to get underneath the conductor and initiate vibrations. These vibrations may cause flashover between conductors of different phase. It is advisable to use the horizontal configuration to reduce the impact of galloping or dancing of conductors.

If conductors are perfect circular, the effect can be minimized. Stranded conductors can be wrapped up with PVC to make the conductor circular. To reduce the effect of ice formation, the high I^2R conductors can be used, which is an economical solution.

PROBLEMS

13.1 A transmission-line conductor consists of a hard drawn copper (weighs 214 kg/km) of 240-mm^2 cross-section (61/2.24 mm) and has a span of 200 m, the supporting structures being level. The conductor has an ultimate tensile stress of 40 kg/mm^2 and safety factor is 5. Ice density is 931.0 kg/m^3. Find

(a) the sag in still air

(b) the sag with wind pressure of 1 kg/m and ice loading of 1 cm

(c) vertical sag in (b).

13.2 An overhead transmission line has a span of 300 m, the conductor weighing 600 kg/km. Calculate the maximum sag if the ultimate tensile strength is 6000 kg. Assume safety factor = 4. Also calculate the length of the wire between the spans.

13.3 In problem 13.2, if supports are not at equal levels and having 1-m difference in levels, determine the minimum sag point.

13.4 An overhead transmission conductor of silicon–bronze having an ultimate tensile strength of 5000 kg/cm^2 and the area of 2.5 cm^2 when erected between supports 600-m apart and having 20-m difference in level, determine the sag which must be allowed so that the factor of safety shall be 2. Assume the wire weighs 2 kg/m, ice loading 1 kg/m and wind loading is 1.5 kg/m. Also, calculate the vertical sag.

13.5 Assume a radial ice thickness 1.0 cm, a wind pressure 40 kg/m^2 of projected area and a temperature of –5°C as the worst conditions, a factor of safety of 2 being required under these conditions. Find the erection sag and tension of a line at a temperature of 65°C in still air. The line has a normal span of 300 m and conductor used is ACSR having the following data:

Area = 240 mm^2; overall diameter = 20 mm; weight = 1.0 kg/m; ultimate strength = 8000 kg; coefficient of linear expansion = 18.44 × 10^{-5}/°C; modulus of elasticity = 9320 kg/mm^2; ice weighs 910 kg/m^3.

13.6 A transmission line conductor is having a diameter of 20 mm and weighs 1.0 kg/m. The span is 280 m. The wind pressure is 40 kg/m^2 of projected area with ice coating of 10 mm. The ultimate strength of conductor is 10000 kg. Calculate the maximum sag if the factor of safety is 2 and ice weighs 910 kg/m^3.

14

Corona and Radio Interference

14.1 Introduction

The literal meaning of *corona* is a ring of light that appears around the sun. This term is borrowed to describe the partial discharges that develop in the presence of high electric field. Corona is one of the main concerns for power transmission engineers because of the power loss it causes in the lines and the noise it causes in radio and TV receptions.

If the potential difference is increased between two conductors spaced some distance apart in air, at some potential a faint luminous glow of violet colour will appear adjacent to the conductor surface with a hissing noise. There is also formation of ozone gas. If the potential is further increased, the intensity of glow and noise will increase. This phenomenon is known as corona, which is due to the ionization of air near power conductor. Since free electrons are normally present in the free space due to radio and cosmic rays, these electron get accelerated due to the voltage of the power conductors and collide with other molecules of air and they dislodge electrons from molecules. Thus the number of electrons increases. This process is known as *ionization of air* surrounding the conductor. Normally, the distance between the conductors is sufficiently high compared to their radius, therefore, corona occurs before flashover. Thus, the 'corona' is defined as a self-sustained electric discharge in which the field intensified ionization is localized only over a portion of distance between the electrodes (lines).

In practice, a flashover may occur with no or very little corona if ratio of conductor spacing to the radius is less than 15. This ratio is always greater than 15 for overhead lines.

The discharge process depends on the polarity of the applied voltage. However in the case of ac, the polarity changes alternatively. In the case of dc, the appearance of corona is different. The positive wire has more uniform bluish white glow and on negative polarity wire reddish tufts or beads are formed. The ac corona can be easily seen with stroboscope.

14.2 CRITICAL VOLTAGES

Consider a two-conductor transmission line, as shown in Figure 14.1. If the charge density at conductor A is q coulomb/m and radius of each conductor is r, the electricity field intensity at point P situated at x metre from the centre of the first conductor A, is

$$E = \frac{q}{2\pi\varepsilon_0 x}$$

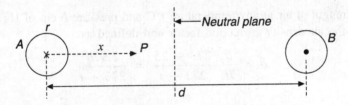

FIGURE 14.1 Two-wire transmission system.

However, the electricity field intensity at point P from the centre of conductor B having charge density $-q$ coulomb/m (return path of current I), is

$$E = \frac{-q}{2\pi\varepsilon_0 (d - x)}$$

Since both the fields are in the same direction, the total electricity field intensity at point P is

$$E_x = \frac{q}{2\pi\varepsilon_0 x} + \frac{q}{2\pi\varepsilon_0 (d - x)} = \frac{q}{2\pi\varepsilon_0}\frac{d}{x(d - x)} \tag{14.1}$$

If V' is the voltage of one conductor with respect to neutral plane, we can write

$$V' = -\int_{d/2}^{r} E_x \, dx = \frac{q}{2\pi\varepsilon_0} [\ln x - \ln (d - x)]_r^{d/2} = \frac{q}{2\pi\varepsilon_0} \ln \frac{d - r}{r} \text{ volt} \tag{14.2}$$

Substituting the value of $q/(2\pi\varepsilon_0)$ in Equation (14.1) from Equation (14.2), we get

$$E_x = \frac{V'}{\ln [(d - r)/r]} \frac{d}{x(d - x)}$$

Since $d \gg r$, we get

$$E_x = \frac{V'}{\ln(d/r)} \frac{d}{x(d - x)} \tag{14.3}$$

It is to note that the value of V' for single-phase line is $V/2$ and for 3-phase lines, it is $V_L/\sqrt{3}$, where V_L is line-to-line voltage. From Equation (14.3), it is clear that the field intensity (gradient) increases as x decreases. The gradient (g_{max}) is maximum at the surface of conductor ($x = r$) and this will be

$$E_{max} = g_{max} = \frac{V'}{\ln(d/r)} \frac{d}{r(d - r)} \approx \frac{V'}{r \ln(d/r)} \tag{14.4}$$

The value of potential gradient at which ionization of air takes place under normal temperature (25°C) and pressure (76 cm of Hg) and without impurities is equal to 30 kV (peak)/cm or 21.1 kV (rms)/cm and is denoted by g_0. Thus the voltage required to ionize the air

$$V' = rg_0 \ln \frac{d}{r}$$

The dielectric strength of air at any temperature t°C and pressure b cm of Hg will be given by $g_0\delta$, where δ is the air density correction factor and defined as

$$\delta = \frac{b}{76} \frac{273 + 25}{273 + t} = \frac{3.92b}{273 + t} \tag{14.5}$$

Then

$$V' = rg_0\delta \ln \frac{d}{r} \tag{14.6}$$

Critical disruptive voltage

It is a voltage at which complete disruption of dielectric occurs. It corresponds to the gradient at the surface of conductors equal to the breakdown strength of air. This voltage can be calculated using Equation (14.6), if the conductor is solid and smooth. Normally, stranded conductors are used in the lines and their surfaces are not smooth. The breakdown voltage will be somewhat less than smooth conductors. Due to irregularity of surface, dust and dirt on its surface there is a further reduction in the breakdown voltage. Allowing the surface irregularity factor m of the wire and the air density correction factor, the critical disruptive voltage (phase to neutral) will be

$$V_c = rg_0 m\delta \ln \frac{d}{r} \tag{14.7}$$

The values of m lie between 0.8 and 1.0. It should be noted that above voltage is valid for a fair weather condition. In case of a foul and bad weather condition, the value of V_c is decreased considerably. While calculating the critical disruptive voltage for corona, the units of g_0 and r must be taken carefully.

Visual critical disruptive voltage

At critical disruptive voltage corona occurs, but it is not visible because the charged ions in air must receive some finite energy to cause further ionization by collision. When the voltage further increases at some point, the corona becomes visible. This voltage is called *visual critical disruptive* voltage (V_v). The gradient for critical visual corona is denoted by g_v. The distance between g_0 and g_v is called the *energy distance*. Peek gave the following empirical formula for g_v, which are function of radius of conductor. Now, we have

$$g_v = g_0\delta\left(1 + \frac{0.3}{\sqrt{r\delta}}\right) \text{ kV/cm} \tag{14.8}$$

for two wires in parallel. The visual critical disruptive voltage is given by

$$V_v = rg_vm_v \ln \frac{d}{r} = 21.1\, m_vr\delta\left(1 + \frac{0.3}{\sqrt{r\delta}}\right) \ln \frac{d}{r} \text{ kV (rms)} \tag{14.9}$$

where d and r are in centimetres. The value of surface (or roughness) factor m_v is different from the m. As conductor surface is irregular and visual corona occurs at some points of the conductor and is called *local corona*. The surface factor m_v is 0.72 for local corona and 0.82 for general (or decided) corona.

Example 14.1 A 3-phase transmission line is having three conductors equilaterally spaced 6-m apart. The diameter of each conductor is 2 cm. The air temperature is 27°C and pressure is 72 cm of Hg. If the surface factor is 0.82 and irregularity factor is 0.90, find the critical disruptive and visual critical disruptive voltages.

Solution Air density factor

$$\delta = \frac{3.92b}{273 + t} = \frac{3.92 \times 72}{273 + 27} = 0.9408$$

Phase-to-neutral critical disruptive voltage

$$V_c = rg_0m\delta \ln \frac{d}{r} = 1.0 \times 21.1 \times 0.90 \times 0.9408 \times \ln \frac{600}{1} = 114.29 \text{ kV}$$

and

$$\text{Line-to-line critical disruptive voltage} = 114.29 \times \sqrt{3} = 197.95 \text{ kV}$$

Using Equation (14.9), the critical visual disruptive voltage

$$V_v = 21.1\, m_vr\delta\left(1 + \frac{0.3}{\sqrt{r\delta}}\right) \ln \frac{d}{r}$$

$$= 21.1 \times 0.82 \times 1.0 \times 0.9408 \times \left(1 + \frac{0.3}{\sqrt{1.0 \times 0.9408}}\right) \ln \frac{600}{1}$$

$$= 136.33 \text{ kV}$$

Hence

$$\text{Line-to-line critical visual disruptive voltage} = 136.33 \times \sqrt{3} = 236.14 \text{ kV}$$

14.3 CORONA LOSS

The ionized charges near the conductor surface take energy from the supply system and thus there is a loss of some energy due to corona. This is resistive loss. It is not possible to derive any formula for the exact loss that occurs due to corona. Several researchers gave empirical formulas based on the experiments for calculating the corona loss. Peek's empirical formula for corona loss under the fair weather condition is

$$P_c = 241 \times 10^{-5} \times \frac{f + 25}{\delta} \sqrt{\frac{r}{d}} \left(V_p - V_c\right)^2 \text{ kW/phase/km} \qquad (14.10)$$

where V_p is the phase-to-neutral operating voltage in kV and f is the supply frequency in Hz.

For storm or foul weather, the value of critical disruptive voltage is taken as $0.8\ V_c$. Thus approximate real power loss due to corona under foul weather conduction is

$$P_c = 241 \times 10^{-5} \times \frac{f + 25}{\delta} \sqrt{\frac{r}{d}} \left(V_p - 0.8V_c\right)^2 \text{ kW/phase/km} \qquad (14.11)$$

It was found that empirical formula given by Peek gives correct results if

1. Corona loss is predominant.
2. Frequency lies between 25 and 120 Hz.
3. Ratio $V_p/V_c > 1.8$.
4. The radius of conductor is greater than 0.25 cm.

When the ratio V_p/V_c is less than 1.8, Peterson's formula holds good which is

$$P_c = \frac{1.11066 \times 10^{-4} fV^2}{[\ln\ (d/r)]^2}\ F \text{ kW/phase/km} \qquad (14.12)$$

where F is the factor which varies with the ratio V_p/V_c. Typical values for different V_p/V_c in fair weather condition are

V_p/V_c	0.6	0.8	1.0	1.2	1.4	1.6	1.8	2.0	2.2
F	0.012	0.018	0.05	0.08	0.30	1.0	3.5	6.0	8.0

14.4 ADVANTAGES AND DISADVANTAGES OF CORONA

The *advantage* of corona is that it works as safety valve in the event of high-voltage steep waves due to switching or lightning surges. The energy of these waves is dissipated in air as corona loss. Corona does have several beneficial applications as in Van de Graaff generators, electrostatic precipitators, electro-printing, electrostatic deposition and ionization counting.

The main *disadvantage* of corona is the power loss which occurs. It reduces the efficiency of the lines. This loss is significant in the case of extra/ultra high voltage (EHV/UHV) lines especially in bad weather conditions. The capacitance of transmission lines increases due to increase in effective diameter of conductors. The ionized air near conductor surface works as a conducting medium. The increase in capacitance results in increased charging current, which reduces the surge impedance loading of the line. Triple frequency corona current induces the triple frequency voltage in the system and these currents and voltages interfere with the communication system.

14.5   FACTORS AFFECTING CORONA LOSS

Since the corona is due to sustained ionization of air molecules, this will be affected by the physical state of the atmosphere as well as by the conditions of line. The relevant factors that affect corona are:

1. Number of ions
2. Size and charge per ion
3. Mean free path
4. Line voltage
5. d/r ratio
6. State of the conductor surface
7. Shape and size of the surface.

The above listed factors can be further classified into three subgroups:

(a) Atmospheric factors
(b) Electric factors
(c) Condition of line

The effect of various factors on corona loss is explained now.

Atmospheric factors

Temperature. From Equation (14.10), it is clear that corona loss is dependent on air density correction factor δ. This factor is directly appearing in the loss formula however it also has impact on factor V_c which is directly proportional to the air density correction factor (see Equation 14.7). Any decrease in V_c will increase the corona loss significantly, as loss $\propto (V_p - V_c)^2$. Thus effect of δ on corona loss is very severe.

   Since air density factor is inversely proportional to the function of temperature (see Equation 14.5), with any increase in temperature, δ will be reduced and thus corona loss will be increased. Also, a decrease in temperature will increase the value of δ which thus reduces the corona loss.

Pressure. Since air density factor is directly proportional to the pressure (see Equation 14.5), with any decrease in pressure, δ will be reduced and thus corona loss will be increased. Also an increase in pressure will increase the value of δ and thus reduces the corona loss. Therefore corona loss is more in hilly areas than the plain areas. Pressure also affects the term $(V_p - V_c)^2$, that influences corona loss. As the pressure increases so does V_c and thus will be more and thus used will be less corona loss. On the other hand.

Dust and dirt. Due to presence of dust and dirt, less voltage gradient is required for sustained discharge. The critical disruptive voltage is reduced due to dust and dirt and therefore the corona loss is more.

Rain, snow, hail and fog. Bad weather conditions such as rain, storm, hails, etc. reduce the critical disruptive voltage and thus there is more corona loss. Corona loss is less in a fair weather condition. In calculation, the critical disruptive voltage under foul weather condition is taken as $0.8V_c$, where V_c is the critical disruptive voltage under fair weather condition.

Electrical factors

Frequency. Equation (14.10) shows that corona loss is proportional to $(f + 25)$. If the frequency is more, corona loss will also be more. The corona loss is less in dc-transmission system than the ac-transmission system. Due to presence of harmonics, the corona loss is always higher.

Supply voltage. If the voltage supply is high, corona loss will be high. In low-voltage lines, corona is absent due to insufficient field to maintain the self-sustained ionization.

Effect of line conditions

Conductor configurations. Conductors of 3-phase overhead transmission lines can be placed in either vertical configuration or horizontal configuration. The field intensity at the middle conductor surface is higher than the outer conductors. Thus the critical disruptive voltage for middle conductor will be less than other two conductors and thus there will be more loss in middle conductor. If they are equilaterally spaced, the average field at each conductor will be same. Since the ground is an equipotent surface, the field distribution is affected by the presence of earth. If conductors are placed at more height, the corona loss will be less.

Diameter of conductor. Since corona loss is proportional to $(V_p - V_c)^2 \sqrt{(r/d)}$, it can be separated in two terms as:

$$\text{Loss} \propto \sqrt{r} \quad \text{and} \quad \text{Loss} \propto (V_p - V_c)^2$$

If the radius of the conductor increases, the critical disruptive voltage V_c will increase because V_c is directly proportional to $r \ln (d/r)$ as $d \gg r$. Therefore, from the first corona-loss relation, it is seen that an increase in conductor diameter will increase the corona loss. However, the second term indicates that the increase in diameter will increase V_c and thus will reduce corona loss. The second term is more predominant than the first term. Thus the increase in conductor diameter will reduce the corona loss.

Profile of conductor. Electric field around a conductor depends on the shape of conductor. If the conductor is round, the field will be uniform around the conductor but if it is flat or oval, the field will be more at sharp ends. Thus corona loss in cylindrical conductors will always be less compared to any other shapes.

Surface condition. If the surface is polished and uniform, the critical disruptive voltage V_c will be more and thus there will be less corona loss. On the other hand, if the conductor surface is rough, the corona loss will be more.

Number of conductor per phase. For higher voltage lines, bundled conductors are used. By using the bundled conductors the effective radius is increased and thus the reduced field. The critical disruptive voltage V_c will be more in the case of bundled conductors. Thus corona loss is reduced.

Heating of conductor by load current. There is no direct effect of heating of conductor on the corona loss. However it has indirect effect in reducing the corona loss. Due to heating of conductors, there is no condensation of fog or dew, as presence of these increases the corona loss.

Conductor spacing. It is clear from Equation (14.7) that an increase in the conductor spacing will increase the critical disruptive voltage. Since corona loss is proportional to $(V_p - V_c)^2 \sqrt{(r/d)}$ the corona loss will be decreased considerably with the increase in conductor spacing.

14.6 EFFECT OF CORONA ON LINE DESIGN

Since corona loss reduces the efficiency of lines, the transmission lines are designed in such a way that the corona loss is small enough in a fair weather condition. If a line has a critical disruptive voltage of about 10% above the operating voltage, then it is quite satisfactory even though some corona loss will take place under a foul weather condition. An increase in spacing and diameter of conductors increase the critical disruptive voltage, thus reduces the corona loss but it also increases the cost. In properly designed transmission lines, the corona loss is usually insignificant in a fair weather condition. The typical measured values range from 0.3 to 1.7 kW/conductor/km for 500-kV lines and from 0.7–17 kW/conductor/km for 765-kV lines.

Example 14.2 A 3-phase, 50-Hz, 220-kV transmission line consists of conductors of 2.0-cm diameter and spaced equilaterally at a distance of 4 m. The line conductors have smooth surface with value of $m = 0.96$. The barometric pressure is 73 cm of Hg and temperature of 20°C. Determine the fair and stormy weather corona loss per km per phase.

Solution Air density factor

$$\delta = \frac{3.92b}{273 + t} = \frac{3.92 \times 73}{273 + 20} = 0.9767$$

Phase-to-neutral critical disruptive voltage will be

$$V_c = rg_0 m\delta \ln \frac{d}{r} = 1.0 \times 21.1 \times 0.96 \times 0.9767 \times \ln \frac{400}{1} = 118.53 \text{ kV}$$

and

$$\text{Line phase voltage } V_p = \frac{220}{\sqrt{3}} = 127.02 \text{ kV}$$

Since V_p is greater than V_c, corona will be present. Using Peek's formula for corona loss in a fair weather, we get

$$P_c = 241 \times 10^{-5} \times \frac{f + 25}{\delta} \sqrt{\frac{r}{d}} \left(V_p - V_c\right)^2 = 0.67 \text{ kW/phase/km}$$

For rainy weather, the value of critical disruptive voltage will be taken as $0.8V_c$. Thus the loss due to corona will be

$$P_c = 241 \times 10^{-5} \times \frac{f + 25}{\delta} \sqrt{\frac{r}{d}} \left(V_p - 0.8V_c\right)^2 = 9.59 \text{ kW/phase/km}$$

14.7 RADIO INTERFERENCE

The *radio interference*, also called the *radio influence*, is a noise type that occurs in the AM radio reception (0.5–1.6 MHz). It does not take place in the FM band. Radio noise (RI or TVI) is usually expressed in milli-volt per metre or in decibels above 1 μV/m. Corona noise includes interference with radio, TV and other wireless reception. Corona undoubtedly also interferes with carrier signals transmitted along EHV lines. In HVDC lines, the noise level is higher under the positive conductor than the negative conductor. However for ac transmission, lateral decay of radio noise is less steep than for dc lines.

The radio interference (RI) for both ac and dc EHV lines depends on the field strength E_{max} and defined as

$$RI = CE_{max}^{2n} \text{ dB} \qquad (14.13)$$

where C is constant. The exponent n has a value between 5 and 7 in a fair weather and between 1.5 and 3.5 in rain. For the same voltage gradient, RI level increases with the radius as

$$RI = Kr^2 \text{ dB} \qquad (14.14)$$

This relation is independent of conductor bundling.

If the power line is running along the same route as the communication line, there will be an interference in the communication line due to both electromagnetic and electrostatic effects. The electromagnetic effect produces currents, which is superimposed on the communication signal, and thereby it is distorted. However, electrostatic effect induces voltage in communication line, which may be dangerous in handling the telephone receiver. Let us consider these effects separately.

Electromagnetic effect

Figure 14.2 shows a 3-phase line with communication line conductors d and e. If the balanced current through the power conductors are I_a, I_b and I_c then

$$I_a + I_b + I_c = 0$$

The flux linkage to conductor d due to current in conductor a will be

$$\lambda_{ad} = 2 \times 10^{-7} I_a \ln \frac{D_\infty}{D_{ad}}$$

where D_∞ is the infinity. The flux linkage to conductor e due to current in conductor a will be

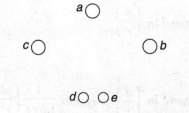

FIGURE 14.2 Three-phase line with communication line.

$$\lambda_{ae} = 2 \times 10^{-7} I_a \ln \frac{D_\infty}{D_{ae}}$$

The mutual flux linkage between conductor d and e due to current I_a

$$\lambda_{ad} - \lambda_{ae} = 2 \times 10^{-7} I_a \ln \frac{D_{ae}}{D_{ad}}$$

The mutual inductance M_a between conductor a and loop de will be

$$M_a = \frac{\lambda_{ad} - \lambda_{ae}}{I_a} = 2 \times 10^{-7} \ln \frac{D_{ae}}{D_{ad}} \quad \text{H/m} \tag{14.15}$$

Similarly, mutual inductances M_b and M_c between conductor b and loop de and between conductor c and loop de respectively will be

$$M_b = 2 \times 10^{-7} \ln \frac{D_{be}}{D_{bd}} \quad \text{H/m} \tag{14.16}$$

and

$$M_c = 2 \times 10^{-7} \ln \frac{D_{ce}}{D_{cd}} \quad \text{H/m} \tag{14.17}$$

Since the currents are displaced by 120°, these mutual inductances have also displacement of 120°. The net mutual inductance M will be the vector sum of three mutual inductances.

$$\overline{M} = \overline{M}_a + \overline{M}_b + \overline{M}_c$$

If I is current in the power conductor and frequency is f, voltage induced in communication conductors d and e will be

$$V = j\omega M I \quad \text{volt/m}$$

The value of M will be small if the distance between power line and communication line is large. Generally, power conductors as systematically spaced, M will be cancelled for power frequency. Presence of harmonics and multiples of harmonics do not cancelled. Due to presence of harmonics, the induced voltage may be dangerous.

Example 14.3 Show that the maximum critical disruptive voltage occurs when the radius of conductor is (d/e)

Solution
$$V' = rg_0 m\delta \ln\left(\frac{d}{r}\right)$$

for max V', $\dfrac{\partial V'}{\partial r} = 0$

$$0 = g_0 m\delta \ln\left(\frac{d}{r}\right) - rg_0 m\delta \frac{1}{(d/r)}\left(\frac{d}{r^2}\right)$$

$$\ln\left(\frac{d}{r}\right) = 1 = \ln e$$

$$\therefore \qquad\qquad r = d/e$$

Example 14.4 A 1ϕ 50 Hz overhead power line is symmetrically supported on a horizontal cross-arm. Spacing between the centres of the conductors (say a and b) in 2.5 m. A telephone line is also symmetrically supported on a horizontal cross-arm 1.8 m directly below the power line. Spacing between the centres of these conductors (say, c and d) is 1.0

(a) Show that the mutual inductance per unit length between centre a-b and centre c-d is given by

$$4 \times 10^{-2} \ln \sqrt{\frac{D_{ad}\, D_{bc}}{D_{ac}\, D_{bd}}} \text{ H/m}$$

where, e.g. D_{ad} denotes the distance in metres between conductors a and d.

(b) Hence, compute the mutual inductance per kilometre between the power line and the telephone line.

(c) Find the 50 Hz voltage per kilometre induced in the telephone line when the power line carries 150 A.

Solution   Flux linkage of conductor a.

$$\psi_a = 2 \times 10^{-4}\left[I \ln \frac{1}{D_{ac}} - I \ln \frac{1}{D_{ad}}\right]$$

$$= 2 \times 10^{-4}\left[I \ln \frac{D_{ad}}{D_{ac}}\right]$$

Flux linkage of conductor b

$$\psi_b = 2 \times 10^{-4} \left[I \ln \frac{1}{D_{bc}} - I \ln \frac{1}{D_{bd}} \right]$$

$$= 2 \times 10^{-4} = \left[I \ln \frac{D_{bd}}{D_{bc}} \right]$$

∴ Total flux linkages of the telephone line $\psi = \psi_a - \psi_b$

$$= 2 \times 10^{-4} \ln \frac{D_{ad} \, D_{bc}}{D_{ac} \cdot D_{ad}}$$

$$= 4 \times 10^{-4} \, I \ln \sqrt{\frac{D_{ad} \, D_{bc}}{D_{ac} \cdot D_{ad}}}$$

Hence, mutual inductance $= \dfrac{\psi}{I} = 4 \times 10^{-4} \ln \sqrt{\dfrac{D_{ad} \, D_{bc}}{D_{ac} \, D_{ad}}}$ H/m

(b) $D_{ad} = D_{bc} = \sqrt{(1.8)^2 + (1.75)^2} = 2.51 \, \text{m}$

$\quad D_{ac} = D_{bd} = \sqrt{(1.8)^2 + (0.75)^2} = 1.95 \, \text{m}$

So, $\quad M = 4 \times 10^{-4} \ln \dfrac{2.51}{1.95} = 0.1 \times 10^{-3}$ H/km/ph

(c) Inductive reactance $= 2\pi f M = 0.0317 \, \pi/\text{km}$

Now, $I = 150\text{A}$

so emf induced in telephone line/km $= I \cdot (jwM)$

$$= 4.76 \text{ V/km}$$

Electrostatic effect

Using the concept of image conductors, the potential of conductor d due to charge q coulomb/m on conductor a will be

$$V_{ad} = \frac{-q}{2\pi\varepsilon_0} \int_{h_a}^{D_{ad}} \left(\frac{1}{x} + \frac{1}{2h_a - x} \right) dx = \frac{q}{2\pi\varepsilon_0} \ln \frac{2h_a - D_{ad}}{D_{ad}} \qquad (14.18)$$

where h_a, as shown in Figure 14.3, is the height of conductor a from the ground. The voltage between conductor a and image conductor a' will be

$$V_{aa'} = -\int_{2h_a-r}^{r} E_x dx = -\int_{2h_a}^{r} \frac{q}{2\pi\varepsilon_0} \left(\frac{1}{x} + \frac{1}{2h_a - x} \right) dx = \frac{q}{2\pi\varepsilon_0} \, 2 \ln \frac{2h_a - r}{r} = 2V_a$$

or

$$V_a = \frac{q}{2\pi\varepsilon_0} \ln \frac{2h_a - r}{r}$$

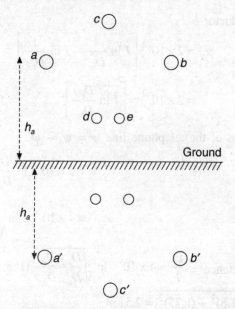

FIGURE 14.3 Electrostatic effect.

where V_a is voltage (phase to ground) of conductor a. Substituting the value of q in Equation (14.18) from above equation, we get

$$V_{ad} = \frac{q}{2\pi\varepsilon_0} \ln \frac{2h_a - D_{ad}}{D_{ad}} = V_a \frac{\ln \dfrac{2h_a - D_{ad}}{D_{ad}}}{\ln \dfrac{2h_a - r}{r}} \qquad (14.19)$$

The potential of conductor d due to charges on the conductors b and c can also be obtained in similar ways. The total potential will be the phasor sum of all the potential as

$$\overline{V}_d = \overline{V}_{ad} + \overline{V}_{bd} + \overline{V}_{cd}$$

The potential due to electrostatic effect in conductor e can also be computed.

PROBLEMS

14.1 Find the disruptive critical voltage and critical voltage for visual corona of a 3-phase 50-km long line consisting of ACSR conductors of area 240-mm², spaced in a 3.5-m delta arrangement. Diameter of conductors is 2 cm. Temperature is 27°C and barometric pressure is 73 cm. Assume $m = 0.85$ and $m_v = 0.72$. If the line is operated at 132 kV, find the coronal loss. What will be the losses in a fair weather and in storm if the line voltage is 220 kV?

14.2 A 3-phase overhead transmission line operates at 132 kV between phases at 50 Hz. The conductors are arranged in a 3.0-m delta configuration. What is the minimum diameter of a conductor that can be used for no corona under a fair weather condition. Assume an air density factor of 0.95 and irregularity factor of 0.85.

14.3 A conductor of 3-phase, 33 kV system having 2.0-cm diameter is passed centrally through a porcelain bushing (relative permeability = 5) having internal and external diameters of 3 cm and 9 cm respectively. Find the maximum potential gradient in the air space between conductor and porcelain and state whether corona will be present or not.

14.4 A conductor of 1 cm diameter passes centrally through a porcelain cylinder of internal diameter 2 cm and external diameter 8 cm. The cylinder is surrounded by a tightly fitting metal sheath. The permittivity of porcelain is 5 and the peak voltage gradient in air must not exceed 34 kV/cm. Determine the maximum safe working voltage.

14.5 A 3-phase 60-Hz, 50-km long, 132-kV transmission line delivers a total load of 25 MW at 0.8-p.f. lagging. The conductor arrangement is shown as in Figure 14.4. The radius of each power conductor equilaterally spaced at 4.0 m apart is 1.0 cm. Calculate the induced voltage at fundamental frequency in telephone circuit (shown in the figure as *d* and *e*) due to electromagnetic effect. Also, determine the potential of telephone conductors *d* and *e* above the earth due to electrostatic effect only.

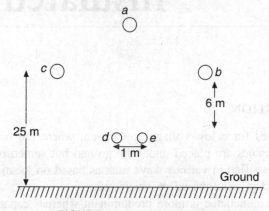

FIGURE 14.4 Problem 14.5.

14.6 The single-phase power line of Example 14.4 is replaced by a 3ϕ line on a horizontal cross-arm in the same position as that of the original single-phase line. Spacing of the conductors of the power line is $D_{13} = 2D_{12} = 2D_{23}$ and equivalent equilateral spacing is 3 m. The telephone line remains is symmetrically supported on a horizontal cross-arm 1.8 m directly below the power line. Spacing between the centres of the conductors (say *c* and *d*) is 1.0 m. If the current in the power line is 150A, find the voltage per kilometre induced in the telephone line. Discuss the phase relation of the induced voltage with respect to the power line current.

15

Insulated Cables

15.1 INTRODUCTION

Cables are normally used for a low-voltage application, where the overhead line erection is impractical. Normally, cables are placed under the ground but sometimes it is also hanged on towers. Cable can be classified in various ways such as based on location, types of insulations used, number of conductors used, based on shield, etc.

In overhead lines, inductance is more predominant whereas capacitance is in the cables. The large charging current in high voltage cables limits the length of its use and therefore overhead transmission lines are preferred for long distance application. Since copper is normally used in cables, the cost of conductor is high in the case of cable compared to overhead lines where aluminium conductors are used. Another cost involved in cables is the cost of insulation which is air in the case of overhead lines. The erection costs of overhead lines are higher than that of the cable. In spite of some limitations, cables are preferred over the overhead transmission lines, where:

  (a) Public safety is involved.
  (b) Scenic beauty of a city is important.
  (c) Submarine crossing is there.
  (d) Connections of substations, transformers, etc., are required.

15.2 CABLE CONDUCTORS

Earlier only stranded copper conductors were used in cables but now aluminium is also used because it is cheaper than copper. However, any saving in the cost must be compensated against its extra-insulation cost required to surround the core. A comparison of copper and aluminium is given in Table 15.1.

Table 15.1 Comparison of Copper and Aluminium Materials

Properties	Copper	Aluminium
Specific gravity	8.890	2.71
Young's modulus	12700 kg/mm^2	5600 kg/mm^2
Ultimate tensile strength	40 kg/mm^2	15 kg/mm^2
Resistivity at 20°C	1.73 μΩ-cm	2.87 μΩ-cm
Resistance temperature coefficient	0.00426 per °C at 0°C	0.00380 per °C at 0°C
Coefficient of linear expansion	16.6 × 10^{-6} per °C	23 × 10^{-6} per °C

Stranded conductors are used to provide a mechanical flexibility. Various conductors are spiraled round the central conductor. If there is more than one layer, alternate layers are spiraled in opposite direction to prevent bird caging when conductor is bent. One complete turn of spiral measured across the axis of cable is called *lay*. Spiraling increases the resistance as the length of each spiraled conductor is greater than the central conductor and thus the weight of cable. The size of conductors are represented as 19/20s, where the first number stands for the number of strands used and the second number is the standard wire gauge (SWG) of each strands. If it is shown as 19/2.9, the first number represents the strands used and the second one the diameter of each strand in millimetres. The different cross-sectional areas are used and they are defined differently.

Nominal cross-section area is the area of one conductor in a plane perpendicular to its length multiplied by the number of conductors. *Actual cross-section area* is the cross-section of oblique cross-section due to cutting of the stranded cable by a plane perpendicular to the core of cable multiplied by the number of conductors. *Equivalent cross-section* is the cross-section of a solid conductor of same length as the cable and having same resistance at same temperature. Thus

Equivalent area < Actual cross-section area > Nominal cross-section area

Calculation of weight

If *l* is the lay and *d* is the pitch diameter of a particular layer, as shown in Figure 15.1. The circumference of this layer is πd. The length of the conductor along the spiral is hypotenuse of a right-angled triangle. The length along the spiral *l'* is

$$l' = \sqrt{l^2 + (\pi d)^2}$$

If *n* is the number of layers (excluding central strand), the total number of conductors in each layer is 6*n* and pitch diameter of each layer is (2*n* + 1)*D*, where *D* is the diameter of each strand. The length of the *n*th layer strands is

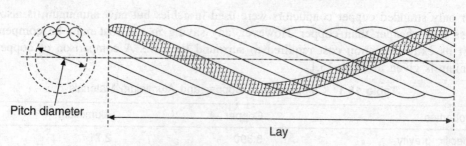

FIGURE 15.1 Lay of a cable.

$$l'_n = \sqrt{l^2 + [\pi(2n + 1)D]^2} \tag{15.1}$$

If there are n layers, the central strand will be of length l and the nth layer-strands have $6n$ strands and the length of each strand is l'_n. The sum of the length will therefore is

$$l + \sum_n (6nl'_n) = l + \sum_n \left\{ 6n\sqrt{l^2 + [\pi(2n + 1)D]^2} \right\} \tag{15.2}$$

If it is not spiraled, the length will be $(3n^2 + 3n + 1)l$. Therefore, increase in length is

$$l + \sum_n \left\{ 6n\sqrt{l^2 + [\pi(2n + 1)D]^2} \right\} - (3n^2 + 3n + 1)l \tag{15.3}$$

Therefore, increase in weight can be calculated using area and density of material.

Calculation of resistance

Since the cross-section area of each conductor is same, the total resistance R' is given by

$$\frac{1}{R'} \propto \frac{1}{l} + \sum_n \frac{6n}{l'_n} = \frac{1}{l} + \sum_n \frac{6n}{\sqrt{l^2 + [\pi(2n + 1)D]^2}} \tag{15.4}$$

If all the strands were of the same length l, the resistance R would be proportional to $l/(3n^2 + 3n + 1)$. Therefore, the change in the resistance is

$$\frac{R'}{R} = \frac{(3n^2 + 3n + 1)/l}{\dfrac{1}{l} + \displaystyle\sum_n \dfrac{6n}{\sqrt{l^2 + [\pi(2n + 1)D]^2}}} \text{ times} \tag{15.5}$$

Example 15.1 Calculate the increase in resistance and weight due to spiraling of the conductor having diameter of each strand of 2 cm and number of layers excluding central strand is one. Lays length is of 40 cm.

Solution For $n = 1$, the total number of strand will be 7 and therefore the length is a strand of layer one, using Equation (15.1), is

$$l_1' = \sqrt{l^2 + [\pi(2n + 1)D]^2} = \sqrt{40^2 + (\pi \times 3 \times 2)^2} = 44.22 \text{ cm}$$

The total length of strands in the lay will be $305.31 (= 40 + 6 \times 44.22)$ cm. If it were not spiraled, the total length would be 280 $(= 7 \times 40)$ cm. Then

$$\% \text{ Increase in weight} = \frac{305.31 - 280}{280} \times 100 = 9.04\%$$

Increase in resistance is calculated as:

$$\frac{1}{R'} \propto \frac{1}{l} + \sum_n \frac{6n}{l_n'} = \frac{1}{40} + \frac{6}{44.22} = 0.16068$$

and

$$\frac{1}{R} \propto \frac{7}{40} = 0.175$$

Therefore

$$\frac{R'}{R} = \frac{0.175}{0.16068} = 1.089$$

Thus, there will be an increase of 8.9% in resistance.

15.3 INSULATING MATERIALS

Besides a cable conductor (used for transmitting power), insulation (to insulate the conductor from earth or other phases) and external protection (against mechanical damage, fire, chemical or other attack) are other important parts of a cable. The main properties of insulating materials of cables are:

1. High-insulation resistance
2. High-dielectric strength
3. Good mechanical properties (elasticity and tenacity)
4. Immunity to chemical attacks over wide range of temperatures
5. Non-hygroscopic (i.e. free from moisture)
6. Being economical
7. Easy handling, manufacture and installation
8. Reasonably long life
9. Sufficiently low-thermal resistivity
10. Low relative permittivity and less tangent angle when used in ac cables.

Various insulating materials used for cable are discussed below.

Vulcanized rubber. Ordinary rubber has a sufficient dielectric strength but it easily absorbs the moisture contents and thus its dielectric strength is reduced. The sulphur used in vulcanizing process has a high dielectric strength and resistant to moisture absorption. The ordinary rubber is not too elastic but a vulcanized rubber is elastic and resilient. Vulcanized rubber insulated cables are normally used for low-voltage application such as wiring of houses, buildings, factories, etc. There are different types of synthetic rubber materials available such as butyl rubber, silicon rubber, neoprene and styrene rubber.

Varnished cambric. A cotton cloth impregnated and coated with varnish is known as *varnished cambric*. The varnish is oil with petroleum bitumen added. The cambric is lapped on to the conductor in the form of a tape and to allow for sliding on one turn over another as the cable is bent. The surfaces are lubricated with a petroleum compound to have good finish. The dielectric strength is about 40 kV/cm and the dielectric constant is 3 to 4. Terylene can be used in place of cambric which is mechanically stronger and non-hygroscopic. It can also be operated at much higher temperature.

Polyvinyl chloride. *Polyvinyl chloride* (PVC) is a polymer and made from acetylene during polymerization process. Different grades such as hard grade, heat resisting, general-purpose type, etc., are possible which depends on the plasticizer. PVC is inferior to the vulcanized rubber in respect of elasticity and insulation resistance but is inert to oxygen, alkalis, acids, oils, etc. PVCs are expensive than vulcanized rubber.

Impregnated paper. Insulating paper is lapped on the conductor until the required thickness, which depends on the operating voltage of cable, is achieved. It is then dried in heat and vacuum and impregnated with insulating compound which should be such that it is plastic at ordinary temperature and has no tendency to drain from higher-end to lower-end. Impregnated paper cables have the advantages of marked durability, high dielectric strength, low cost and low-electrostatic capacitance thus suitable for extra high voltages. The compounds used are paraffinic or naphthaenic mineral oil with resin to improve the impregnating quality. There should not be any voids in finished cable.

Polythene. *Polythene* can be used for high-frequency cables as it has a low-melting point. By cross-linking the molecules, new material is obtained which does not melt. It is known as *cross-linked polythene* (XPLE). It has a good impulse dielectric strength, inert to chemical reactions and has a high-thermal dissipation property. Classification of insulating materials is given in Table 15.2.

Table 15.2 Classification of Insulating Materials

Class	Temperature (°C)	Materials
Class Y (formerly O)	90	Cotton, silk, paper without impregnation
Class A	105	Cotton, silk, paper impregnated suitably or coated or immersed in dielectric liquids
Class E	120	Consists of materials or combination of materials which by experience or accepted test for 120°C temperature
Class B	130	Mica, glass fibre, asbestos, wood, etc.
Class F	150	Mica, glass fibre, asbestos, wood, etc., with suitable binding substances at this temperature operation
Class H	180	Silicon, elastomer and combination of materials such as mica, glass, fibre, etc., with suitable bonding substances such as silicon resin
Class C	above 180	Mica, porcelain, glass and quartz with or without inorganic binder

Mechanical protective covering

Since insulating materials are mechanically weak, the power cables are armoured with steel tapes or steel wires of having enough strength. Tapes are very inflexible and are not suitable for installation where bending of cables is a must and is on the supports above the ground. With ordinary main cable, aluminium sheathing may be used which does not need additional armouring and is usually finished with watertight protection such as rubber or PVC. All cables whether armoured or not, have an external covering or serving. There is some power loss in armouring. Normally, non-magnetic material is used as armouring.

15.4 INSULATION RESISTANCE

Load current flows through cable conductor but leakage current flows radially through insulating material, as shown by dotted lines in Figure 15.2.

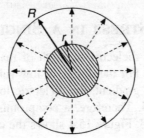

FIGURE 15.2 Insulation material.

Let ρ = specific resistance of material; R = outer radius of insulation; and r = radius of conductor (or inner radius of insulation). Consider a small annular cylinder of width dx at distance x from the centre, as shown in Figure 15.3. Since the leakage current flows from conductor to the sheath through the insulation, the length through which the current is flowing is dx and the area is $2\pi x l$, where l is length of cable. The insulation resistance of the annular cylinder is

$$dR_s = \frac{\rho\, dx}{2\pi x l} \tag{15.6}$$

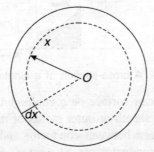

FIGURE 15.3 A small annular cylinder.

Since the insulating material is from r to R, the insulation resistance is obtained by integrating Equation (15.6) as

$$R_s = \frac{\rho}{2\pi l} \int_r^R \frac{dx}{x} = \frac{\rho}{2\pi l} \ln \frac{R}{r} \text{ ohm} \tag{15.7}$$

The insulation resistance per unit length of the cable is

$$R_s = \frac{\rho}{2\pi} \ln \frac{R}{r} \text{ ohm/m} \tag{15.8}$$

It can be seen from Equation (15.7) that the insulation resistance is inversely proportional to the length of the cable. However, the resistance of conductor is directly proportional to the length of conductor. Therefore, as cable length increases, there is less insulation resistance and thus more leakage current. This current is not useful. Therefore, the insulating material should have as minimum leakage current as possible.

15.5   ELECTROSTATIC STRESS IN A SINGLE-CORE CABLE

If the dielectric stress exceeds the dielectric strength of material surrounding the conductors, the insulating material will rapture. For the design of low value of electric stress, the cable size is more however for high value of gradient, the dielectric loss will be more and there may be thermal breakdown of the material. Therefore, a compromise between these has to be made. The electric stress can be computed. Figure 15.4 shows the cross-section of a single-core cable along with dielectric stress distribution.

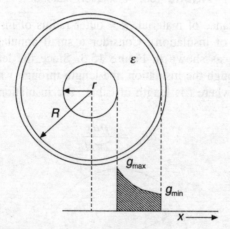

FIGURE 15.4 A cross-section of a single-core cable.

Let the charge on the conductor surface be q coulomb/unit length, ε the permittivity of dielectric, R the inner radius of sheath or outer radius of insulating material, r the radius of conductor, V the potential difference between conductor and sheath. The electric field E_x at distance x from the centre of the conductor can be written, using Equation (10.28), as

$$E_x = \frac{q}{2\pi\varepsilon x} \text{ volt/m}$$

Potential difference V can be found out as

$$V = -\int_R^r E_x \, dx = \frac{q}{2\pi\varepsilon} \ln \frac{R}{r}$$

Thus the electric field (or gradient) can be written in terms of voltage as

$$E_x = \frac{V}{x \ln (R/r)} \tag{15.9}$$

From Equation (15.9), it can be seen that the maximum stress occurs at the surface of the conductor while the minimum stress occurs at the outer surface of the insulation. Average stress is the amount of voltage across the insulation material which is divided by the thickness of the insulation. Thus the maximum electric stress at the surface of conductor $(x = r)$ is

$$E_{max} = \frac{V}{r \ln (R/r)} \tag{15.10}$$

and the minimum electric stress occurs at $x = R$. Hence

$$E_{min} = \frac{V}{R \ln (R/r)} \tag{15.11}$$

From Equation (15.10), it can be seen that for a particular voltage V and the overall size of cable R, there is one particular radius that gives the minimum stress at the conductor surface. To find the optimal value of r such that E_{max} is minimum, Equation (15.10) is differentiated with respect to r and equated to zero as

$$\frac{dE_{max}}{dr} = 0 \tag{15.12}$$

Since the numerator of Equation (15.10) is a constant, the relation can be found out by differentiating the denominator and equating to zero, we have

$$r \times \frac{r}{R} \times \left(-\frac{R}{r^2}\right) + \ln \frac{R}{r} = 0 \tag{15.13}$$

From Equation (15.13), we get

$$\ln \frac{R}{r} = 1 \quad \text{or} \quad \frac{R}{r} = e \tag{15.14}$$

Thus $R = 2.718r$. The actual value of electric stress at the conductor

$$E_{max} = \frac{V}{r} = \frac{Ve}{R} \tag{15.15}$$

The plot of Equation (15.10) with the ratio r/R is shown in Figure 15.5. From the figure, it is also seen that the minimum value of E_{max} occurs when $r/R = 1/e$.

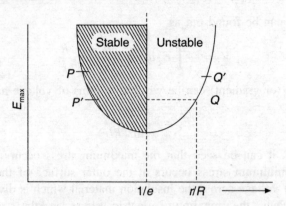

FIGURE 15.5   Plot of E_{max} with r/R ratio.

As the value of r/R ratio is decreased or increased from $1/e$, the electric stress at the conductor will be increased. To know the stable region (r/R ratio values), consider an impurity is at point Q due to design. Due to impurity, the air gets ionized which is trapped due to manufacturing defects. If a thin layer of impurity is at a distance x near the conductor, due to high electric stress it may be ionized and the effective radius of the conductor now becomes $(r + x)$, as shown in Figure 15.6. Now the stress will be more compared to the previous case when there is no impurity. Then the ratio $(r + x)/R$ will shift to Q', stress increases and finally leads to rapture. This design leads to unstable operation.

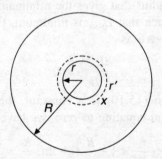

FIGURE 15.6   Cross-section of a conductor.

Let us now consider that the cable is designed in such a way that stress is at point P (Figure 15.5). Due to impurity ionization, the effective radius of conductor is $(r + x)$. Now the stress will be less compared to the previous case when there is no impurity. Then the stress is shifted to P', and the ionization is reduced. This design leads to stable operation. Thus for satisfactory operation of cable, we have

$$\frac{r}{R} < \frac{1}{e} \quad \text{or} \quad \frac{R}{r} > e \tag{15.16}$$

Example 15.2   A single-core cable has a conductor of diameter 3 cm and inside diameter of lead sheath is 6 cm. If the cable is designed for operating voltage of 33 kV (line-to-neutral), find:

(a) Maximum and minimum values of electric stress
(b) Optimal value of conductor radius for the smallest value of the maximum stress.

Solution (a) From Equations (15.10) and (15.11), we get

$$E_{max} = \frac{V}{r \ln (R/r)} = \frac{33}{1.5 \ln (3/1.5)} = 31.74 \text{ kV/cm}$$

and

$$E_{min} = \frac{V}{R \ln (R/r)} = \frac{33}{3 \ln (3/1.5)} = 15.87 \text{ kV/cm}$$

(b) From Equation (15.14), for minimum E_{max}, the optimal value of the conductor radius,

$$r = \frac{R}{2.718} = \frac{3.0}{2.718} = 1.104 \text{ cm}$$

Therefore, we get

$$E_{max} = \frac{V}{r \ln (R/r)} = \frac{33}{1.104 \ln (3/1.104)} = 29.90 \text{ kV/cm}$$

Example 15.3 Find the overall economic diameter of a single-conductor cable working at 11-kV voltage and having insulation of dielectric strength of 50 kV/cm with safety factor of 2.

Solution Since the dielectric strength is 50 kV/cm and safety factor is 2, the maximum stress allowed is 25 (=50/2) kV/cm. From Equation (15.15), we have outer insulation radius R as

$$E_{max} = \frac{Ve}{R} \quad \text{or} \quad 25 = \frac{11e}{R}$$

Thus $R = 1.20$ cm and the radius of the conductor $r = R/e = 0.44$ cm.

15.6 GRADING OF CABLES

Since the electric stress distribution in insulating material is not uniform, even at optimal size of conductor for given operating voltage and cable size, the insulating material is not properly utilized. By grading, the utilization of insulating materials can be improved. *Grading* means distribution of dielectric material such that the difference between E_{max} and E_{min} is reduced. Thereby a cable of same size can be operated for high voltage or for the same operation voltage, the size can be reduced. Grading can be broadly classified into two groups as:

(a) *Capacitance grading* (more than one dielectric materials are used)
(b) *Intersheath grading* (the same dielectric material is used but potentials at certain radius are held constant by using metal sheaths).

15.6.1 Capacitance Grading

If the electric stress or gradient throughout the insulating material is the same (Figure 15.7), the utilization factor is maximum. Ideally, it is possible only by having the decreasing permittivity of insulation starting with a high value at the surface of conductor. If q is charge per unit length, the gradient at point x from the centre of the cable is

$$E_x = \frac{q}{2\pi\varepsilon x} = k$$

The permittivity (ε) is:

$$\varepsilon = \frac{k_1}{x}$$

This can be realized by having infinite number of dielectric material of varying permittivities (Figure 15.7). It is practically impossible. Normally, two or three materials are used which do not give the constant gradient through the cable but it improves the gradient distribution.

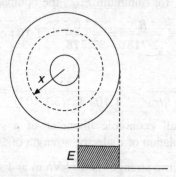

FIGURE 15.7 Uniform gradient.

Let us consider three materials be used with permittivities ε_1, ε_2 and ε_3 placed at between the distances r and r_1, r_1 and r_2, and r_2 and R respectively, as shown in Figure 15.8. Let dielectric strength of the materials be G_1, G_2 and G_3.

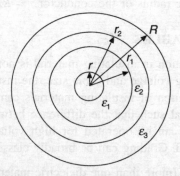

FIGURE 15.8 Capacitance grading.

The main objective is to find the locations of these materials so that their utilization can be better. The criterion may be based on the same safety factors or the same working stresses.

For the same safety factor

Let the safety factor is F for all the materials. The value of ε_1 will be such that the electric stress at the surface of conductor should be G_1/F which can be related as

$$\frac{q}{2\pi\varepsilon_1 r} = \frac{G_1}{F} \tag{15.17}$$

The electric stress at the radius r_1 should be G_2/F and can be given by

$$\frac{q}{2\pi\varepsilon_2 r_1} = \frac{G_2}{F} \tag{15.18}$$

Similarly at the radius r_2, the electric stress should be G_3/F and can be given by

$$\frac{q}{2\pi\varepsilon_3 r_2} = \frac{G_3}{F} \tag{15.19}$$

From Equations (15.17)–(15.19), we get the following relations

$$q = 2\pi\varepsilon_1 r\frac{G_1}{F} = 2\pi\varepsilon_2 r_1\frac{G_2}{F} = 2\pi\varepsilon_3 r_2\frac{G_3}{F} \tag{15.20}$$

or

$$\varepsilon_1 r G_1 = \varepsilon_2 r_1 G_2 = \varepsilon_3 r_2 G_3$$

since $r < r_1 < r_2$. Therefore

$$\varepsilon_1 G_1 > \varepsilon_2 G_2 > \varepsilon_3 G_3 \tag{15.21}$$

Thus material having the highest product of permittivity and dielectric strength will be kept near the conductor. The operating voltage of cable can be obtained as

$$V = \int_r^{r_1} E_1 \, dx + \int_{r_1}^{r_2} E_2 \, dx + \int_{r_2}^{R} E_3 \, dx$$

$$= \frac{q}{2\pi}\left(\frac{1}{\varepsilon_1} \ln \frac{r_1}{r} + \frac{1}{\varepsilon_2} \ln \frac{r_2}{r_1} + \frac{1}{\varepsilon_3} \ln \frac{R}{r_2}\right) \tag{15.22}$$

In Equation (15.22), the value of q can be replaced by knowing the stress in any of the Sections using Equation (15.20).

With the same maximum stresses

If all the materials are subjected to the same maximum stress, the stresses at r, r_1 and r_2 should be same, as shown in Figure 15.9. The relationship can be written as

$$E_{\max} = \frac{q}{2\pi\varepsilon_1 r} = \frac{q}{2\pi\varepsilon_2 r_1} = \frac{q}{2\pi\varepsilon_3 r_2}$$

or

$$\varepsilon_1 r = \varepsilon_2 r_1 = \varepsilon_3 r_2$$

Since

$$r < r_1 < r_2, \quad \varepsilon_1 > \varepsilon_2 > \varepsilon_3 \tag{15.23}$$

Thus for the same maximum stress, the material having the highest permittivity should be placed near the conductor and next highest is placed after that and so on.

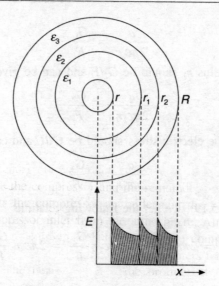

FIGURE 15.9 Stress distribution.

The operating voltage can be obtained using Equation (15.22) as

$$V = E_{1(\max)}r \ln \frac{r_1}{r} + E_{2(\max)}r_1 \ln \frac{r_2}{r_1} + E_{3(\max)}r_2 \ln \frac{R}{r_2} \qquad (15.24)$$

Since $E_{1(\max)} = E_{2(\max)} = E_{3(\max)} = E_{\max}$

$$V = E_{\max} \left(r \ln \frac{r_1}{r} + r_1 \ln \frac{r_2}{r_1} + r_2 \ln \frac{R}{r_2} \right) \text{volt} \qquad (15.25)$$

15.6.2 Intersheath Grading

Consider two metal sheath having radii r_1 and r_2 kept at potentials V_2 and V_1 respectively, as shown in Figure 15.10. The potentials at intersheaths are maintained with the help of an auxiliary transformer. Due to this arrangement, the stress distribution are forced to be lower than the gradient without intersheath for the same operating voltage V and overall size of the cable R. If the insulating material is homogeneous, using Equation (15.10), the electric stress at the conductor surface is given by

$$E_{\max} = \frac{V - V_2}{r \ln (r_1/r)}$$

Similarly, the electric stresses at radius r_1 and r_2 are given by

$$\frac{V_2 - V_1}{r_1 \ln (r_2/r_1)} \quad \text{and} \quad \frac{V_1}{r_2 \ln (R/r_2)}$$

Since the material is the same, the maximum stress must be same. Therefore,

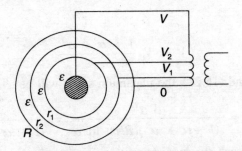

FIGURE 15.10 Intersheath grading.

$$\frac{V - V_2}{r \ln (r_1/r)} = \frac{V_2 - V_1}{r_1 \ln (r_2/r_1)} = \frac{V_1}{r_2 \ln (R/r_2)} \tag{15.26}$$

The stress can also be made to vary between the same maximum and minimum value by choosing r_1 and r_2, such that

$$\frac{r_1}{r} = \frac{r_2}{r_1} = \frac{R}{r_2} = \alpha \text{ (say)} \tag{15.27}$$

From Equations (15.26) and (15.27), we have

$$\frac{V - V_2}{r} = \frac{V_2 - V_1}{r_1} = \frac{V_1}{r_2} \tag{15.28}$$

It is now necessary to represent the stresses in terms of operating voltage V, conductor radius r and cable size R. For this calculation, the voltages V_1 and V_2 in terms of V, r and R is required. From relation

$$\frac{V_2 - V_1}{r_1} = \frac{V_1}{r_2}$$

We get

$$\frac{V_2}{r_1} = V_1 \left(\frac{1}{r_1} + \frac{1}{r_2} \right) = V_1 \left(\frac{r_1 + r_2}{r_1 r_2} \right)$$

Thus

$$V_2 = V_1 \frac{r_1 + r_2}{r_2} = V_1 \frac{1 + (r_2/r_1)}{r_2/r_1}$$

or

$$V_2 = V_1 \frac{1 + \alpha}{\alpha} \tag{15.29}$$

From relation

$$\frac{V - V_2}{r} = \frac{V_1}{r_2}$$

We have

$$V = V_2 + \frac{rV_1}{r_2} = V_1 \frac{1 + \alpha}{\alpha} + V_1 \frac{r}{r_1} \frac{r_1}{r_2} = V_1 \left(\frac{1 + \alpha}{\alpha} + \frac{1}{\alpha^2} \right)$$

or

$$V = V_1 \frac{1 + \alpha + \alpha^2}{\alpha^2} \tag{15.30}$$

From Equations (15.30) and (15.27), the maximum stress will be

$$E_{max} = \frac{V_1}{r_2 \ln (R/r_2)} = \frac{V\alpha^2}{(1 + \alpha + \alpha^2)(R/\alpha) \ln \alpha} = \frac{V\alpha^3}{(1 + \alpha + \alpha^2)R \ln \alpha} \tag{15.31}$$

If intersheaths are not present, the maximum stress is at conductor surface and is equal to

$$E'_{max} = \frac{V}{r \ln (R/r)} = \frac{V}{(R/\alpha^3) \ln \alpha^3} = \frac{V\alpha^3}{3R \ln \alpha} \tag{15.32}$$

Therefore

$$\frac{E_{max}}{E'_{max}} = \frac{3}{1 + \alpha + \alpha^2} \tag{15.33}$$

Since the value of α is greater than unity, the ratio $3/(1 + \alpha + \alpha^2)$ is less than unity. This shows that the gradient due to intersheath is less than that of without the intersheath. Hence, it is advantageous. Using Equation (15.24), the operating voltage of the cable with intersheath can be given by

$$V = E_{max} \left(r \ln \frac{r_1}{r} + r_1 \ln \frac{r_2}{r_1} + r_2 \ln \frac{R}{r_2} \right) = E_{max}(r + r_1 + r_2) \ln \alpha \tag{15.34}$$

Equation (15.34) can further be simplified as

$$V = E_{max} r \left(1 + \frac{r_1}{r} + \frac{r_2}{r} \right) \ln \alpha = E_{max} r(1 + \alpha + \alpha^2) \ln \alpha \tag{15.35}$$

Grading of cables in practical system is difficult due to several reasons, such as:

(a) Non-availability of varying permittivity of insulating materials.

(b) Change in the permittivity with time, which changes the distribution of stress that may lead to rapture of insulating material at normal working voltage.

(c) Damage of intersheath during laying or due to aging may lead to severe stress.

(d) Charging current flows through the intersheath which may damage the cable due to overheating.

(e) There may be resonance problem in intersheath grading due to inductance of transformer and capacitance of cable.

(f) Grading may not be economical in low-voltage cables.

Due to these reasons, grading is avoided in modern practice in favour of oil- and gas-filled cables.

Example 15.4 A single-core cable is having conductor diameter of 2 cm and consisting of three *A*, *B* and *C* insulating materials of permittivities 5, 4 and 2 and permissible stresses of

50.0, 40.0 and 30.0 kV/cm respectively. If the line is designed for 110 kV, find the minimum internal sheath radius of the cable.

Solution Since the stress at the cable core is highest followed by at the next insulating material and so on, the placement of insulating material from the conductor core will be A, B and C, respectively. Assuming the same safety factor of unity for each material, from Equation (15.20), we get

$$\varepsilon_1 r G_1 = \varepsilon_2 r_1 G_2 = \varepsilon_3 r_2 G_3$$

From the relation, $\varepsilon_1 r G_1 = \varepsilon_2 r_1 G_2$, we can calculate the outer radius of insulating material A as,

$$r_1 = \frac{\varepsilon_1 r G_1}{\varepsilon_2 G_2} = \frac{5 \times 1 \times 50}{4 \times 40} = 1.56 \text{ cm}$$

Similarly, the outer radius of insulating material B can be calculated from relation, $\varepsilon_2 r_1 G_2 = \varepsilon_3 r_2 G_3$, as

$$r_2 = \frac{\varepsilon_2 r_1 G_2}{\varepsilon_3 G_3} = \frac{4 \times 1.56 \times 40}{2 \times 30} = 4.16 \text{ cm}$$

From Equation (15.24), we have

$$V = E_{1(max)} \, r \, \ln \frac{r_1}{r} + E_{2(max)} r_1 \, \ln \frac{r_2}{r_1} + E_{3(max)} r_2 \, \ln \frac{R}{r_2}$$

or

$$110 = 50 \times 1 \times \ln \frac{1.56}{1} + 40 \times 1.56 \ln \frac{4.16}{1.56} + 30 \times 4.16 \ln \frac{R}{4.16}$$

By solving we get the outer radius of material C, $R = 5.15$ cm. This is the outer sheath radius.

Example 15.5 Prove that the ratio of gradient with and without intersheath will be $2/(1 + \alpha)$, when there is only one layer.

Solution Let the intersheath is at r_1 distance from the centre and at voltage V_1. If the core radius is r and the outersheath radius is R, then

$$\frac{r_1}{r} = \frac{R}{r_1} = \alpha$$

The gradients at cable core and at the intersheath are

$$\frac{V - V_1}{r \, \ln \, (r_1/r)} \quad \text{and} \quad \frac{V_1}{r_1 \, \ln \, (R/r_1)}$$

Since the material is same, the maximum stress must be same and therefore

$$\frac{V - V_1}{r \, \ln \, (r_1/r)} = \frac{V_1}{r_1 \, \ln \, (R/r_1)}$$

Above relation can also be written as

$$\frac{V - V_1}{r} = \frac{V_1}{r_1}$$

Then

$$V = rV_1\left(\frac{1}{r} + \frac{1}{r_1}\right) = V_1\frac{r + r_1}{r_1}$$

or

$$V = V_1\frac{1 + \alpha}{\alpha}$$

The maximum stress

$$E_{max} = \frac{V_1}{r_1 \ln (R/r_1)} = \frac{V\alpha}{(1 + \alpha)(R/\alpha) \ln \alpha} = \frac{V\alpha^2}{(1 + \alpha) R \ln \alpha}$$

If intersheaths are not present, the maximum stress is at the conductor surface which is equal to

$$E'_{max} = \frac{V}{r \ln (R/r)} = \frac{V}{(R/\alpha^2) \ln \alpha^2} = \frac{V\alpha^2}{2R \ln \alpha}$$

Therefore

$$\frac{E_{max}}{E'_{max}} = \frac{2}{1 + \alpha}$$

Thus proved.

15.7 CAPACITANCE OF A SINGLE-CORE CABLE

A capacitance is formed between a core and sheath, which is separated by insulating material. The electric field at a point x from the centre of the core is given, using Equation (9.28), by

$$E_x = \frac{q}{2\pi\varepsilon x} \text{ volt/m}$$

where the charge on the conductor surface is q coulomb/unit length and ε is the permittivity of dielectric. If R is the inner radius of the sheath or outer radius of the insulating material and r is the radius of conductor, potential difference V can be calculated as

$$V = -\int_R^r E\,dx = \frac{q}{2\pi\varepsilon} \ln \frac{R}{r} \text{ volt}$$

Therefore, the capacitance C can be given by

$$C = \frac{q}{V} = \frac{2\pi\varepsilon}{\ln (R/r)} \text{ F/m} \qquad (15.36)$$

This capacitance is much more than the overhead transmission line due to the following reasons:

(a) High value of permittivity of insulating material

(b) Distance between the core and the earthed sheath is small

(c) Small distances between the cores (phases) itself.

15.8 CAPACITANCE OF A THREE-CORE CABLE

In a three-core belted cable, two insulations are required: the *conductor* insulation of thickness d and the *belt* insulation of thickness t, as shown in Figure 15.11. The belt insulation is required, because with operating voltage V, the conductor insulation is only suitable for $V/2$ voltage whereas the voltage between the conductor and the sheath is $V/\sqrt{3}$.

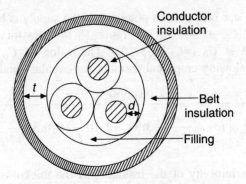

FIGURE 15.11 Three-core belted cable.

Since conductors of the cable are not surrounded by isotropic homogeneous insulation of a known permittivity, the capacitances cannot be easily calculated; they are generally obtained by measurement. There are six capacitances formed. Three capacitances will be formed between the phases and are connected in the form of a delta, as shown in Figure 15.12, and represented as C_2. Other three capacitances are formed between each conductor and sheath and represented as C_1 in Figure 15.12.

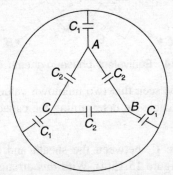

FIGURE 15.12 Capacitance of a three-core cable.

The capacitances formed between the phases can be represented in terms of equivalent star connection, as shown in Figure 15.13. The values of capacitances now become $3C_2$, where C_2 is the capacitance between phases represented in delta connection.

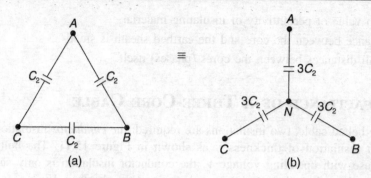

FIGURE 15.13 Equivalent star of delta.

Since the neutral point of star is at ground potential, if the supply is balanced, the capacitances C_1 are in parallel with $3C_2$, as shown in Figure 15.14. The total equivalent capacitance between phases-to-sheath is C_0 ($=C_1 + 3C_2$). The value of C_0 can be calculated with acceptable accuracy by following empirical formula for circular conductors.

$$C_0 = \frac{0.0298\varepsilon_r}{\log_{10}\left[1 + \dfrac{T + t}{d}\left(3.84 - 1.70\dfrac{t}{T} + 0.52\dfrac{t^2}{T^2}\right)\right]} \text{ μF/km} \tag{15.37}$$

where ε_r is the relative permittivity of the insulation, t the thickness of belt insulation, d the diameter of the conductor and T the conductor insulation thickness.

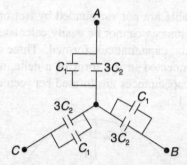

FIGURE 15.14 Equivalent phase-to-sheath capacitance.

From Figure 15.14, it can be seen that two unknown values must be measured to find out the capacitance per phase of the cable. In determining the capacitances of the three-core cable, the common tests performed are:

1. Measure the capacitance C_x between the sheath and all the three conductors joined together, as shown in Figure 15.15(a). With this arrangement, the entire conductor-to-sheath capacitances will be in parallel, therefore $C_x = 3C_1$.
2. Connect any two cores to the sheath and measure capacitance C_y between remaining conductor and sheath as shown in Figure 15.15(b). With this arrangement, $C_y = C_1 + 2C_2$.

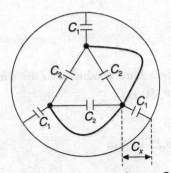 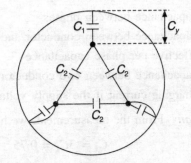

(a) Measuring the capacitance C_x (b) Connecting two cores to the sheath

FIGURE 15.15 Capacitance measurements.

From these measurements, we get

$$C_2 = \frac{C_y - (C_x/3)}{2} = \frac{1}{2}\left(C_y - \frac{C_x}{3}\right) \tag{15.38}$$

Therefore

$$C_0 = C_1 + 3C_2 = \frac{3}{2}C_y - \frac{1}{6}C_x \tag{15.39}$$

3. Measure the capacitance C_z between two conductors by means of a Schering bridge and connecting the third conductor to the sheath to eliminate one of the C_1s, as shown in Figure 15.16. Thus

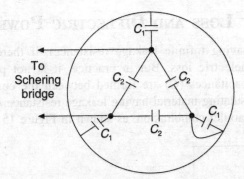

To Schering bridge

FIGURE 15.16 Measurement by Schering bridge.

$$C_z = C_2 + \frac{1}{2}(C_1 + C_2) = \frac{1}{2}(C_1 + 3C_2) \tag{15.40}$$

or

$$C_0 = 2C_Z \tag{15.41}$$

Example 15.6 A 2-km long 3-core, 3-phase cable has capacitance 0.5 µF/km between two conductors bunched with sheath and the third conductor. The capacitance between the conductors is also measured when bunched together and the sheath and found to be 0.75 µF/km. Determine:

(a) Capacitance between phases

(b) Capacitance between conductor and sheath

(c) Effective per phase capacitance

(d) Capacitance between two conductors connecting a third conductor to the sheath

(e) Charging current if the supply voltage is 11 kV, 50 Hz.

Solution   From the measurement, we have

$$C_x = 3C_1 = 0.75 \quad \text{or} \quad C_1 = 0.25 \ \mu\text{F/km}$$

and

$$C_y = C_1 + 2C_2 = 0.50$$

Therefore, (a) the capacitance between phases $C_2 = 0.125 \ \mu\text{F/km}$ and (b) the capacitance between conductor and sheath, $C_1 = 0.25 \ \mu\text{F/km}$.

(c) The effective per phase capacitance is

$$C_0 = C_1 + 3C_2 = \frac{3}{2}C_y - \frac{1}{6}C_x = 0.625 \ \mu\text{F/km}$$

(d) The capacitance between two conductors connecting a third conductor to the sheath, using Equation (15.41), is $C_0/2 = 0.3125 \ \mu\text{F/km}$.

(e) The charging current per phase per km is

$$\frac{V}{\sqrt{3}}\omega C_0 = \frac{11 \times 10^3}{\sqrt{3}} \times 2\pi \times 50 \times 0.625 \times 10^{-6} = 1.25 \ \text{A}$$

15.9 DIELECTRIC LOSS AND DIELECTRIC POWER FACTOR

In a perfect dielectric (having infinite leakage resistance), if there is no flow of leakage current, so will be no dielectric loss. But in practice, it is not possible to get a perfect dielectric. In a cable, capacitances (C) are formed between the conductors and the sheath, which are separated by insulating material having leakage resistance R_s. The equivalent circuit can be represented by a parallel combination, as shown in Figure 15.17.

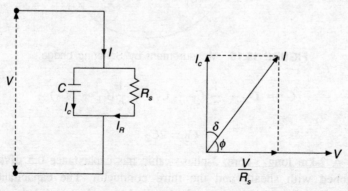

FIGURE 15.17 Equivalent circuit of cable and its phasor diagram.

The dielectric loss due to loss in leakage resistance is

$$P_l = \frac{V^2}{R_s} \qquad (15.42)$$

The cosine of the angle ϕ is the power factor of dielectric which provides a useful measure of the quality of the dielectric. The dielectric power factor, which is different from the supply factor, represents the loss and therefore tried to reduce it whereas it is tried to increase the power factor of supply near to unity. The power factor of impregnated paper is approximately 0.003. For a good dielectric, the value of ϕ is very close to 90°. The angle δ (in radians) is called the dielectric loss angle, which is very small for a good dielectric. Therefore

$$\delta \approx \tan \delta \approx \sin \delta \approx \sin (90 - \phi) = \cos \phi \qquad (15.43)$$

From the phasor diagram

$$\frac{V/R_s}{V\omega C} = \tan \delta \quad \text{or} \quad \frac{V}{R_s} = V\omega C \tan \delta$$

Therefore, the dielectric power loss

$$P_l = V^2 \omega C \tan \delta = V^2 \omega C \delta \text{ watt} \qquad (15.44)$$

The power factor of the dielectric of a cable depends on the quality of insulating material, the electric stress and the frequency. It varies with the temperature. With increase in temperature, the power factor increases and thus there is more loss in the dielectric, which results into further increase in temperature. If a cable operates under condition where change in power factor with change in temperature is significantly large, the temperature continues to increase until the insulation damage.

The dielectric power-loss in the cable is less when the applied voltage is dc. In the case of ac, the dielectric loss consists of hysteresis loss which is much larger than the leakage loss. The total dielectric loss can be measured by the Schering bridge (refer to Figure 15.16).

15.10 LOCATION OF FAULTS IN UNDERGROUND CABLES

There are two types of faults in the cables: *conductor* failure and *insulation* failure. Conductor failures, in general, are located by comparing the capacity of the insulated conductors whereas insulation failures are located by fault tests. In short cables, the faults are located by inspection of manholes, listening the cracking sound, etc. In long cables, the locations of ground faults are determined by the balance-bridge principle.

15.10.1 Murray Loop Test

It is one of the best methods for locating high-resistance faults in low-conductor resistance circuits. This test is useful where more than one conductor of same size in the cable are present. Figure 15.18 shows a Murray loop. L is the length in cable conductor (MO and NO) and having the same cross-sectional area. The fault is in the section NO at distance x from N. Murray loop can be established if the conductor is broken at any point. In order to avoid earth current, a galvanometer is connected as shown in the figure. A battery is used to energize the bridge. The balance is obtained by adjusting the resistances. If the unfaulted line and faulted line have the same resistances per unit length, the following relation can be written at the balance point:

$$\frac{R_1}{R_2} = \frac{2L - x}{x} \quad \text{or} \quad x = \frac{2LR_2}{R_1 + R_2} \tag{15.45}$$

Thus the location of fault can be determined.

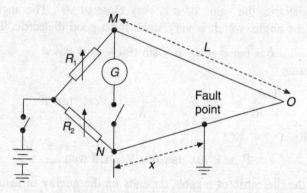

FIGURE 15.18 Murray loop.

15.10.2 Varley Loop Test

This test is also used when there is a second conductor of the same size as the one with the fault. A Varley loop is shown in Figure 15.19.

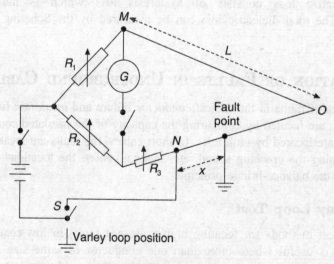

FIGURE 15.19 Varley loop.

With the balance condition, we have

$$\frac{R_1}{R_2} = \frac{(2L - x)r_c}{R_3 + xr_c} \quad\quad (15.46)$$

or

$$x = \frac{R_1}{R_1 + R_2}\left(2L\frac{R_2}{R_1} - \frac{R_3}{r_c}\right) \text{ unit of length} \quad\quad (15.47)$$

where r_c is the conductor resistance in ohm per unit length. If the conductor resistance is not known, it can be found out by changing the switch to S position and measuring the resistance of the conductor $2L$ by using the wheatstone bridge method.

15.11 CLASSIFICATION OF CABLES

Cables can be classified according to voltage, location of use, insulation material used, etc. Table 15.3 shows the classification of cables:

Table 15.3 Classification of Cables

Based on location	(a) Underground
	(b) Submarine
	(c) Aerial
According to voltage	(a) Low voltage or LT cables (up to 1000 volt)
	(b) High voltage or HT cables (up to 11 kV)
	(c) Super tension or ST cables (up to 33 kV)
	(d) Extra-high voltage or EHT cables (up to 132 kV)
	(e) Extra-super voltage power cables (above 132 kV)
According to types of insulation and protective covering	(a) Rubber and rubber like compound (VIR cables)
	(b) PVC cables
	(c) Lead sheathed cables
	(d) Paper insulated lead covered cables
	(e) Paper insulated aluminium covered cables
	(f) Paper insulated lead covered steel armoured cables
	(g) Varnished cambric cables
	(h) Oil-filled cables
	(i) Gas-filled cables
	(j) External pressure cables
According to the number of conductors or cores	(a) One-core
	(b) Two-core
	(c) Three-core
	(d) Three-and-a-half core
	(e) Four core
Based on protective finish	(a) Metallic (a lead sheath)
	(b) Non-metallic (plastic)

(*Cont...*)

Table 15.3 Classification of Cables (*Cont...*)

Presence or absence of metallic shield over the insulation	(a) Shielded (Hochstadter or type H) (b) Nonshielded
According to construction and arrangement of conductors and insulation	(a) Belted cables (b) Solid cable (c) H type (d) SL type (e) HSO type

PROBLEMS

15.1 Find the overall diameter of a one-core cable and its most economical core diameter when working on a 400-kV, 3-phase system. The peak permissible stress in dielectric is not to exceed 300 kV/cm.

15.2 Find the maximum working voltage of a one-core lead sheathed cable joint with conductor of 2-cm diameter and sheath of 6-cm inside diameter. Two insulating materials are used: Inner maximum working potential gradient 60 kV/cm, relative permittivity 4; outer maximum working potential gradient 40 kV/cm, relative permittivity 3.

15.3 A 3-phase metal sheathed cable 1-km long gave the following results on a test for capacitance:

(a) Capacitance between two conductors bunched with the sheath and the third conductor 0.5 μF.

(b) Capacitance between bunched conductors and the sheath 1 μF. With sheath insulated, find the capacitance (i) between any two cores, (ii) between any two bunched conductors and the third conductors and (iii) calculate the charging current per phase per km when connected to 11-kV, 50-Hz supply.

(c) Find the capacitance to neutral.

15.4 Prove that for a concentric cable of given dimensions and given maximum potential gradient in the dielectric, the maximum permissible voltage between the core and the sheath is independent of the permittivity of the insulating material.

16.1   INTRODUCTION

In earlier days, dc power was used but due to limitations of low-voltage dc systems, ac systems became popular. With increasing interconnection and loading of power system, the following factors impose limitations on the amount of power to be transmitted over ac lines.

(a) *Reactive power loss:* The requirement of reactive power in transmission, generation and distribution is of major concerns in ac system. Depending upon the loading of transmission lines, the reactive power loss which is defined as the sum of the reactive power generation (due to capacitance of line) and absorption (due to inductance of line) varies. During light load condition, the reactive power absorbed by the line inductance is less than the reactive power generated by the line capacitance. This situation is reversed in the case of peak-load condition. Thus, to maintain the voltages (within the limits) at both the end of the line, the reactive supports are required.

(b) *Stability:* An ac system must operate in synchronism. Power transfer in line is governed by $P_{12} = (V_1 V_2/x) \sin(\delta_1 - \delta_2)$, where V_1 and V_2 are voltage magnitudes at the two ends of the line whereas δ_1 and δ_2 are the voltage angles. The power flow from bus-1 to bus-2 (P_{12}) is dependent on the line reactance (x). During steady-state power flow, the difference between voltage angles may be 90° but during transient it is small, and beyond this, the system becomes unstable. Stability imposes serious limitation on the distance of power transmission.

(c) *Current-carrying capacity:* Even during the no-load at the receiving end, due to capacitance of the line, ac current flows (called *charging current*) from the sending end. The charging current is more predominant in the case of cable, due to high capacitance. Therefore, it is not possible to build cables for longer distance. The length of cable, when charging current becomes equal to the thermal current limit is known as *critical length*. This is not possible to use cables more than its critical length.

(d) *Operation and control:* It is not possible to connect to different frequency ac systems. At the same time, ac power cannot be smoothly controlled without use of any extra device. Current in ac systems flows according to impedance.

Advent of high-voltage semiconductor devices has made it possible to go for high-voltage dc (HVDC) transmission for long-distance power transfer. Through semiconductor devices, it is also possible to control the ac power over the line. Flexible ac transmission systems (FACTS) are the name given to the application of power electronics devices to the control of flows and other quantities in power systems. Semiconductor technology enabled the manufacture of powerful thyristors and later new elements such as the gate turn-off thyristor (GTO) and insulated gate bipolar transistor (IGBT). Development based on the semiconductor devices first established high-voltage dc transmission (HVDC) technology as an alternative to long distance ac transmission. HVDC technology, in turn, has provided the basis for the development of FACTS equipment which can solve problems of ac transmission. FACTS devices, by controlling the power flows in the network without generation rescheduling or topological changes, can improve both static and dynamic performances considerably.

16.2   ADVANTAGES AND DISADVANTAGES OF HVDC TRANSMISSION

Advantages

The main advantages of HVDC transmission over HVAC transmission are:

(a) Requires less space compared to ac for same voltage rating and size

(b) Ground can be used as return conductor

(c) Less corona loss and radio interference (RI)

(d) No charging current

(e) Cheaper for long-distance transmission

(f) No skin and Ferranti effect

(g) Asynchronous operation possible

(h) No switching transient

(i) No transmission of short-circuit power in case of fault

(j) Power control possible

(k) No compensation problem

(l) No stability problem

(m) No reactive power-loss

(n) Low short-circuit current

(o) No technical limit for transfer of power except thermal limit and

(p) Fast fault clearing time.

Disadvantages

(a) *High cost of terminal equipments:* HVDC transmission system requires converters at both the ends and those are very expensive than ac equipments. Converters also have less overload capability. But the total cost of dc system is less compared to ac system for long- distance transmission. Figure 16.1 shows the comparative costs of ac and dc overhead transmission lines (including terminal equipments) with distance. The cost curve of dc transmission intersects the cost curve of ac transmission at distance that is known as *breakeven distance*. This distance is about 600–800 km.

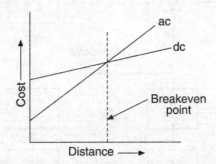

FIGURE 16.1 Cost comparison of ac and dc lines.

(b) *Introduction of harmonics:* Converters generate considerable amount of harmonics both on ac and dc sides. Some harmonics are filtered out but some harmonics still enter into the system and affect the apparatus. These harmonics may also interfere with com-munication system.

(c) *Blocking of reactive power:* DC lines block the flow of reactive power from one end to another end. These reactive powers are required by some load that must be fulfilled by the inverters.

(d) *Point-to-point transmission not possible:* It is not possible to tap dc power at several locations in the line. Wherever power is to be tapped, a control station is required and coordinated with other terminals. This increases the complexity and cost of the system. However, there is no problem in the case of ac line. When the power is controlled at both the ends of the line, it is called *two-terminal* dc system or line. If there are more than two control stations in the line, it is known as *multi-terminal* HVDC system.

16.3 TYPES OF HVDC LINKS

HVDC links can be classified into three categories: monopolar, bipolar and homopolar. *Monopolar* lines have only one conductor normally operated at negative polarity to reduce the corona loss. Here, earth is used as return path. Figure 16.2(a) shows a monopolar line.

In *bipolar* type of links, two conductors (poles) are needed. One pole operates at negative polarity and the other operates at positive polarity, as shown in Figure 16.2(b). The main advantage of bipolar links compared to monopolar links is that it can be operated as single monopolar in the case of fault in any line. In normal operation, there is no current through ground but is grounded because of its operation as monopolar in the event of faults in any line. The rating of bipolar links is expressed as $\pm X$ kV, where X is the voltage magnitude of each line in kV.

Homopolar lines have two or more conductors having the same polarity. Normally negative polarities are used due to less corona loss and radio interference. Ground is always used as return path, as shown in Figure 16.2(c). In this case also, it can be operated as single monopolar link in case of fault in anyone line.

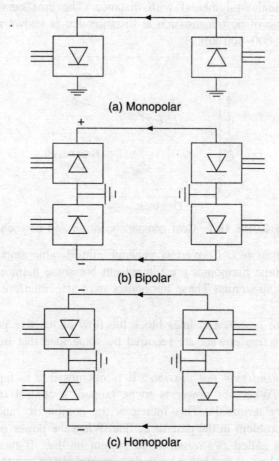

(a) Monopolar

(b) Bipolar

(c) Homopolar

FIGURE 16.2 Types of HVDC links.

16.4 MAIN COMPONENTS OF HVDC TRANSMISSION

Main components of HVDC transmission are discussed now.

Converters. *Converters* are the main part of the HVDC system. Each HVDC line has at least two converters, one at each end. Sending-end converter works as rectifier (converts ac power to dc power), however converter at the receiving-end works as an inverter (converts dc power to ac power). Several thyristors are connected in series/parallel to form a valve to achieve higher voltage/current ratings. Bridge converters are used for HVDC application. The current rating of converter stations can be increased by putting:

- Valves in parallel
- Thyristors in parallel
- Bridges in parallel
- Some combinations of above

Voltage rating of converter station is increased by:

- Valves in series
- Bridges in series
- Thyristors in parallel
- Combination of above

The main requirements of the valves are:

(a) To allow current-flow with low-voltage drop across it during the conduction phase and to offer high resistance during non-conducting phase

(b) To withstand high-peak inverse voltage during non-conducting period

(c) To allow a reasonably short-commutation margin angle during inverter operation

(d) Smooth control of conducting and non-conducting phases.

Normally, a six-pulse operation is adopted in HVDC systems but sometimes a 12-pulse is also used. Figure 16.3 shows the components of a 12-pulse operational HVDC system.

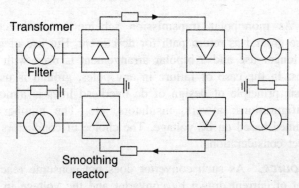

FIGURE 16.3 Components of HVDC transmission.

Converter transformers. For a 6-pulse converter, a conventional 3-phase or three single-phase transformers are used. However, for a 12-pulse converter configuration, following transformers are used:

(a) Six single-phase two winding
(b) Three single-phase three winding
(c) Two 3-phase two winding.

In converter transformer, it is not possible to use winding close to yoke since the potential of its winding connection is determined by conducting valves. Hence, the entire winding is completely insulated. As leakage flux of a converter transformer contains very high harmonic contents, it produces greater eddy current loss and hot spots in the transformer tank. In case of a 12-pulse configuration, if two 3-phase transformers are used, one will have star–star connection and second will have star–delta connection to give phase shift of 30° so that operation of two-bridge converter can give 12-pulse.

Since fault current (due to fault across valve) is predominantly controlled by transformer impedance, the leakage impedance of converter transformer is higher than the conventional transformer. Online tap changing is used to control the voltage and reactive power demand.

Smoothing reactors. As its name, these reactors are used for smoothing the dc current output in the dc line. It also limits the rate of rise of the fault current in the case of dc line short circuit. Normally, partial or total air cored magnetically shielded reactors are used. Disc coil type winding are used and braced to withstand the short circuit current. The saturation inductance should not be too low.

Harmonic filters. Harmonics generated by converters are of the order of $pn \pm 1$, where p is number of pulses and n is integer. Filters are used to provide low-impedance path to the ground for the harmonic currents. They are connected to the converter terminals so that harmonics should not enter the ac system. However, it is not possible to protect all harmonics from entering the ac system. Magnitudes of some harmonics are high and filters are used for them only. These filters also provide some reactive power compensation at the terminals.

Overhead lines. As monopolar transmission scheme is most economical, the first consideration is to use ground as return path for dc current. But use of ground as conductor is not permitted for longer use and a bipolar arrangement is used with equal and opposite currents in both poles. In the case of failure in any poles, ground is used as a return path temporarily. The basic principle of design of dc overhead lines is almost same as ac lines design such as configurations, towers, insulators, etc. The number of insulators and clearances are determined based on dc voltage. The choice of conductors depends mainly on corona and field-effect considerations.

Reactive power source. As such converter does not consume reactive power but due to phase displacement of current drawn by converter and the voltage in ac system, reactive power requirement at a converter station is about 50–60% of real power transfer, which is supplied by filters, capacitors and synchronous condensers. Synchronous condensers do not only supply the reactive power but also provide ac voltages for natural commutation of the inverter. Due to harmonics and transients, a specially-designed machine is used.

Earth electrodes. The earth resistivity at upper layer is higher (~4000 ohm-m) and electrodes cannot be kept directly on the earth surface. The electrodes are buried into the earth where resistivity is around 3–10 ohm-m to reduce transient over-voltages during line faults and also gives low-dc electric potential and potential gradient at the surface of earth. The location of earth electrodes is also important due to:

  (a) Possible interference of dc current ripple to power lines, communication systems of telephone and railway signals, etc.
  (b) Metallic corrosion of pipes, cable sheaths, etc.
  (c) Public safety.

The electrodes must have low resistance (less than 0.1 ohm) and buried up to 500 m into the earth.

16.5 SELECTION FOR CONFIGURATION FOR CONVERTERS

For a particular pulse number, p, there are several possible ways to realize. The number of pulsations or ripples of dc voltage per cycle of ac voltage is known as *pulse number* of a converter. If q is the number of valves in a commutation group and r of these are connected in parallel and s of them are connected in series, the pulse number can be given by

$$p = qrs \tag{16.1}$$

A group of valves in which only one valve conducts at a time (neglecting the overlap) is known as a *commutation group*. The suitable configuration of converters is decided on following requirements:

  1. High pulse number
  2. PIV/V_{do} should be as low as possible
  3. V_{do}/E should be as high as possible
  4. Transformer utilization factor (TUF) should be near to unity.

The *first* requirement gives the low-harmonic generation. But the pulse number is limited, as it increases the numbers of valves and thus the cost. The *second* requirement indicates the utilization of valve. Each valve must withstand the peak inverse voltage (PIV) of the converter. It is always preferred if a converter configuration provides less PIV and at the same time it should produce higher dc voltage (V_{do}). The ratio V_{do}/(PIV) gives the utilization efficiency of the valve. It can be calculated as follows:

  If there are q valves in a commutation group, each valve will conduct for $2\pi/q$ period in an ac cycle. The average maximum dc voltage output of the converter is

$$V_{do} = \frac{1}{2\pi/q} \int_{-\pi/q}^{\pi/q} E_m \cos(\omega t)\, d(\omega t) = \frac{q}{\pi} E_m \sin \frac{\pi}{q} \tag{16.2}$$

where E_m $(=E\sqrt{2}\,)$ is the peak value of alternating voltage and ω $(=2\pi f)$ is supply frequency in radian/second. If there are s numbers of series valves, the dc output is

$$V_{do} = \frac{qs}{\pi} E_m \sin \frac{\pi}{q} \qquad (16.3)$$

If q is even, and when the valve with a phase displacement of 180° is conducting, we obtain PIV $= 2E_m$. On the other hand, if q is odd, PIV occurs when the valve with a phase displacement of $\pi \pm (\pi/q)$ is conducting and is equal to.

$$\text{PIV} = 2E_m \cos \frac{\pi}{2q}$$

Thus

$$\text{PIV} = \begin{cases} 2E_m & \text{for } q \text{ even} \\ 2E_m \cos \dfrac{\pi}{2q} & \text{for } q \text{ odd} \end{cases} \qquad (16.4)$$

and

$$\frac{\text{PIV}}{V_{do}} = \begin{cases} \dfrac{2\pi}{sq \sin \dfrac{\pi}{q}} & \text{for } q \text{ even} \\ \dfrac{\pi}{sq \sin \dfrac{\pi}{2q}} & \text{for } q \text{ odd} \end{cases} \qquad (16.5)$$

Third consideration is the ratio of V_{do}/E should be as high as possible to have a high-dc output voltage. Using Equation (16.3), we get

$$\frac{V_{do}}{E} = \frac{\sqrt{2}qs}{\pi} \sin \frac{\pi}{q} \qquad (16.6)$$

where $E = E_m/\sqrt{2}$.

The *fourth* criteria is the transformer utilization factor. It is defined as the ratio of transformer rating (valve side or secondary side) to the dc power output. This value should be as low as possible. The current rating of transformer is given by

$$I_t = \frac{I_d}{r\sqrt{q}}$$

where I_d is the dc current in dc link. The transformer rating will be

$$P_t = p\frac{E_m}{\sqrt{2}}I_t = p\frac{E_m I_d}{r\sqrt{2q}} \qquad (16.7)$$

Thus TUF can be calculated using Equations (16.3) and (16.7) as

$$\text{TUF} = \frac{P_t}{V_{do}I_d} = \frac{p\dfrac{E_m I_d}{r\sqrt{2q}}}{\dfrac{qsI_d}{\pi}E_m \sin\dfrac{\pi}{q}} = \frac{\pi}{\sqrt{2}\sqrt{q}\sin(\pi/q)} \tag{16.8}$$

This shows that TUF is a function of q only. The optimum value of q is 3. For a 6-pulse converter, various values are presented in Table 16.1.

Table 16.1 Different Configuration of 6-Pulse Converters

Serial no.	q	r	s	PIV/V_{do}	V_{do}/E	TUF
1	2	1	3	1.047	2.700	1.571
2	2	3	1	3.142	0.900	1.571
3	3	1	2	1.047	2.340	1.481
4	3	2	1	2.094	1.169	1.481
5	6	1	1	2.094	1.350	1.814

From the table, it can be seen that serial numbers 1 and 3 are suitable but TUF is better for the serial number 3. Since ac supply is 3-phase and commutation group of three valves can be easily arranged. The current rating of transformers can further be increased by a factor of $\sqrt{2}$ while decreasing the number of winding by a factor 2. For a six-pulse converter, Graetz circuit is the best circuit, as shown in Figure 16.4.

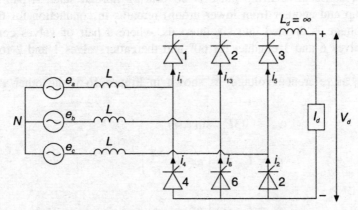

FIGURE 16.4 3-Phase bridge conveter (Graetz circuit).

For a 12-pulse converter, the same analysis can be performed and it is found that two 6-pulse converters connected in series by two transformers with phase displacement of 30° are the best choice. That is, if one transformer is in star–star, another should be in star–delta.

16.6 ANALYSIS OF CONVERTERS

A 6-pulse converter circuit as shown in Figure 16.4 is analyzed. To make analysis simpler following assumptions are made:

1. Power sources (or sinks) consisting of balance sinusoidal emf of constant voltage and frequency in series with equal lossless inductances.
2. The dc current is constant, i.e. ripple free.
3. Valves have zero forward resistance when on (conducting) and infinite resistance when off (not conducting).
4. Ignition of valves at equal intervals of 60° (1/6 of the cycle).

Different cases depending on the conduction of valves in a commutating group can be analyzed separately. If at all instants, only one valve in a commutating group conducts, there will be no overlap. In this case two valves conduct: one valve from upper-commutation group and second from lower-commutation group. This case is also known as *two-valve* conduction. Due to leakage inductance the current cannot be changed suddenly and therefore commutation from one valve to another is not instantaneous and it takes finite time for current transfer. This time is known as *overlap angle*. There will be more than two valves conduction at sometimes. It may be 3 or 4 valve conduction.

16.6.1 Without Overlap

Under this assumption, the transfer of current (commutation) between valves on the same side of the bridge (upper or lower) takes place instantaneously. Although, this assumption is not correct due to the presence of source reactance. The numbering of valves in Figure 16.4 is done in the sequence in which they are fired. Each valve conducts for 120° and the interval between consecutive firing pulse is 60° during normal state. A pair of valves (one from upper group and another from lower group) remains in conduction for 60°. Each cycle of ac supply voltage is divided into six intervals, where a pair of valves conducts for 60°. For example, valves 6 and 1 conduct for 60° and thereafter valves 1 and 2 for the next 60°, and so on.

Taking e_{ba} as reference voltage, as shown in Figure 16.5, the other voltages can be written as:

$$e_{ba} = \sqrt{3}E_m \sin(\omega t)$$

$$e_a = E_m \sin\left(\omega t + \frac{5\pi}{6}\right)$$

$$e_b = E_m \sin\left(\omega t + \frac{\pi}{6}\right)$$

$$e_c = E_m \sin\left(\omega t - \frac{\pi}{2}\right)$$

$$e_{cb} = e_c - e_b = \sqrt{3}E_m \sin(\omega t - 120°)$$

$$e_{ac} = \sqrt{3}E_m \sin(\omega t + 120°)$$

$$e_{bc} = \sqrt{3}E_m \sin(\omega t + 60°)$$

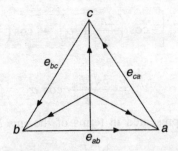

FIGURE 16.5 Phasor voltages.

where E_m is the peak voltage magnitude of phase to neutral voltage.

A valve can only be fired if the voltage appearing across it is positive and there is a gate signal available. Let us consider valves 1 and 2 are conducting. Voltage appearing at the cathode of valve 3 is e_a since valve 1 is conducting (see Figure 16.4) and e_b at the anode of valve 3. Valve 3 conducts only when the voltage e_b is greater or equal to e_a, i.e. when voltage e_{ba} is positive. This is known as the commutation voltage of valve 3. Valve 3 can now be fired using gate pulse with any delay angle α which is $\alpha°$ after the zero crossing of the commutation voltage of valve 3. Since no overlapping is assumed, when valve 3 is fired, the current instantaneously transfers from valve 1 to valve 3 and now valves 2 and 3 will continue to conduct for another 60°. Figure 16.6 shows the conduction of valves 2 and 3.

In valves 2, 3 conduction case, we have

$$i_b = I_d = i_3 = i_2 = -i_c, \qquad i_a = 0 = i_1 = i_4 = i_5 = i_6, \qquad V_d = e_{bc}$$

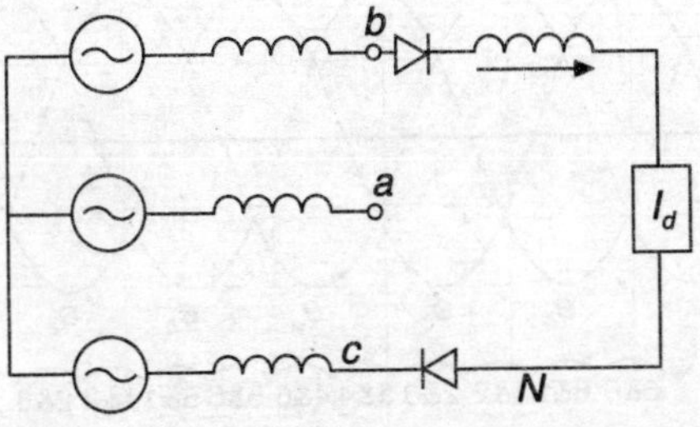

FIGURE 16.6 Valves 2 and 3 conduction.

where i_n is the instantaneous current through valve n. i_a, i_b and i_c are the phase a, b and c currents respectively.

Since the pair of valves 2 and 3 conduct for 60° and valves 3 and 4 conduct for next 60°, for the dc output voltage, only one interval can be considered. If the delay angle is $\alpha°$, the instantaneous dc voltage e_{bc} will appear across dc terminal from α to $60 + \alpha$. The average dc voltage will be given by

$$V_d = \frac{\sqrt{3}E_m}{\pi/3} \int_\alpha^{(\pi/3)+\alpha} e_{bc} \, d(\omega t)$$

$$= \frac{3\sqrt{3}}{\pi} E_m \int_\alpha^{(\pi/3)+\alpha} \sin\left(\omega t + \frac{\pi}{3}\right) d(\omega t)$$

$$= \frac{3\sqrt{3}}{\pi} E_m \left[-\cos\left(\frac{2\pi}{3} + \alpha \right) + \cos\left(\frac{\pi}{3} + \alpha \right) \right]$$

or

$$V_d = \frac{3\sqrt{3} E_m}{\pi} \cos \alpha \tag{16.9}$$

Equation (16.9) can also be represented in terms of the rms line-to-line voltage (E_{LL}) as

$$V_d = \frac{3\sqrt{2} E_{LL}}{\pi} \cos \alpha \tag{16.10}$$

When delay angle or the firing angle is zero, Equation (16.9) can be written as

$$V_d = \frac{3\sqrt{3} E_m}{\pi} = V_{do}$$

Therefore, Equation (16.9) can again be written as

$$V_d = V_{do} \cos \alpha \tag{16.11}$$

This equation indicates that the average dc voltage across the bridge will vary with firing angle α. The dc output voltage is maximum when α is $0°$ and zero at $\alpha = 90°$. When the voltage across the bridge is positive, it acts as rectifier and when it is negative, it is known as inversion operation of bridge. Figure 16.7 shows the valve conduction sequence and dc output voltage waveform.

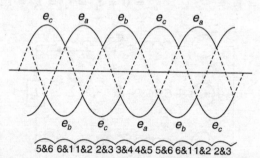

FIGURE 16.7   Conduction sequence and dc output voltage waveform.

Although delay angle α can vary from 0 to $180°$, the delay angle can not be less than certain minimum limit (say $5°$) in order to ensure the firing of all the series-connected thyristors. Similarly, the upper limit of the delay angle is also restricted due to the turn-off time of a valve. The delay angle α is not allowed to go beyond ($180° - \gamma$), where γ is called *extinction angle*. It is also known as *minimum margin angle*, which is typically $10°$. However, in normal operation of inverter, it is not allowed to go below $15°$. The values of γ between $15°$ and $20°$ are typically used.

AC current waveform.   If the reactance of a smoothing reactor is very large, the output dc current can be assumed as constant (ripple free). It means that there is no harmonics in dc current. The ac current, which flows in the secondary winding of transformer, is shown in Figure 16.8.

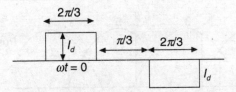

FIGURE 16.8 AC current waveform.

Since current is not a sinusoidal current, there is harmonics in the converter transformer. The rms value of the fundamental component of the current using Fourier analysis is given by

$$I_1 = \frac{\sqrt{2}}{\pi} \int_{-\pi/3}^{\pi/3} I_d \cos \theta \, d\theta = \frac{\sqrt{6}}{\pi} I_d \tag{16.12}$$

The rms value of the current (not the rms value of fundamental component of current) can be calculated as

$$I = \left(\frac{1}{2\pi} \int_0^{2\pi} I_d^2 \, d\theta \right)^{1/2} = \sqrt{\frac{2}{3}} I_d \tag{16.13}$$

This shows that I is increased by $\sqrt{2}$ times as compared to I_t in Eq. (16.7).

The rms value of hth harmonics is given by

$$I_h = \frac{I_1}{h} \tag{16.14}$$

where $h = np \pm 1$ (n is an integer and p is the pulse number)

Effect of firing angle on voltage waveforms. The effect of firing-angle delay on the voltage waveforms is shown in Figures 16.9(a) and (b). Moreover the voltage across valve 1 is shown in Figure 16.9(c).

Power factor. Neglecting other harmonics component, the ac power supplied by the converter

$$P_{\text{ac}} = \sqrt{3} E_{LL} I_1 \cos \phi \tag{16.15}$$

where $\cos \phi$ is the power factor.
Using Equation (16.10), the dc output power is given by

$$P_{\text{dc}} = V_d I_d = \frac{3\sqrt{2}}{\pi} E_{LL} I_d \cos \alpha \tag{16.16}$$

Ignoring the losses in the converters, ac power will be equal to dc power. Therefore, substituting the value of I_1 in Equation (16.15) from Equation (16.12) and equating with Equation (16.16), we get

$$\sqrt{3} E_{LL} \frac{\sqrt{6}}{\pi} I_d \cos \phi = \frac{3\sqrt{2}}{\pi} E_{LL} I_d \cos \alpha$$

Thus

$$\cos \phi = \cos \alpha \tag{16.17}$$

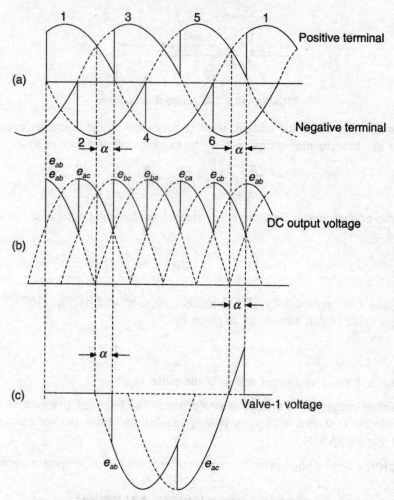

FIGURE 16.9 Different voltage waveforms.

This equation shows that when delay angle increases, the power factor reduces and thus more reactive power requirement. Voltage waveforms on full inversion (without delay) are shown in Figure 16.10.

The real and reactive powers in different modes of operation are shown in Figure 16.11.

16.6.2 With Overlap

The shift of current from one conducting valve to another conducting valve is not sudden due to leakage inductance of converter transformer and the supply system. The duration when current is shared by conducting valves is called *overlap angle* and is measured by the overlap (commutation) angle u. Figure 16.12 shows the conduction patterns of the valves.

The value of u can be different. Based on the overlap angle, three modes of converter operation is classified as:

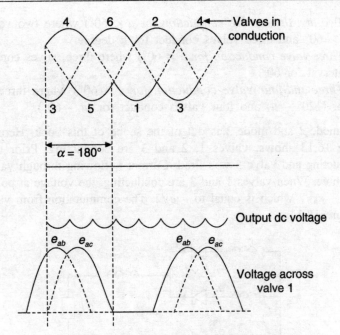

FIGURE 16.10 Voltages in inverter mode.

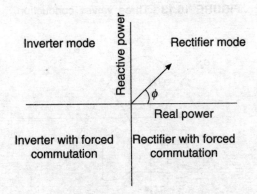

FIGURE 16.11 Power factor.

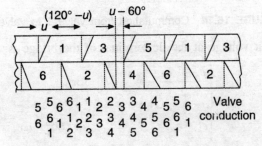

FIGURE 16.12 Conduction with overlap.

Mode 1 (*Two-and-three valve conduction for $u < 60°$*) where two valves conduct for $u - 60°$ and three valves conduct for u degree.

Mode 2 (*Three-valve conduction for $u = 60°$*) where three valves conduct during each interval for $60°$.

Mode 3 (*Three-and-four valve conduction for $u > 60°$*) where three valves conduct for $(120° - u)$ and four valves conduct for $(u - 60°)$.

The analysis of mode-2 and mode-3 is out of the scope of this book. Here only mode-1 is analyzed. Figure 16.13 shows, valves 1, 2 and 3 are conducting. Prior to this, valves 1 and 2 were conducting and valve 3 was fired. Current i_1 flowing through valve 1 will not be shifted to valve three. When valves 1 and 3 are conducting, the voltage at positive terminal of the bridge is $(e_a + e_b)/2$ which is equal to $-e_c/2$. The commutation from valve 1 to valve 3 is shown in Figure 16.14.

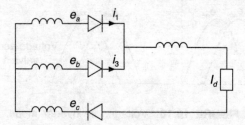

FIGURE 16.13 Three valves conduction.

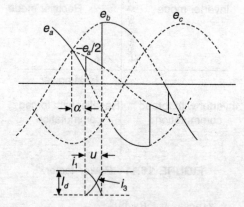

FIGURE 16.14 Commutation from valve 1 to valve 3.

The instantaneous output voltage at the dc terminal of the bridge is

$$
v_{dc} = \begin{cases} \dfrac{e_a + e_b}{2} - e_c & \text{for } u \\[4mm] e_b - e_c & \text{for } (60° - u) \end{cases}
$$

The average dc voltage can be obtained by taking average over period of 60°. Thus

$$V_d = \frac{3}{\pi}\left[\int_{\alpha}^{\alpha+u}\left(\frac{e_a + e_b}{2} - e_c\right)d(\omega t) + \int_{\alpha+u}^{\alpha+60}(e_b - e_c)\,d(\omega t)\right] \quad (16.18)$$

Since

$$\frac{e_a + e_b}{2} = -\frac{e_c}{2}$$

Equation (16.18) can be written as

$$V_d = \frac{3}{\pi}\left[\int_{\alpha}^{\alpha+u} -\frac{3e_c}{2}\,d(\omega t) + \int_{\alpha+u}^{\alpha+60}(e_b - e_c)\,d(\omega t)\right]$$

$$= \frac{3}{\pi}\left[\int_{\alpha}^{\alpha+u}\frac{3}{2}E_m \cos(\omega t)\,d(\omega t) + \int_{\alpha+u}^{\alpha+60}\sqrt{3}E_m \sin(\omega t + 60)\,d(\omega t)\right]$$

$$= \frac{3}{\pi}\left\{\frac{3E_m}{2}[\sin(\alpha + u) - \sin\alpha] + \sqrt{3}E_m[\cos(\alpha + u + 60) - \cos(\alpha + 120)]\right\}$$

$$= \frac{3}{\pi}E_m\left[\frac{3}{2}\sin(\alpha+u) - \frac{3}{2}\sin\alpha + \frac{\sqrt{3}}{2}\cos(\alpha+u) - \frac{3}{2}\sin(\alpha+u) + \frac{\sqrt{3}}{2}\cos\alpha + \frac{3}{2}\sin\alpha\right]$$

$$= \frac{3}{\pi}E_m\left[\frac{\sqrt{3}}{2}\cos(\alpha+u) + \frac{\sqrt{3}}{2}\cos\alpha\right]$$

$$= \frac{3\sqrt{3}}{2\pi}E_m[\cos\alpha + \cos(\alpha+u)] \quad (16.19)$$

or

$$V_d = \frac{V_{do}}{2}[\cos\alpha + \cos(\alpha+u)] \quad (16.20)$$

From Figure 16.13, we can write voltage equation using KVL as

$$e_a - L\frac{di_1}{dt} = e_b - L\frac{di_3}{dt}$$

or

$$L\frac{di_3}{dt} - L\frac{di_1}{dt} = e_b - e_a \quad (16.21)$$

Since dc current is always I_d, we have $i_1 = I_d - i_3$. Integrating, we get

$$\frac{di_1}{dt} = -\frac{di_3}{dt}$$

Now, Equation (16.21) can be written as

$$2L\frac{di_3}{dt} = e_b - e_a = \sqrt{3}E_m \sin(\omega t) \quad (16.22)$$

Solving, we get

$$i_3 = -\frac{\sqrt{3}E_m}{2\omega L}\cos(\omega t) + A$$

where A is an integration constant. This can be obtained by using initial condition, at $\omega t = \alpha$, $i_3 = 0$. Therefore

$$i_3 = I_s[\cos\alpha - \cos(\omega t)], \quad \alpha \le \omega t \le \alpha + u \qquad (16.23)$$

where

$$I_s = \frac{\sqrt{3}E_m}{2\omega L}$$

At $\omega t = \alpha + u$, $i_3 = I_d$, Equation (16.23) becomes

$$I_d = I_s[\cos\alpha - \cos(\alpha + u)] \qquad (16.24)$$

Eliminating u from Equations (16.24) and (16.20), we get

$$V_d = V_{do}\left(\cos\alpha - \frac{I_d}{2I_s}\right) = V_{do}\cos\alpha - R_c I_d \qquad (16.25)$$

where R_c is called *equivalent commutation resistance* and is given by

$$R_c = \frac{3}{\pi}\omega L = \frac{3}{\pi}X_c$$

Equation (16.25) can be represented by an equivalent analogous circuit consisting of one variable dc source with resistance R_c, as shown in Figure 16.15.

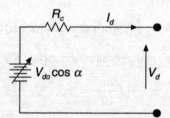

FIGURE 16.15 Equivalent circuit of rectifier.

Current and voltage waveforms of a 6-pulse bridge rectifier operation are shown in Figure 16.16. Figure 16.16(a) represents dc positive and negative terminal voltages across the rectifier output, whereas Figure 16.16(b) shows the dc output voltage. The voltage across valve-1 is shown in Figure 16.16(c). Figure 16.16(d) shows the currents in valves of upper group and lower group, whereas Figure 16.16(e) shows the phase a line current.

Inverter operation. The analysis of inverter operation is not different from the rectification. However, inverter equations are normally expressed in terms of the angle of advance $\beta(=\pi - \alpha)$ or the extinction angle $\gamma(=\beta - u)$.

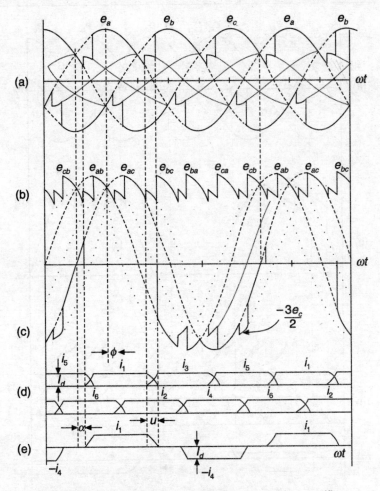

FIGURE 16.16 Waveforms of a 6-pulse bridge rectifier.

Current and voltage waveforms of a 6-pulse bridge inverter operation are shown in Figure 16.17. Figure 16.17(a) represents dc positive and negative terminal voltages across the inverter output, whereas Figure 16.17(c) shows the dc output voltage. The voltage across valve-1 is shown in Figure 16.17(b). Figure 16.17(d) shows currents in valves of upper group and lower group, whereas Figure 16.17(e) shows the phase *a* line current.

The dc output voltage in inverter operation can be given by

$$V_{di} = -\frac{V_{doi}}{2}[\cos\alpha + \cos(\alpha + u)]$$

$$= -\frac{V_{doi}}{2}[\cos(\pi - \beta) + \cos(\pi - \gamma)]$$

$$= \frac{V_{doi}}{2}(\cos\beta + \cos\gamma) \tag{16.26}$$

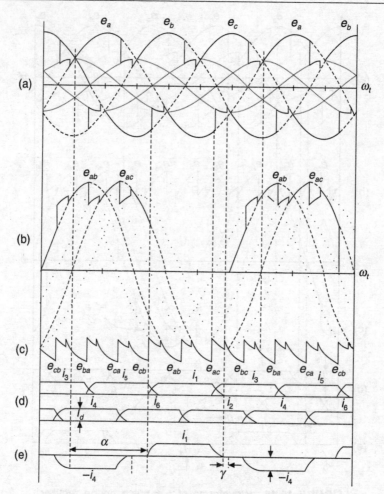

FIGURE 16.17 Waveforms of a 6-pulse bridge inverter.

The dc voltage V_{doi} is taken as negative because the inverter uses opposite polarity. From Equation (16.25), we get,

$$V_{di} = -V_{doi} \cos(\pi - \beta) + R_c I_d = V_{doi} \cos \beta + R_c I_d \qquad (16.27)$$

Similarly, we can also write

$$V_{di} = V_{doi} \cos \gamma - R_c I_d \qquad (16.28)$$

Equations (16.27) and (16.28) can be represented by an equivalent analogous circuit consisting of one variable dc source with resistance R_c, as shown in Figure 16.18.

16.7 HVDC CONTROL

Controlling the firing angle of valves can control the output of converters and thereby the power control over HVDC link. The power control is one of the best features of HVDC system. The ideal control system for an HVDC converter should have the following features.

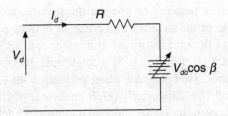

FIGURE 16.18 Equivalent circuit of inverter.

1. Control should not be sensitive to normal variation in voltage and frequency of the ac supply system.
2. Control should be fast, reliable and easy (simple).
3. There should have continuous operating range from full rectification to full inversion.
4. Control should be such that it should require less reactive power.
5. Under steady-state conditions, the valve must be fired symmetrically.
6. Control should be such that it must control the maximum current in the link, and limit the fluctuation of current.
7. Power can be controlled independently and smoothly which can be done by controlling the current and/or the voltage simultaneously in the link.
8. Control should be such that it can be used for protection of line and converter.

From Figure 16.15 and Figure 16.18, a two terminal HVDC link can be represented as equivalent circuit which is shown in Figure 16.19.

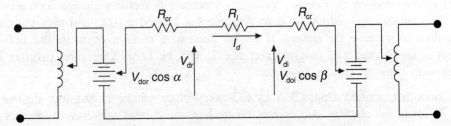

FIGURE 16.19 Equivalent circuit of HVDC link.

Here, R_{cr}, R_{ci} are the commutation resistances of rectifier and inverter respectively. R_l is the resistance of smoothing reactor and line. The dc link current can be obtained as

$$I_d = \frac{V_{dor} \cos \alpha - V_{doi} \cos \beta \text{ (or } \cos \gamma)}{R_{cr} + R_l \pm R_{ci}} \qquad (16.29)$$

In Equation (16.29), negative sign is used when γ is used in place of β, in the numerator. For maintaining safe commutation margin, γ is used as control variable instead of β. To control power in a two-terminal dc link it is desirable to have current control in one converter and voltage control in the second converter. From Equation (16.29), the increase of power in the link can be achieved by either (a) reducing α, which will also improve the power factor or (b) increasing γ or β, which will worsen the power factor and higher loss in the valvesnubber circuit. Therefore, it is required to operate the inverter at minimum γ. The operation of minimum extinction angle at the inverter and constant current control at rectifier results in better voltage regulation than the operation with minimum α at rectifier and current control at inverter. To avoid commutation failure, it is economical to operate inverter at constant extinction angle (CEA) control. However, the main problem with CEA control is the negative resistance characteristics of the converter which makes it difficult to operate stably if connected with a weak ac system. Under normal condition, rectifier operates at constant current (CC) control and inverter at constant extinction angle (CEA) control. With this control, let us examine the effects of ac voltages on the dc link current.

(a) *Increase in rectifier-end ac voltage:*   Due to this, current in link increases which can be seen from Equation (16.29). To control the current, rectifier-end controller increases the delay angle α while the inverter-end controller maintains a constant extinction angle (CEA). Increase in α will worsen the power factor and generally is controlled up to some fixed angle and thereafter tap changer is used.

(b) *Increase in inverter-end ac voltage:*   Due to this, the current in link reduces and to maintain the constant current in the link, angle α is reduced up to α_{min}, which is required for the complete firing of the valve thyristors. If still current in link is less than the reference current, the tap changer is to be operated to increase the ac voltage at rectifier.

(c) *Decrease in inverter-end ac voltage:* Due to decrease in inverter voltage, dc current in the link increases and to control the current, the rectifier-end controller increases the delay angle α. Increase in α will worsen the power factor and generally is controlled up to certain angle and thereafter tap changer is used.

(d) *Decrease in rectifier-end ac voltage:*   Decrease in rectifier voltage decreases the dc current. To maintain this current, α is to decrease but limited to α_{min} and then tap changers is to be used to increase the current. If further decreased, rectifier characteristic falls below and CEA characteristic will not intersect and I_d will be zero. Therefore, inverter is also equipped with constant current controller.

A smooth transition from CEA to CC takes place whenever the link current starts falling. To avoid the clash of two current controllers, the current reference at inverter end is kept below the current reference at rectifier end. The difference between their current settings is called *current margin* and it is normally 10% of the rated current of the link. The power reversal in the link can be obtained, without altering the current direction, by the reversal of dc voltage, which can be achieved by increasing the delay angle at the station initially operating as rectifier while reducing the delay angle at the station initially operating as inverter. Thus, it is necessary to have both CEA and CC controllers at both the stations. Figure 16.20 shows the control characteristics of both the stations.

From Figure 16.20, it can be seen that each station control characteristic has three parts (Table 16.2):

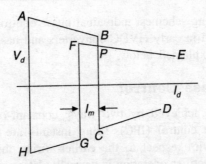

FIGURE 16.20 Controllers characteristics.

Table 16.2 Types of Station Control Characteristic

Station-I	Station-II	Controller type
AB	HG	Minimum α
BC	GF	Constant current
CD	EF	CEA (minimum γ)

The point P is the operating point. Figure 16.21 shows the operating point after the power reversal. The basic control characteristic is modified due to several problems. During the ac faults at the inverter end, commutation failure is caused and it is important to reduce the stress on the inverter valves which can be achieved by a low-voltage-dependent current limit (LVCL) to rectifier control characteristic. Figure 16.22 shows a control characteristic including a voltage-dependent current-order limit (VDCOL).

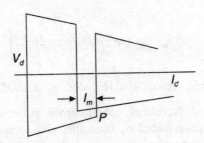

FIGURE 16.21 Power reversal controllers' characteristics.

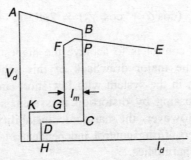

FIGURE 16.22 Modified controllers' characteristics with VDCOL.

There are two basic firing schemes: individual phase control (IPC) and equidistant pulse control (EPC). IPC was used in early HVDC converters and has now been replaced by EPC. These control schemes are explained below.

16.7.1 Individual-phase Control

This control scheme can be achieved by two ways: constant-α control and inverse-cosine control. In individual-phase control (IPC), firing instants are determined individually for each valve in steady state with respect to the earliest firing instant (i.e. voltage crossing). The constant delay angle in rectifier operation is normally determined from a negative feedback current loop, as shown in Figure 16.23. Whereas at the inverter end, the individual firing scheme requires the following for safe operation with minimum reactive power requirements.

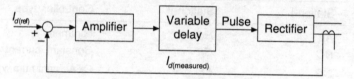

FIGURE 16.23 Negative feedback current loop.

(a) Calculation (a continuous) of the available voltage integral for commutation.

(b) A continuous calculation of required voltage integral for safe commutation.

Optimum firing is achieved when (a) and (b) coincides.

Time integral of commutating voltage is equal to the overall voltage change produced by commutating current i_c.

$$\int_\alpha^{\pi-\gamma_0} \sqrt{3}E_m \sin(\omega t)\, d(\omega t) = 2\omega L \int_0^{I_d} di_c$$

or

$$\sqrt{3}E_m \cos\alpha + \sqrt{3}E_m \cos\gamma_0 = 2\omega L I_d$$

During large or small system disturbances, actual current at the end of commutation period is different from the magnitude anticipated by controller and compensation is made for the rate of change of current. Thus equation used as a basis for a predictive constant extinction angle control is

$$\sqrt{3}E_m (\cos\alpha + \cos\gamma_0) = 2\omega L\left(I_d + u\frac{dI_d}{d\omega t}\right) \tag{16.30}$$

The main advantage of this control is to achieve the highest dc voltage under asymmetrical and distorted waveform. The major drawback of this scheme is the aggravation of the harmonic instability problem in the system with low short-circuit ratio. This is mainly due to perturbation in the zero crossing by distortion in system supply voltage which shifts the instants of firing pulses. However, the harmonic instability can be overcome by several measures such as using filters, firing control independent of zero crossing and changing the ac network behaviour with harmonics.

16.7.2 Equidistant Pulse Control (EPC)

The firing pulses, in this scheme, are generated at equal intervals of $1/(pf)$ through a ring counter in steady state. There are three variations of the EPC schemes:

(a) Pulse frequency control (PFC)

(b) Pulse period control

(c) Pulse phase control (PPC)

The main drawbacks of the EPC schemes are:

1. Under unbalanced voltage conditions, EPC results in less dc voltage compared to IPC.
2. Higher negative damping contribution to torsional oscillations when HVDC is the major transmission from generating stations.

16.8 CONVERTER FAULTS

According to the origin of the malfunction, converter faults can be divided into three broad groups:

1. Faults due to malfunction of valves and controllers.
   (a) Arc backs (or back fire) in mercury valves only
   (b) Arc through (or fire through or short through)
   (c) Quenching (arc quenching or arc chopping)
   (d) Misfire
2. Commutation failure in inverters (or break through), i.e. failure to complete commutation before commutating emf reverses.
3. Short circuit within converter stations.

The voltages across valves during rectifier and inversion operation are shown in Figure 16.24 and the malfunction can be explained through this.

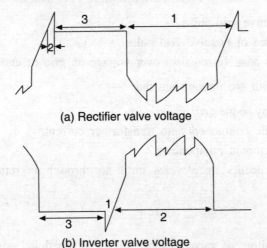

(a) Rectifier valve voltage

(b) Inverter valve voltage

FIGURE 16.24 Valve voltages: 1. inverse voltage period; 2. blocking period; 3. conduction period.

16.8.1 Arc Back

This mis-operation, which is conduction in the inverse voltage period of valves, occurs mainly in rectifiers because inverse voltage period in rectifiers are much more than that of inverters that can be seen in Figure 16.24. It is the most common and serve malfunction in mercury valve rectifier and random in nature. On average, it is one or two arc back per valve/month. Modern thyristors do not suffer from arc backs. Factors that increases the arc back are:

1. High PIV
2. High voltage jump, especially of the jump at arc extinction
3. High rate of change of current at the end of conduction
4. Over current
5. Impurity of anode and grid
6. High rate of rise of inverse voltage.

Factors 1 and 2 can be reduced by having low voltage whereas having low current can reduce factors 3 and 4. These reduce power handling/valve and increase the cost of converter. Factors 2 and 3 can be improved by using small (α, β, γ, δ) but they are larger for control operation (momentary). Factor 6 is minimized by use of RC damper in parallel to each valve. However, factor 3 can be improved with high u.

This malfunction of valves results into line-to-line short circuit and sometimes 3-phase short circuit. It also generates some harmonics.

16.8.2 Arc Through

This is also known as *fire through* or *short through*. It occurs during blocking period of valve that is when the voltage across the valves is positive. Since the positive voltage across the valve is more during the inverter operation, the chance of this malfunction is also more in inverters than the rectifiers. It is similar to commutation failure. This malfunction is mainly due to

- failure of negative grid pulse
- early occurrence of positive grid pulse
- sufficient high-positive transient over voltage on grid or anode.

The main problems with arc through are that

- It reduces delay angle (α).
- It introduces dc component into transformer current.
- It changes harmonic components.
- Short circuit occurs once/cycles until arc-through is removed or the bridge is bypassed.

16.8.3 Misfire

As its name, it is a failure of valve to ignite during a scheduled conducting period whereas arc through is the failure to block a valve during a scheduled non-conducting period. This can occur either in rectifier or in inverter but it is more severe when occurs in inverters. It may be either due to negative gate pulse or positive anode to cathode voltage or fault in valves. The effect of misfire in inverter is similar to commutation failure and arc through. Let valves 6 and 1 are conducting and valve 2 fails to ignite. Valves 6 and 1 continue to conduct and thereafter valve 3 will conduct and dc short circuit occurs for smaller durations. There is a small jump of voltage at the beginning of short-circuit and large jump at the end of short-circuit.

16.8.4 Quenching

It is a premature extinction of valve in normal conduction period. This malfunction has the same effect as misfire (almost) and causes short-circuit of dc terminal.

16.8.5 Commutation Failure

This fault, which is more common in an inverter, is the result of a failure of the incoming valve (due to insufficient extinction time) to take over the direct current before the commutating voltage reverses its polarity. It is not due to malfunctioning of valve but due to ac or dc condition outside the bridge. It causes decrease in dc current, low ac voltage (due to ac short circuit). The failure of two successive commutations in the same cycle is called *double commutation failure*.

To illustrate the commutation failure, let us take example that valves 1 and 2 are conducting and now valve 3 has to be ignited to take the complete current of valve 1 which is in the upper limb of converter. If current in incoming valve 3 diminishes to zero, the current in valve 1 will continue to carry full link current. Firing of valve 4 (next in sequence) will result in short circuit of the bridge, as both valve of same arm will conduct. If the commutation from valve 2 to valve 4 is successful, only valves 1 and 4 will conduct. Firing of valve 5 (in sequence) will be unsuccessful as voltage across it is negative and valves 1 and 4 will still continue. Now valve 6 will be fired and if commutation from valve 4 to 6 is successful, valves 6 and 1 will conduct which is normal pattern of conduction. Thus a single commutation failure is self-clearing.

The double commutation failure is more severe and should be averted which depends on the current control of link and the magnitude of ac voltage. Converter differential protection can also be used. The initial rate of rise of current in inverter is limited by smoothing reactor and the current at rectifier end limits the current in persistent commutation failures.

Example 16.1 A 6-pulse bridge connected converter is fed from 238 kV/110 kV transformer which is connected with 3-phase, 238 kV, 50 Hz supply. Calculate the direct voltage output when the commutation angle (overlap angle) is 20° and delay angle (a) 30 degree, (b) 90 degree and (c) 150 degree.

Solution Using Equation (16.20), the output voltage is given by

$$V_d = \frac{V_{do}}{2}[\cos\alpha + \cos(\alpha + u)]$$

where

$$V_{do} = \frac{3\sqrt{3}E_m}{\pi} = \frac{3\sqrt{3}}{\pi} \frac{\sqrt{2} \times 110}{\sqrt{3}} = 148.55 \text{ kV}$$

(a) For $\alpha = 30°$, the dc output voltage is

$$V_d = \frac{148.55}{2}[\cos 30 + \cos(30 + 20)] = 112.07 \text{ kV}$$

(b) For $\alpha = 90°$, the dc output voltage is

$$V_d = \frac{148.55}{2}[\cos 90 + \cos(90 + 20)] = -25.40 \text{ kV}$$

Negative sign shows the output voltage has negative polarity and works as inverter.

(c) For $\alpha = 150°$, the dc output voltage is

$$V_d = \frac{148.55}{2}[\cos 150 + \cos(150 + 20)] = -137.47 \text{ kV}$$

Example 16.2   Find the effective commutation resistance of a 6-pulse rectifier, which is fed from 400 kV, 3-phase ac voltage, when the dc current in HVDC link is 1 kA and the rectifier dc voltage is 500 kV at firing angle of 20°.

Solution   Using Equation (16.25), the dc voltage is given by

$$V_d = V_{do} \cos \alpha - R_c I_d$$

where

$$V_{do} = \frac{3\sqrt{3}E_m}{\pi} = \frac{3\sqrt{3}}{\pi} \frac{\sqrt{2} \times 400}{\sqrt{3}} = 540.19 \text{ kV}$$

Therefore, we have

$$500 = 540.19 \cos 20 - (R_c \times 1.0)$$

Thus $R_c = 7.61$ ohm.

Example 16.3   A 6-pulse bridge inverter is fed from 500-kV dc voltage. Find the ac voltage output of the inverter if the advance angle is 20° and extinction angle is 10°.

Solution   Using Equation (16.26), the dc voltage is given by

$$V_{di} = \frac{V_{doi}}{2}(\cos \beta + \cos \gamma) = \frac{V_{doi}}{2}(\cos 20 + \cos 10) = 0.96225 \, V_{doi} = 500 \text{ kV}$$

or

$$V_{doi} = \frac{3\sqrt{3}E_m}{\pi} = \frac{500}{0.96225}$$

Thus

$$E_m = 314.16 \text{ kV} \quad \text{or} \quad V_L = 384.77 \text{ kV}$$

16.9 INTERCONNECTION OF HVDC TRANSMISSION INTO AC SYSTEMS

Since it is efficient and economical to have ac generation and distribution but for transmission and control of power, HVDC links can be used. The main areas of application based on the economics and technical performances, are:

(a) Long-distance bulk power transmission

(b) Underground or submarine cables

(c) Asynchronous connection of ac system with different frequencies

(d) Control and stabilize the power system with power flow control.

Based on the interconnection, three types of HVDC links are possible:

1. HVDC transmission system, where bulk power is transmitted from one point to another point over long distance.

2. Back-to-back dc link, where rectification and inversion is carried out in the same converter station with very small or no dc lines. This is basically used to control the power and stabilize the system. It is also used, sometimes, to connect two different frequencies systems.

3. Parallel connection of ac and dc links, where both ac and dc lines run parallel. It is mainly used to modulate the power of ac line. Due to its fast control, the dc line can improve the transient stability of the system.

16.10 FLEXIBLE AC TRANSMISSION SYSTEMS (FACTS) TECHNOLOGY

With the development of modern power systems, it becomes very important to control the power flow along the transmission corridor. The normal evolutionary process in late 1970s by introducing power electronics based control for reactive power has been greatly accelerated by more recent developments in the electric power industry, which have aggravated the early problems and highlighted the structural limitations of power systems in a greatly changed socio-economical environment. The desire to find solutions to these problems and limitations led to focuss technological developments under the Flexible AC Transmission System (FACTS).

The gate-turn off thyristor (GTO) and insulated gate bipolar transistor (IGBT) are more promising switching devices presently and potentially available in the near future. However in longer future (10 years or more), MOS-controlled thyristor (MCT) devices will be competitive to GTO and IGBT devices. A comparison of various power switching devices is presented in Table 16.3.

Table 16.3 Comparison of Power Semiconductor Devices

	Thyristor	GTO	IGBT	SI thyristor	MCT	MOSFET
Maximum voltage rating (V)	8000	6000	1700	2500	3000	1000
Maximum current rating (A)	4000	6000	800	800	400	100
Voltage blocking [(Symmetrical/asymmetrical)]	S/A	S/A	A	A	S/A	A
Gating	Pulse	Current	Voltage	Current	Voltage	Voltage
Conduction drop (V)	1.2	2.5	3	4	1.2	Resistive
Switching frequency (kHz)	1	5	20	20	20	100
Development target maximum voltage rating (kV)	10	10	3.5	5	5	2
Development target maximum current rating (kA)	8	8	2	2	2	0.2

Note: SI, static induction thyristor; MOSFET, MOS field effect transistor; S, Symmetrical; A, Asymmetrical.

At present, the most high-voltage transmission lines are operating below thermal ratings due to constraints such as voltage and transient stability limits. Power electronics based FACTS technology can enhance transmission system control and increase line loading in some cases all the way up to thermal limits, thereby without compromising reliability. Based on these capabilities, bottlenecks can be eliminated, line capacity can be increased, and reliability can be improved. These capabilities allow transmission system owners and operators to maximize asset utilization and execute additional bulk power transfers, with immediate bottom-line benefits. Moreover, FACTS devices can also enable companies to avoid or minimize the time-consuming, source-intensive process of constructing new transmission facilities and concentrate instead on maximizing profitability of existing sets as the market for transmission services expands.

Several energy companies are realizing the benefits of FACTS installations. Tennessee Valley Authority (TVA) installed the first static synchronous compensator (STATCOM) in 1995 to strengthen ties between its Sullivan substation and the rest of its network while avoiding more labour and space-intensive installation of an additional transformer bank. The device provides instantaneous control of transmission voltage and increasing capacity to provide TVA with greater flexibility in bulk power transactions. It also increases reliability and damps out major grid oscillations.

Thereafter, in 1998, installation of the first unified power flow controller (UPFC) was completed at the Inez substation owned by American Electric Power (AEP). The device employs dual back-to-back voltage-source converters with a STATCOM and a static synchronous series compensator (SSSC) coupled to a dc link capacitor, enabling it to function as an ideal ac-to-ac power converter. It represents the first controller capable of providing complete control of all the three basic transmission system parameters (voltage, line impedance, and phase angle) simultaneously. AEP installed the UPFC as the first major element in a regional reinforcement. It is mitigating line loading and low-voltage problems caused by rapid growth in area far from the company's generating sources. It also ensures that a new, high-capacity 138-kV line carries its share of regional load.

Up to now, installed FACTS equipments have been put forward over time due to a significant advantages of FACTS devices, its potential benefits together with the rapid developments of modern power electronics technology. Consequently, as power semiconductor devices continue to improve, the cost of FACTS controllers continues to decrease. Large-scale use of FACTS technology is eventually an assured scenario.

16.11   OBJECTIVES OF FACTS

The basic transmission challenge of the evolving deregulated power system (competitive power market), whatever final form it may take, is to provide a network capable of delivering contracted power from any supplier to any consumer over a large geographic area under market forces-controlled, and thus continuously varying patterns of contractual arrangements. Due to cost, right-of-way, and environmental problems, the network expansion is restricted.

The FACTS initiative was originally launched to solve the emerging system problems in the late 1980s due to restrictions on the construction of transmission line, and to facilitate the growing power of export and import and wheeling transactions among utilities, with two main objectives:

(a) To increase the power transfer capability of transmission systems

(b) To keep power flow over designated routes.

The first objective implies that power flow in a given line can be increased up to the thermal limit by forcing the necessary current through the series line impedance if, at the same time, stability of the system is maintained via appropriate real-time control of power flow during and following system faults. The second objective implies that the power flow can be restricted to select (contracted) transmission corridors by controlling the current in a line (by, for example, changing the effective line impedance and phase angle), while parallel and loop-flows can be mitigated.

The achievement of the two basic objectives would significantly increase the utilization of existing (and new) transmission assets, and could play a major role in facilitating deregulation with minimal requirements for new transmission lines. The implementation of the above two basic objectives requires the development of high-power compensators and controllers. N.G. Hingorani, in 1988, first defined the concepts of Flexible AC Transmission Systems (FACTS), "FACTS controllers can control the interrelated parameters that govern the operation of transmission systems including series impedance, shunt impedance, current, voltage, phase angle and the damping of oscillations at various frequencies below the rated frequency". They are having many benefits to the power system in terms of operation, control and transmission line planning and finance.

In summary, the FACTS controllers offer the following advantages:

- Control of power flow in transmission corridors by controlling line impedance, angle and voltage.
- Optimum power flow for certain objectives.
- Increase the loading capability of lines to their thermal capabilities, including short term and seasonal. This can be accomplished by overcoming other limitations, and sharing of power among lines according to their capability.

- Increase the system security through raising the transient stability limit, limiting short-circuit currents and overloads.
- Provide secure and controllable tie line connections to neighbouring utilities and regions thereby decreasing overall generation reserve requirements on both the sides.
- Damp out of power systems' oscillations, which could damage equipment and limit useable transmission capacity by rapidly modulating the effective impedance in response to power system dynamics.
- Prevent cascading outages by limiting the impacts of faults and equipment failures.
- Provide greater flexibility in sitting new generation.
- Upgrade of lines.
- Reduce reactive power flows, thus allowing the lines to carry more active power.
- Reduce loop flows.
- Increase utilization of the lowest cost generation. One of the principal reasons for transmission interconnections is to utilize the lowest cost generation. When this cannot be done, it follows that there is not enough cost-effective transmission capacity. Cost-effective enhancement of capacity will therefore allow increased use of the lowest cost generation.

16.12 Basic Types of FACTS Controllers

After years of rapid development, many types of FACTS devices have been put forward. Some of them are already brought into the operation or under construction. However, much work is still needed to fully make use of the new characteristics of FACTS devices. Presently, the studies on FACTS are mainly focused on the FACTS devices, power flow modulation and control, stability enhancement and oscillation damping. Figure 16.25(a) shows the general symbol of FACTS controller.

FACTS controllers, in general, can be divided into four categories:

1. *Series controllers:* This controller could be of variable impedance, such as capacitor, reactor, etc., or power electronics based variable source of main frequency, sub-synchronous and harmonic frequencies to serve the desired need. In principle, all the series controllers inject voltage in series with the line. Even variable impedance, multiplied by the current flow through it, represents an injected series voltage in the line. As long as the voltage is in phase quadrature with the line current, the series controller only supplies or consumes variable reactive power. Any other phase relationship will involve handling of real power as well. Figure 16.25(b) shows a typical series FACTS controller.

2. *Shunt controllers:* As in the case of series controllers, the shunt controllers may be of variable impedance, variable source, or a combination of these. In principle, all the shunt controllers inject current into the system at the point of connection. Even variable shunt impedance connected to the line voltage causes a variable current flow and hence represents injection of current into the line. As long as the injected current is in phase quadrature with the line voltage, the shunt controller only supplies or

consumes variable reactive power. Any other phase relationship will involve handling of real power as well. Figure 16.25(c) represents a schematic diagram of shunt FACTS controller.

3. *Combined series–series controllers* (Figure 16.25d): This could be a combination of separate series controllers, which are controlled in a coordinated manner, in a multi-line transmission system. Or, it could be a unified controller, in which series controllers provide independent series reactive compensation for each line but also transfer real power among the lines via the power link. The real power transfer capability of the unified series–series controller, referred to as interline power flow controller, makes it possible to balance both the real and reactive power flow in the lines and thereby maximize the utilization of the transmission system. Note that here the term 'unified' means that the dc terminals of all the controller converters are all connected together for real power transfer.

4. *Combined series–shunt controllers* (Figures 16.25e and 16.25f): This could be a combination of separate shunt and series controllers, which are controlled in a coordinated manner or a unified power flow controller with series and shunt elements. In principle, combined shunt and series controllers inject current into the system with the shunt part of the controller, and voltage in series in the line with the series part of the controller. However, when the shunt and series controllers are unified, there can be a real power exchange between the series and shunt controllers via the power link.

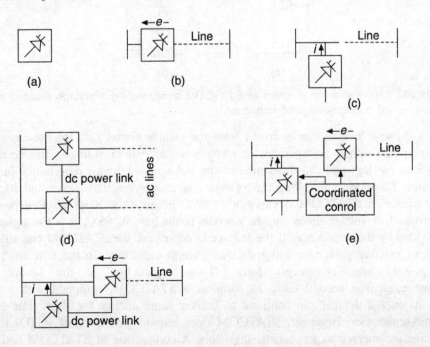

FIGURE 16.25　(a) General symbol for FACTS controller; (b) series controller; (c) shunt controller (d) unified series-series controller; (e) coordinated series and shunt controller; and (f) unified series-shunt controller

16.13   FACTS Devices

16.13.1   Static Synchronous Compensator (STATCOM)

STATCOM is a static synchronous generator operated as a shunt-connected static VAr compensator (SVC) whose capacitive or inductive output current can be controlled independently of the ac system voltage. Figure 16.26 shows a simple one-line diagram of STATCOM. For the voltage-source converter, its ac output voltage is controlled such that it is just right for the required reactive current flow for any ac bus voltage and dc capacitor voltage is automatically adjusted as required to serve as a voltage source for the converter. STATCOM can also be designed as an active filter to absorb system harmonics. In this scheme converters are used, whereas in SVC thyristors are used.

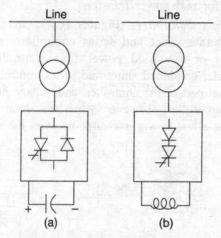

FIGURE 16.26   Simple one-line diagram of STATCOM based on (a) a voltage-sourced converter, (b) a current-sourced converter.

It is a 3-phase inverter that is driven from the voltage across a dc storage capacitor and whose three-phase output voltages are in phase with ac system voltages, the current flow causes to lead (or lag) and the difference in the voltage amplitudes determines how much current flows. Therefore, controlling the voltage can change reactive power and its polarity. The performance of STATCOM is superior to SVC because the most reactive power, that can be delivered, is voltage times current whereas in the case of SVC, it is the square of the voltage divided by the impedance. If the voltage is depressed, the STATCOM can still deliver high level of reactive power by using its over-current capability. In the case of SVC, the reactive power capability steeply falls off as a function of the square of the voltage just when it is needed most. In addition, a STATCOM, equipped with a large dc capacitor or storage device, can continue to deliver some energy for short time just as a synchronous condenser. However, STATCOM does require gate-turn off (GTO) thyristors which is costly compared to the normal thyristors. A comparison of STATCOM and SVC is given in Table 16.4.

Table 16.4 Comparison between a STATCOM and SVC

STATCOM	SVC
It acts as a voltage source behind a reactance.	It acts as a variable susceptance.
It is insensitive to transmission system harmonics.	It is sensitive to a transmission system harmonic resonance.
It has a larger dynamic range.	It has smaller dynamic range.
It generates less harmonics.	It generates more harmonics.
It has faster response (within ms) and better performace during transients.	Its performance is slow during the transients.
Both inductive and capacitive regions of operation are possibie.	It operates mostly in capacitive region.
It can maintain a stable voltage even with a very weak ac system.	It has difficulty in operating with a very weak ac system.
It can be used for small amount of energy storage.	
Temporary overload capacity translates into improved voltage stability.	

16.13.2 Static Synchronous Generator (SSG)

SSG is a self-commutated static switching power converter commuted with a static synchronous electric energy source (such as battery, flywheel, super conducting magnet, large dc storage capacitor). It is operated to produce a set of adjustable multiphase output voltages, which may be coupled to an ac power system for the purpose of exchanging independently controllable real and reactive power. Simple model of SSG is shown in Figure 16.27.

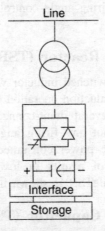

FIGURE 16.27 Model of SSG.

16.13.3 Static VAr Compensator (SVC)

SVC is a shunt-connected static VAr generator or absorber whose output is adjusted to control capacitive or inductive current so as to maintain or control specific parameters of the electrical power system (typically bus voltage magnitude). SVC is based on a thyristor without the gate turn-off capability. It includes separate equipment for leading and lagging VAr. SVC is considered as a lower cost alternative to STATCOM, although this may not be the case if the comparison is made based on the required performance and not just the MVA size. A simple model of SVC is shown in Figure 16.28. A comparative performance of SVC and STATCOM is given in Table 16.4.

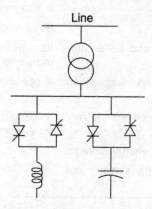

FIGURE 16.28   SVC system.

16.13.4   Thyristor Controlled Reactor (TCR)

TCR is a shunt-connected, thyristor-controlled inductor whose effective reactance is varied in a continuous manner by partial-conduction control of the thyristor valve. TCR is a subset of SVC in which conduction time and hence, current in a shunt reactor is controlled by a thyristor-based ac switch with firing angle control. Simple model of TCR is shown in Figure 16.29.

16.13.5   Thyristor Switched Reactor (TSR)

TSR is a shunt-connected, thyristor-switched inductor whose effective reactance is varied in a stepwise manner by full or zero conduction operation of the thyristor valve. TSR is another subset of SVC. TSR is made up of several shunt-connected inductors, which are switched in and out by thyristor switches without any firing angle controls in order to achieve the required step changes in the reactive power consumed from the system. Use of thyristor switches without firing angle control results in lower cost and losses, but without a continuous control. A simple model of TSR is shown in Figure 16.29.

16.13.6   Thyristor Switched Capacitor (TSC)

TSC is a shunt-connected, thyristor-switched capacitor whose effective reactance is varied in a stepwise manner by full or zero conduction operation of the thyristor valve. TSC is also a subset of SVC in which thyristor based ac switches are used to switch in and out (without firing angle control) shunt capacitors units, in order to achieve the required step change in the reactive power supplied to the system. Unlike shunt reactors, shunt capacitors cannot be switched continuously with variable firing angle control. Simple model of TSC is shown in Figure 16.29.

16.13.7 Static VAr Generator or Absorber (SVG)

SVG is a static electrical device, equipment, or system that is capable of drawing controlled capacitive and inductive current from an electrical power system and thereby generating or absorbing reactive power. Generally considered to consist of shunt connected, thyristor-controlled reactor(s) and thyristor-switched capacitors. The SVG is simply a reactive power (VAr) source that, with appropriate controls, can be converted into any specific or multipurpose reactive shunt compensator. Thus, both the SVC and the STATCOM are static VAr generators equipped with appropriate control loops to vary the VAr output so as to meet specific compensation objectives. A simple model of SVG is shown in Figure 16.29.

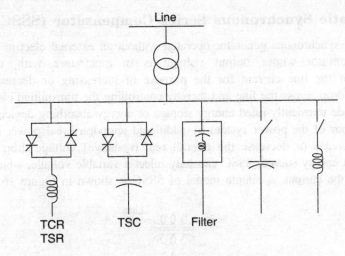

FIGURE 16.29 Simple models of SVG, SVS, TCR, TSR and TSC.

16.13.8 Static VAr System (SVS)

SVS is a combination of different static and mechanically switched VAr compensators whose outputs are coordinated. A simple model of SVS is shown in Figure 16.29.

16.13.9 Thyristor-controlled Braking Resistor (TCBR)

TCBR is a shunt-connected thyristor-switched resistor, which is controlled to aid stabilization of a power system or to minimize power acceleration of a generating unit during disturbances. TCBR involves cycle-by-cycle switching of a resistor (usually a linear resistor) with firing angle control of a thyristor-based ac switch. For lower cost, TCBR may be thyristor switched without firing angle control. However, with firing control, half-cycle by half-cycle firing control can be utilized to selectively damp low-frequency oscillations. Simple model of TCBR is shown in Figure 16.30.

Line

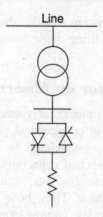

FIGURE 16.30 Simple model of TCBR.

16.13.10 Static Synchronous Series Compensator (SSSC)

SSSC is a static synchronous generator operated without an external electric energy source as a series compensator whose output voltage is in quadrature with, and controllable independently of the line current for the purpose of increasing or decreasing the overall reactive voltage drop across the line and thereby controlling the transmitted electric power. The SSSC may include transiently-rated energy storage or energy-absorbing devices to enhance the dynamic behaviour of the power system by additional temporary real power compensation, to momentarily increase or decrease the overall real (resistive) voltage drop across the line. Without an extra energy source, SSSC can only inject a variable voltage, which is 90° leading or lagging with the current. A simple model of SSSC is shown in Figure 16.31.

Line

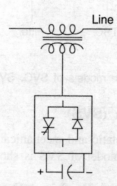

FIGURE 16.31 Simple model of SSSC.

16.13.11 Interline Power Flow Controller (IPFC)

IPFC is a combination of two or more static synchronous series compensators which are coupled via a common dc link to facilitate a bi-directional flow of real power between the ac terminals of the SSSCs, and are controlled to provide independent reactive compensation for the adjustment of real power flow in each line and maintain the desired distribution of reactive power flow among the lines. The IPFC structure may also include a STATCOM coupled with the IPFC's common dc link, to provide shunt reactive compensation and supply or absorb the overall real power deficit of the combined SSSCs.

16.13.12   Thyristor-controlled Series Capacitor (TCSC)

TCSC is a capacitive reactance compensator, which consists of a series capacitor bank shunted by a thyristor-controlled reactor in order to provide a smoothly variable series capacitive reactance. The TCSC is based on thyristors without the gate turn-off capability. It is an alternative to SSSC (discussed earlier) and like an SSSC, it is a very important FACTS controller. A variable reactor such as a thyristor-controlled reactor (TCR) is connected with a series capacitor. When the TCR firing angle is 180°, the reactor becomes non-conducting and the series capacitor has its normal impedance. If the firing angle reduces from 180°, the capacitive impedance increases. On the other end, when the TCR firing angle is 90°, the reactor becomes fully conducting, and the total impedance becomes inductive, because the reactor impedance is designed to be much lower than the series capacitor impedance. With 90° firing-angle, the TCSC helps in limiting fault current. The TCSC may be a single, large unit, or may consist of several equal or different-sized smaller capacitors in order to achieve a superior performance. A simple model of TCSC is shown in Figure 16.32.

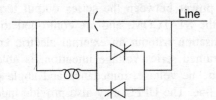

FIGURE 16.32   Simple model of TCSC and TSSC.

16.13.13   Thyristor-switched Series Capacitor (TSSC)

TSSC is a capacitive reactance compensator, which consists of a series capacitor bank-shunted by a thyristor-switched reactor to provide a step-wise control of series capacitive reactance. Instead of continuous control of capacitive impedance, this approach of switching inductors at firing angle of 90° or 180° but without firing angle control could reduce cost and losses of the controller. It is reasonable to arrange one of the modules to have thyristor-controlled, while others could be thyristor-switched. A simple model of TSSC is shown in Figure 16.32.

16.13.14   Thyristor-controlled Series Reactor (TCSR)

TCSR is an inductive reactance compensator, which consists of a series reactor shunted by a thyristor-controlled reactor in order to provide a smoothly variable series inductive reactance. When the firing angle of the thyristor-controlled reactor is 180°, it stops conducting, and the uncontrolled reactor acts as a fault current limiter. As the angle decreases below 180°, the net inductance decreases until firing angle of 90°, when the net inductance is the parallel combination of the two reactors. A simple model of TCSR is shown in Figure 16.33.

16.13.15 Thyristor-switched Series Reactor (TSSR)

TSSR is an inductive reactance compensator, which consists of a series reactor shunted by a thyristor-controlled switched reactor in order to provide a step-wise control of series inductive reactance. This is a complement of TCSR, but with thyristor switches fully on or off to achieve a combination of stepped series inductance. A simple model of TSSR is shown in Figure 16.33.

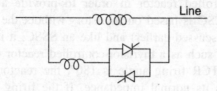

FIGURE 16.33 Simple model of TCSR and TSSR.

16.13.16 Unified Power Flow Controller (UPFC)

UPFC is a combination of static synchronous compensator (STATCOM) and a static synchronous series compensator (SSSC), which are coupled via a common dc link, to allow bidirectional flow of real power between the series output terminals of the SSSC and the shunt output terminals of the STATCOM, and are controlled to provide concurrent real and reactive series line compensation without an external electric energy source. The UPFC, by means of angular unconstrained series voltage injection, is able to control, concurrently or selectively, the transmission line voltage, impedance and angle or, alternatively, the real and reactive power flow in the line. The UPFC may also provide independently controllable shunt reactive compensation. Additional storage such as a super-conducting magnet connected to the dc link via an electronic interface would provide the means of further enhancing the effectiveness of the UPFC. As mentioned before, the controlled exchange of real power with an external source, such as storage, is much more effective in controlling the system dynamics than modulation of the power transfer within a system. A simple model of UPFC is shown in Figure 16.34.

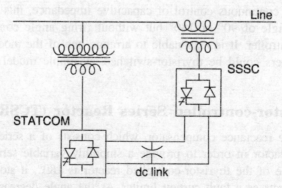

FIGURE 16.34 Simple model of UPFC.

16.13.17 Thyristor-controlled Phase Shifting Transformer (TCPST)

TCPST is a phase shifting transformer adjusted by thyristor switches to provide a rapidly variable phase angle. In general, phase shifting is obtained by adding a perpendicular voltage vector in series with a phase. This vector is derived from the other two phases via shunt-connected transformers. The perpendicular series voltage is made variable with a variety of power electronics topologies. A circuit concept that can handle voltage reversal can provide phase shift in either direction. This controller is also referred to as thyristor-controlled phase angle regulator (TCPAR). A simple model of TCPST is shown in Figure 16.35.

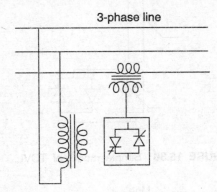

FIGURE 16.35 Simple model of TCPST or TCPAR.

16.13.18 Interphase Power Controller (IPC)

IPC is a series-connected controller of active and reactive power consisting, in each phase, of inductive and capacitive branches subjected to separately phase-shifted voltages. The active and reactive power can be set independently by adjusting the phase shifts and the branch impedances, using mechanical or electronic switches. In a particular case where the inductive and capacitive impedance form a conjugate pair, each terminal of the IPC is a passive current source dependent on the voltage at the other terminal.

16.13.19 Thyristor-controlled Voltage Limiter (TCVL)

TCVL is a thyristor-switched metal-oxide varistor (MOV) used to limit the voltage across its terminals during transient conditions. The thyristor switch can be connected in series with a gapless arrester, or part of the gapless arrester (10–20%) can be bypassed by a thyristor switch in order to dynamically lower the voltage limiting level. In general, the MOV would have to be significantly more powerful than the normal gapless arrester, in order that TCVL can suppress dynamic over-voltages, which can otherwise last for tens of cycles. A simple model of TCVL is shown in Figure 16.36.

16.13.20 Thyristor-controlled Voltage Regulator (TCVR)

TCVR is a thyristor-controlled transformer, which can provide variable in-phase voltage with continuous control. For practical purposes, this may be a regular transformer with a thyristor-controlled tap changer [Figure 16.37(a)] or with a thyristor-controlled ac-to-ac voltage converter for injection of variable ac voltage of the same phase in series with the line [Figure 16.37(b)]. Such a relatively low-cost controller can be very effective in controlling the flow of reactive power between two ac systems.

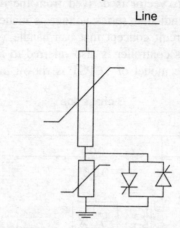

FIGURE 16.36 Simple model of TCVL.

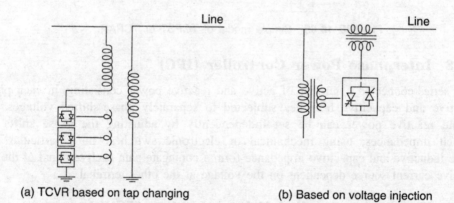

(a) TCVR based on tap changing   (b) Based on voltage injection

FIGURE 16.37 Simple model of TCVR.

Table 16.5 shows the summary of control attributes for various FACTS controllers.

Table 16.5 Control Attributes for Various FACTS Controllers

FACTS controllers	Control attributes
STATCOM	Voltage control, VAr compensation, damping oscillations and voltage stability
SVC, TCR, TCS and TRS	Voltage control, VAr compensation, damping oscillations, transient and dynamic stability, and voltage stability
TCBR	Damping oscillations and transient and dynamic stability

(cont...)

Table 16.5 Control Attributes for Various FACTS Controllers (*cont...*)

FACTS controllers	Control attributes
SSSC, TCSC, TSSC, TCSR and TSSR	Current control, damping oscillations, transient and dynamic stability, voltage stability, and fault current limiting.
TCPST	Active power control, damping oscillations, transient and dynamic stability and voltage stability.
UPFC	Active and reactive power control, voltage control, VAr compensation, damping oscillations, transient and dynamic stability, voltage stability and fault current limiting.
TCVL	Transient and dynamic voltage limit.
TCVR and IPFC	Reactive power control, voltage control, damping oscillations, transient and dynamic stability and voltage stability.

PROBLEMS

16.1 Find the best values of q, s and r for a 12-pulse converter configuration.

16.2 If a 6-pulse bridge rectifier is operating from 220-kV voltage supply through the transformer. Find the output voltage of the rectifier when the firing (delay) angle is (a) 0° (b) 15° and (c) 90°. Assume there is no source reactance.

16.3 If the delay angle and commutation angle of a 6-pulse bridge converter is 15° and 10° respectively, find the secondary voltage of a transformer when the dc output voltage of converter is 500 kV.

16.4 In a HVDC link the dc current is 1 kA and the rectifier-end dc voltage is 500 kV when delay angle is 15°. Find the commutation reactance if the rectifier ac voltage is 400 kV.

16.5 A 6-pulse bridge inverter is fed from 500-kV dc voltage. Find the ac voltage output of the inverter if the delay angle is 160° and commutation angle is 5°.

Chapter 17

Distribution Systems

17.1 INTRODUCTION

Electrical power (which is normally ac power except some non-conventional sources) can be generated by several methods from various energy sources. There are several advantages of having ac generation. Normally, the generating stations are very far from the load centres. Generated power is transmitted over the high-voltage long transmission lines. However the utilization of power is restricted to low voltage because the high capital cost of appliances at high voltage, difficulties in maintenance, safety, etc. The power supply required by the various appliances may be dc or ac depending upon the use. However, ac distribution of supply is common.

17.2 EFFECT OF VOLTAGE ON TRANSMISSION EFFICIENCY

The main advantages of transmitting power over transmission lines on high voltage are:

(a) Cost of conductor is reduced for given power.

(b) Voltage drop in lines is reduced.

(c) Efficiency of transmission line is increased.

Let V be the line to neutral voltage and I be the current lagging V by an angle ϕ, the power transmitted by each phase will be

$$P = VI \cos \phi \qquad (17.1)$$

If P_l is the power loss in each conductor due to flow of current in the conductors of transmission line having the resistance R per phase, then

$$P_l = I^2 R \qquad (17.2)$$

Therefore, the power loss in each conductor in terms of operating voltage V and transmitted power P, using Equations (17.1) and (17.2), will be

$$P_l = \frac{P^2 R}{V^2 \cos^2 \phi} \qquad (17.3)$$

From Equation (17.3), we can conclude that power loss in conductors will be minimum with high voltage and high power factor. If resistivity, length of line and cross-sectional area of conductor are ρ, l and A respectively, the resistance will be

$$R = \rho \frac{l}{a}$$

Substituting the value of R in Equation (17.3), we get

$$P_l = \frac{P^2}{V^2 \cos^2 \phi} \frac{\rho l}{a} \quad \text{or} \quad a = \frac{P^2 \rho l}{P_l V^2 \cos^2 \phi} \qquad (17.4)$$

Therefore, the volume of conductor (v) will be

$$v = al = \frac{P^2 \rho l^2}{P_l V^2 \cos^2 \phi} \qquad (17.5)$$

Since the cost of conductor depends on the weight, which is proportional to the volume, the increase in voltage and power factor will save the cost of conductor for a given power transfer over a particular length of line.

From Equation (17.1), it is clear that at high voltage operation the current will be low for the same power transmitted. The voltage drop in the line will be IZ, where Z is the impedance of the line. Therefore

$$\text{Voltage drop } \Delta V = \frac{PZ}{V \cos \phi} \qquad (17.6)$$

Thus it is evident from Equation (17.6) that high voltage and high power factor will reduce the line voltage drop. The transmission efficiency for delivering per phase power P will be

$$\text{Transmission efficiency } \eta = \frac{\text{Power output}}{\text{Power input}} = \frac{\text{Power output}}{\text{Power output} + \text{Loss}}$$

Therefore, using Equation (17.4), we get

$$\eta = \frac{P}{P + P_l} = \frac{P}{P + \dfrac{P^2}{V^2 \cos^2 \phi} \dfrac{\rho l}{a}} = \frac{1}{1 + \dfrac{P \rho l}{V^2 a \cos^2 \phi}} \qquad (17.7)$$

This shows that at higher voltage and higher power factor, the efficiency will be higher.

The same derivation is also valid for dc power transmission where power factor is unity. Thus, a high-voltage transmission increases the efficiency, reduces the line drop and the cost of conductors of transmission lines. However, there is a limit to increase the voltage level, which is due to increased cost of insulation, switchgear, transformers and terminal equipments. Therefore, an economic study is performed to select the operating voltage level, which is based on the level of power transmission.

17.3 Comparison of Various Transmission and Distribution systems

Nowadays, dc distribution system is phased out in almost every country. However, some applications of dc power still exist, whereas in transmission, both dc and ac exist. Therefore, it is beneficial to analyze various possible distribution systems, which are:

(a) DC 2-wire system (monopolar operation)

(b) DC 2-wire system with mid-point earthed (bipolar operation)

(c) DC 3-wire (homopolar operation)

(d) AC 1-phase, 2-wire

(e) AC 3-phase, 3-wire

(f) AC 3-phase, 4-wire

Some other possible arrangements are:

(a) AC single-phase, 2-wire system with mid-point earthed

(b) AC single-phase, 3-wire system with neutral cross-section of 1/2 of the outers

(c) AC 2-phase, 4-wire system

(d) AC 2-phase, 3-wire system.

But these configurations are not common and therefore not compared. For the comparison of various systems, certain assumptions made are:

(a) The power transmitted is the same in all the cases.

(b) Distance of transmission lines is the same.

(c) Power loss is same in all the cases.

(d) The lines should have the same insulation level.

Two cases based on the equal maximum potential difference (a) between any conductor and earth and (b) between any two conductors are considered here:

17.3.1 Equal Maximum Potential Difference between any Conductor and Earth

Let the voltage V is the maximum potential difference between any conductor and the earth and I_1 is the line current.

(a) *DC 2-wire system:* Figure 17.1 shows the 2-wire dc system without mid-point earthed. If R is the resistance of each conductor having cross-sectional area of a, then

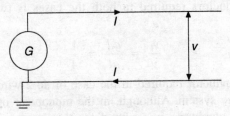

FIGURE 17.1 DC 2-wire system.

$$\text{Power transmitted } P = VI$$

and

$$\text{Power loss} = 2I^2R = \frac{2P^2R}{V^2} \tag{17.8}$$

(b) *DC 2-wire system mid-point earthed:* Figure 17.2 shows the dc 2-wire mid-point earthed system. If R_1 is the resistance of each conductor having cross-sectional area of a_1, then

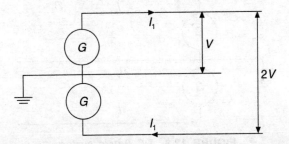

FIGURE 17.2 DC 2-wire mid-point earthed system.

$$\text{Power transmitted } P = 2VI_1$$

and

$$\text{Power loss } P_l = 2I_1^2R_1 = \frac{P^2R_1}{2V^2} \tag{17.9}$$

If power loss is same in both the cases (a) and (b), then from Equations (17.8) and (17.9), we get

$$\frac{P^2R_1}{2V^2} = \frac{2P^2R}{V^2}$$

or

$$R = \frac{R_1}{4} \tag{17.10}$$

Since the resistance is inversely proportional to the area of cross-section, Equation (17.10) can be written in terms of area of cross-section as

$$a_1 = \frac{a}{4} \tag{17.11}$$

Since the number of conductors required in both the cases is two, the ratio of volume of conductors will be

$$\frac{v_1}{v} = \frac{a_1 l}{al} = \frac{1}{4} \tag{17.12}$$

Thus the volume of the conductor required in the case of dc 2-wire mid-point earthed is only (1/4)th that of the dc 2-wire system. Although, in the monopolar operation, ground is used as return path. But here one conductor is assumed for this purpose. If only one conductor is used in case (a), the saving of conductor volume will be 1/2 only. It can be seen as

$$\frac{v_1}{v} = \frac{a_1(2l)}{al} = \frac{1}{2} \tag{17.13}$$

(c) *DC 3-wire system:* Figure 17.3 shows the dc 3-wire system. The current in the return circuit is twice the line current. Assume the balance condition, the power transmitted is

$$P = 2VI_2$$

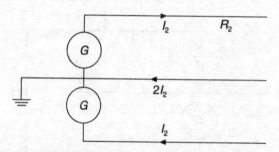

FIGURE 17.3　DC 3-wire system.

If the current density is same in all the cases, the area of return conductor is twice the outer conductors. Therefore, the resistance of return conductor is half of the outer conductors. The loss in return conductor is $4I_2^2 R_2/2$. Therefore

$$P_l = 2I_2^2 R_2 + 4I_2^2 \frac{R_2}{2} = 4I_2^2 R_2 = \frac{2P^2}{V^2} R_2 \tag{17.14}$$

For the same loss as compared to dc 2-wire system, we get

$$\frac{2P^2 R_2}{V^2} = \frac{2P^2 R}{V^2} \quad \text{or} \quad R_2 = R$$

Since resistance is inversely proportional to the area of cross-section, $a_2 = a$. Taking the area of cross-section of return wire double that of the outer wire, the ratio of volume of conductors in dc 3-wire system to that of dc 2-wire system will be

$$\frac{v_2}{v} = \frac{(a_2 + a_2 + 2a_2)l}{(a + a)l} = \frac{2a_2}{a} = 2 \tag{17.15}$$

In case when bipolar dc 3-wire system with return conductor is used, the return conductor current will be zero under the balance condition. The cross-section area of return conductor may be half of the outer conductor. Moreover there will be no loss in return conductor during the balance condition. Therefore, Equation (17.14) gives

$$P_l = 2I_2^2 R_2 = \frac{P^2}{V^2} R_2 \tag{17.16}$$

The ratio of resistance (R_2/R) is 2 and the ratio of cross-sectional area (a_2/a) is 1/2. Thus, the ratio of volume of conductors in dc 3-wire system to that of dc 2-wire system will be

$$\frac{v_2}{v} = \frac{[a_2 + a_2 + (a_2/2)]l}{(a + a)l} = \frac{2.5a_2}{2a} = \frac{2.5}{4} = 0.625 \tag{17.17}$$

(d) *AC* single-*phase, 2-wire system:* Figure 17.4 shows the ac single-phase, 2-wire system with mid-point earthed. It is also possible to have single phase with neutral return. Since the

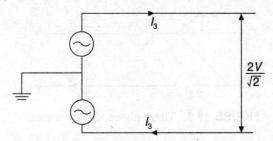

FIGURE 17.4 AC single-phase, 2-wire system.

maximum voltage is V between conductor and earth, the rms voltage between the conductor and earth is $V/\sqrt{2}$, as

$$V_{\text{rms}} = \frac{V_{\text{max}}}{\sqrt{2}}$$

If power factor $= \cos \phi$,

$$P = \sqrt{2}VI_3 \cos \phi \quad \text{and} \quad P_l = 2I_3^2 R_3$$

where R_3 is the resistance of each conductor having cross-sectional area of a_3 and I_3 is the current in each conductor. If power transmission is the same as dc 2-wire system with conductor return, we have

$$I_3 = \frac{I}{\sqrt{2} \cos \phi} \tag{17.18}$$

For the same power loss in the systems, we obtain

$$2I_3^2 R_3 = 2I^2 R \quad \text{or} \quad \frac{R_3}{R} = \left(\frac{I}{I_3}\right)^2 = 2 \cos^2 \phi$$

The ratio of area of conductors is

$$\frac{a_3}{a} = \frac{1}{2 \cos^2 \phi}$$

Since both the systems require the same number of conductors,

$$\frac{\text{Volume of conductors required for 1-phase, 2-wire system}}{\text{Volume of conductors required for dc 2-wire system}} = \frac{2a_3 l}{2al} = \frac{1}{2\cos^2 \phi} \quad (17.19)$$

(e) *Three-phase, 3-wire system:* Figure 17.5 shows a 3-phase system consisting of 3 wires. If the maximum voltage between the conductor and earth is V, the rms voltage is $V/\sqrt{2}$. Thus the power transmitted is

$$3\frac{V}{\sqrt{2}} I_4 \cos \phi$$

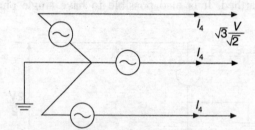

FIGURE 17.5 Three-phase, 3-wire system.

and line-to-line voltage is

$$V_{LL} = \sqrt{3}\frac{V}{\sqrt{2}}$$

If the power transmitted in this case is equal to the dc 2-wire system, then, we have

$$I_4 = \frac{\sqrt{2}}{\sqrt{3}\cos\phi} I \quad (17.20)$$

If R_4 is the resistance of each conductor, the power loss

$$P_l = 3I_4^2 R_4$$

For the same loss as compared to dc 2-wire system, we get

$$3I_4^2 R_4 = 2I^2 R$$

or

$$\frac{R_4}{R} = \frac{2}{3}\left(\frac{I}{I_4}\right)^2 = \frac{2}{3}\frac{3\cos^2\phi}{2} = \cos^2\phi \quad (17.21)$$

The ratio of cross-sectional area of conductors is

$$\frac{a_4}{a} = \frac{1}{\cos^2\phi}$$

Since the required number of conductors in this case is 3

$$\frac{\text{Volume of conductors required for 3-phase, 3-wire system}}{\text{Volume of conductors required for dc 2-wire system}} = \frac{3a_4l}{2al} = \frac{3}{2\cos^2\phi} \quad (17.22)$$

(f) *Three-phase, 4-wire system:* Figure 17.6 shows a 3-phase, 4-wire system. In this case one extra line is increased as compared to 3-phase, 3-wire system. Under balance condition there will be no current in the neutral wire. In practice, the cross-section area of

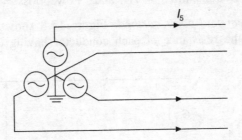

FIGURE 17.6 Three-phase, 4-wire system.

neutral wire is generally kept half of the line wires. Therefore, the comparison will be done in the same manner as done for ac 3-phase, 3-wire system, i.e. the ratio of resistances for each wire of the dc 2-wire system and that of this will remain the same as in Equation (17.21).

$$\frac{R_5}{R} = \cos^2\phi \quad (17.23)$$

where R_5 is the resistance of line conductors.
The ratio of cross-sectional area of conductors is

$$\frac{a_5}{a} = \frac{1}{\cos^2\phi}$$

Since the required number of conductors in this case is 3 and a half,

$$\frac{\text{Volume of conductors required for 3-phase, 4-wire system}}{\text{Volume of conductors required for dc 2-wire system}} = \frac{3.5a_5l}{2al} = \frac{1.75}{\cos^2\phi} \quad (17.24)$$

17.3.2 Equal Maximum Potential Difference between any Two Conductors

In the underground cables, the insulation requirement is based on the voltage between conductors. Now comparison of required conductor volume is based on the equal maximum potential different between any two conductors with assumption that power transmitted and power loss are the same.

(a) *DC 2-wire system:* Figure 17.7 shows the dc 2-wire system with potential difference V between two conductors.

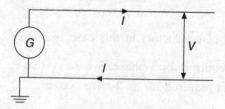

FIGURE 17.7   DC 2-wire system.

Then

$$\text{Power transmitted} = VI \quad \text{and} \quad \text{Power loss} = 2I^2R$$

(b) *DC 2-wire system mid-point earthed:* Figure 17.8 shows the dc 2-wire mid-point earthed system. If R_1 is the resistance of each conductor having cross-sectional area of a_1, then

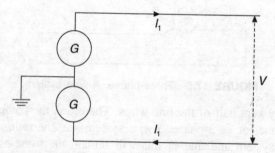

FIGURE 17.8   DC 2-wire system mid-point earthed.

$$\text{Power transmitted } P = VI_1 \quad \text{and} \quad \text{Power loss } P_l = 2I_1^2R_1$$

Since power transmitted and power loss are the same, the volume of conductor required in the dc 2-wire system and this system would be the same.

(c) *DC 3-wire system:* Figure 17.9 shows the dc 3-wire system with a common return path. This is a homopolar configuration. Then

$$P = VI_2$$

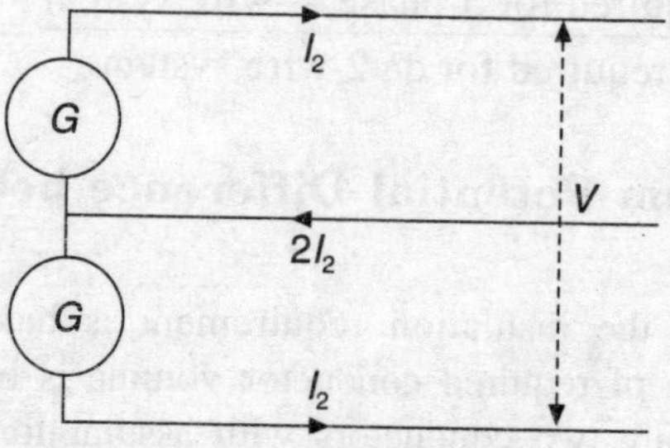

FIGURE 17.9   DC 3-wire system.

If the current density is the same in all the cases, the area of return conductor will be twice that of the outer conductors. Therefore, the resistance of return conductor will be half that of the outer conductors. The loss in return conductor is $4I_2^2 R_2/2$. Then

$$P_l = 2I_2^2 R_2 + 4\frac{I_2^2 R_2}{2} = 4I_2^2 R_2 \tag{17.25}$$

Since the power transfer in this system is the same as that of the dc 2-wire system, the ratio of their currents is unity. For the same loss, using Equation (17.25), we get

$$4I_2^2 R_2 = 2I^2 R$$

or

$$\frac{R_2}{R} = \frac{1}{2}\left(\frac{I}{I_2}\right)^2 = \frac{1}{2}$$

The ratio of cross-section

$$\frac{a_2}{a} = 2$$

Therefore, the ratio of volume of conductors in this case and in dc 2-wire system is

$$\frac{v_2}{v} = \frac{(a_2 + a_2 + 2a_2)l}{(a + a)l} = \frac{4a_2}{2a} = 4 \tag{17.26}$$

A similar analysis can be made for the bipolar operation of the dc system, where return path current is zero under the balance condition and thus there is no loss in return path. It is also assumed that the cross-section of return path is half of the outer conductors. Thus

$$P_l = 2I_2^2 R_2 + 0 = 2I_2^2 R_2$$

Therefore, the ratio of resistances and area of conductor is:

$$\frac{R_2}{R} = \left(\frac{I}{I_2}\right)^2 = 1 = \frac{a}{a_2}$$

Thus the ratio of volume of conductors in this case and in dc 2-wire system is:

$$\frac{v_2}{v} = \frac{[a_2 + a_2 + (a_2/2)]l}{(a + a)l} = \frac{2.5a_2}{2a} = \frac{2.5}{2} = 1.25 \tag{17.27}$$

(d) *Single-phase 2-wire system:* Figure 17.10 shows the ac single-phase, 2-wire system with mid-point earthed. It is also possible to have single phase with neutral return. Since the maximum voltage is V between conductors. The rms voltage between the conductors will be $V/\sqrt{2}$.

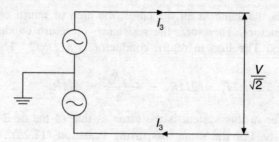

FIGURE 17.10   AC single-phase, 2-wire system.

If power factor = $\cos \phi$, then

$$P = \frac{V}{\sqrt{2}}I_3 \cos \phi \quad \text{and} \quad P_l = 2I_3^2 R_3$$

Equating power transmitted in this case and the power transmitted through the dc 2-wire system, we get

$$I_3 = \frac{\sqrt{2}I}{\cos \phi} \tag{17.28}$$

For the same losses in these two cases, we get

$$2I_3^2 R_3 = 2I^2 R \quad \text{or} \quad \frac{R_3}{R} = \left(\frac{I}{I_3}\right)^2 = \frac{a}{a_3}$$

Substituting the value of current from Equation (17.28), we have

$$\frac{a_3}{a} = \frac{2}{\cos^2 \phi}$$

Since the number of conductor used is the same as in the dc 2-wire system, the ratio of volume is

$$\frac{v_3}{v} = \frac{2a_3 l}{2al} = \frac{2}{\cos^2 \phi} \tag{17.29}$$

   (e) *Three-phase, 3-wire system:* Figure 17.11 shows the 3-phase system consisting of 3-wire. If the maximum voltage between the conductors is V, the rms voltage will be $V/\sqrt{2}$. Thus the power transmitted is $\sqrt{3}(V/\sqrt{2})I_4 \cos\phi$.

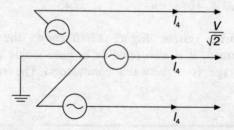

FIGURE 17.11   Three-phase, 3-wire system.

If power transmitted in this case is equal to the dc 2-wire system, we have

$$I_4 = \frac{\sqrt{2}}{\sqrt{3}\cos\phi} I \qquad (17.30)$$

If R_4 is the resistance of each conductor, the power loss is

$$P_l = 3I_4^2 R_4$$

For the same loss as compared to the dc 2-wire system, we get

$$3I_4^2 R_4 = 2I^2 R$$

or

$$\frac{R_4}{R} = \frac{2}{3}\left(\frac{I}{I_4}\right)^2 = \frac{2}{3}\frac{3\cos^2\phi}{2} = \cos^2\phi$$

The ratio of cross-sectional area of conductors is

$$\frac{a_4}{a} = \frac{1}{\cos^2\phi}$$

Since required number of conductors in this case is 3, we get

$$\frac{\text{Volume of conductors required for 3-phase, 3-wire system}}{\text{Volume of conductors required for dc 2-wire system}} = \frac{3a_4 l}{2al} = \frac{1.5}{\cos^2\phi} \qquad (17.31)$$

(f) *Three-phase, 4-wire system:* Figure 17.12 shows the 3-phase, 4-wire system. Only difference is one extra line as compared to the previous case. Under balance condition, there is no current in the neutral wire. In practice, the cross-section area is generally kept half of the line wires. Therefore, the comparison will be done in the same manner as done in the ac 3-phase, 3-wire system, i.e. the ratio of resistances for each wire of the dc 2-wire system and that of this will remain the same.

$$\frac{R_5}{R} = \cos^2\phi$$

where R_5 is the resistance of line conductors.

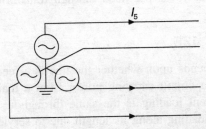

FIGURE 17.12 Three-phase, 4-wire system.

The ratio of cross-sectional area of conductors is

$$\frac{a_5}{a} = \frac{1}{\cos^2 \phi}$$

Since required number of conductors in this case is 3 and a half, we have

$$\frac{\text{Volume of conductors required for 3-phase, 4-wire system}}{\text{Volume of conductors required for dc 2-wire system}} = \frac{3.5a_4 l}{2al} = \frac{1.75}{\cos^2 \phi} \qquad (17.32)$$

It should be noted that if the neutral wire was having the same cross-section area, then the Equation (17.32) would become $2/\cos^2 \phi$.

Summary of both the comparisons are given in Table 17.1.

Table 17.1 Comparison between the Two Systems

Systems	Volume of conductor required	
	Equal maximum potential difference between conductor and earth	Equal maximum potential difference between two conductors other than neutral
DC 2-wire	1	1
DC 2-wire (mid-point earthed)	0.5	1
DC 3-wire (homopolar)	2.0	4.0
DC 3-wire (bipolar)	0.625	1.25
Single-phase, 2-wire (mid-point earthed)	$1/(2\cos^2\phi)$	$2/(\cos^2\phi)$
Three-phase, 3-wire	$1.5/(\cos^2\phi)$	$1.5/(\cos^2\phi)$
Three-phase, 4-wire	$1.75/(\cos^2\phi)$	$1.75/(\cos^2\phi)$

On the basis of comparison shown in Table 17.1, we conclude the following:

(a) The dc transmission is economical compared to the ac transmission. Normally, we use ground as return, the monopolar, bipolar and homopolar are the most suitable ones.

(b) For the distribution system, normally 3-phase, 3-wire system is the best, which is preferred due to greater efficiency of polyphase generation and convenience.

(c) Although, in the ac distribution, power factor is involved whereas its voltage can be stepped up to down as per need through transformers.

17.4 CONDUCTOR SIZE

Choice of conductor size depends upon whether the line is a feeder or a distributor. A *feeder* in a distribution network is a circuit carrying power from a main substation to a secondary substation such that the current loading is the same throughout its length. A distributor, on the other hand, has variable loading along its length due to service connections, tapped off at several positions. The voltage at consumer's terminal must be maintained within ±5% for satisfactory operation of appliances. Therefore, in case of distributor, the allowable voltage drop decides the cross-section of the conductor, whereas cross-section of a feeder is decided on its current-carrying capacity. For transmitting the power through feeder and to choose most economical cross-section or current density, the annual financial loss is to be worked out. The cross-section, which gives minimal annual financial loss, is to be adopted. This is known as *Kelvin's law*.

17.5 KELVIN'S LAW

Kelvin's law gives the cross-section of a feeder conductor based on an economic balance between capital cost and operating cost (running cost). The annual capital cost includes interest and depreciation, cost of conductors, insulators, supports and their erection, etc., if the feeder is carried on overhead line. For underground cables, it consists of cost of conductors, insulation and cost of laying the cable. For a particular voltage, the cost of insulation is constant and does not change with the cross-sectional area. For overhead lines, the cost of support and erection may be partly constant and partly proportional to the cross-section. The cost of conductor is directly proportional to the area of the cross-section of both the cables and overhead lines. Thus the annual capital cost can be represented as $(C_1 + C_2a)$, where C_1 and C_2 are the constants and a is the cross-section of conductor.

The running cost of a feeder is the cost associated with the energy wasted in the conductor and not the total input cost (fuel cost). The annual cost of energy wasted in the conductor is due to its resistance, and due to dielectric loss in the insulation and sheath loss in underground cables, which is very small in low-voltage application compared to the loss in resistance. Since ohmic loss is inversely proportional to the area of cross-section (because resistance is inversely proportional to the cross-sectional area), the annual cost of energy wasted can be represented as C_3/a, where C_3 is a constant. Thus the total annual cost (C) will be sum of the annual capital cost and the cost of energy wasted per annum:

$$C = C_1 + C_2a + \frac{C_3}{a} \tag{17.33}$$

From Equation (17.33), for economical area of cross-section of the feeder, the total annual cost must be minimum.

For minimum condition:

$$\frac{d}{da}\left(C_1 + C_2a + \frac{C_3}{a} \right) = 0 \quad \text{or} \quad C_2 - \frac{C_3}{a^2} = 0$$

Thus, we get

$$a = \sqrt{\frac{C_3}{C_2}} \tag{17.34}$$

or

$$C_2a = \frac{C_3}{a}$$

This shows that the variable part of annual capital charges must be equal to the cost of annual losses due to energy wastage in conductor for the most economical working. It is Kelvin's Law. Figure 17.13 shows the cost variation with respect to cross-section area of conductor.

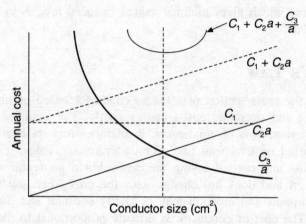

FIGURE 17.13 Cost variation with respect to cross-section area of conductor.

From Figure 17.13, it can also be seen that the minimum of the curve $C_1 + C_2a + (C_3/a)$ lies when $C_2a = C_3/a$. From Kelvin's law, several factors have not been considered but it is theoretically possible to apply this law. Main limitations of this law is discussed now.

Limitations of Kelvin's law

1. As annual charges depend partly on the area of cross-section and partly it is constant, the total annual capital cost $(C_1 + C_2a)$ is not strictly true especially for underground cables.

2. The calculation of energy waste is difficult because load on the feeder is not constant. The cost of generation depends, up to some extent, on the load factor and load factors for losses may be difficult to determine correctly especially in case of cables due to sheath loss. Moreover, the losses like dielectric and hysteresis also occur with high-voltage system and are dependent on load. Even if the load factor is estimated with a fairly good degree of accuracy, it may not suffice to calculate the unit of energy wasted. The load factor gives the average current from maximum current but heating is proportional to the rms current. Since

$$\text{Load factor (LF)} = \frac{\text{Average current}}{\text{Maximum current}} = \frac{I_{\text{av}}}{I_{\text{max}}}$$

and

$$\text{Form factor (FF)} = \frac{\text{rms Value of current}}{\text{Average current}} = \frac{I_{\text{rms}}}{I_{\text{av}}}$$

We get

$$\text{Average losses} \propto \left(I_{\text{max}} \times \text{LF} \times \text{FF}\right)^2$$

The quantity (load factor × form factor)^2 is known as the *loss load factor* or the load factor for the losses. There is also an empirical formula to calculate the load loss factor (LLF) and is given by

$$\text{Load loss factor (LLF)} = 0.2(\text{LF}) + 0.8(\text{LF})^2 \qquad (17.35)$$

The loss load factor is also given by

$$\frac{\text{Total loss per annum}}{I_m^2 R \times 8760}$$

where I_m is the current for which a feeder is to be designed.
3. Kelvin's law does not consider the physical aspect of problem such as line resistance, voltage drop, temperature rise, mechanical strength, etc.
4. The loss due to corona is not considered which may be very high for small diameter of conductor, bad weather condition and high-voltage operation.

Kelvin's law is practically not true but useful in providing the rough idea about the conductor's cross-section. In case of cable, the deviation is significant as explained above. After considering the temperature rise and voltage drop, chances of acceptable result of Kelvin's law for overhead lines (not for underground cables) are up to 30 kV.

Example 17.1 The cost of a 3-phase overhead transmission line having the cross-section area a cm^2 is Rs (500 + 2000a) per kilometre. Calculate the most economical current density for the conductor if the rate of interest and depreciation is 12% per annum and the cost of energy wasted is 5 paise per kWh. The resistivity of the conductor may be taken as 1.7 μΩ-cm. Take load factor of 12%.

Solution Maximum loss in the line = $3I^2R$, where I is the maximum current. Since the load factor for losses (load-loss factor) = 12% = 0.12,

Annual average line-loss = $0.12 \times 3I^2R$ watt

Annual line-loss during the whole year = $0.12 \times 3I^2R \times 8760 \times 10^{-3}$ kWh

$$\text{Resistance of conductor} = \frac{1.7 \times 10^{-6} \times 10^{-2} \times 10^3}{a \times 10^{-4}} = \frac{0.17}{a} \text{ ohm/km}$$

$$\text{Cost of line-losses} = 0.12 \times 3I^2 \times \frac{0.17}{a} \times 8760 \times 10^{-3} \times \frac{5}{100} = \text{Rs } \frac{0.0268I^2}{a}$$

and

Variable part of the annual fixed cost of the conductor = $2000 \times a \times 0.12$

$$= \text{Rs } 240a$$

Hence, from Kelvin's Law

$$240a = \frac{0.0268I^2}{a} \quad \text{or} \quad \frac{I}{a} = \sqrt{\frac{240}{0.0268}} = 94.5 \text{ A/cm}^2$$

Example 17.2   For a 3-phase 110-kV transmission system, the daily load cycle is given below:

   (a)   30 MW for 5 hours at 0.8-p.f. lagging
   (b)   15 MW for 10 hours at 0.9-p.f. lagging
   (c)   8 MW for 9 hours at unity p.f.

If the cost of the line per km is Rs $(3000 + 16000a)$, where a is the cross-sectional area in cm^2 and interest and depreciation cost on the capital cost is 10%, find the most economical cross-section area of the conductor. The cost of energy is 50 paise per kWh and the resistance of the conductor is $0.17/a$, where a is in cm^2.

Solution   Load currents for different loads are:

   (a) For 30-MW load, $I_1 = \dfrac{30 \times 10^6}{\sqrt{3} \times 110 \times 10^3 \times 0.8} = 196.8$ A

   (b) For 15-MW load, $I_2 = \dfrac{15 \times 10^6}{\sqrt{3} \times 110 \times 10^3 \times 0.9} = 87.5$ A

   (c) For 8-MW load, $I_3 = \dfrac{8 \times 10^6}{\sqrt{3} \times 110 \times 10^3 \times 1.0} = 41.99$ A

Daily energy-loss in all the three conductors = $3R\left(I_1^2 \times 5 + I_2^2 \times 10 + I_3^2 \times 9\right)$

$$= 8.583 \times 10^5 R$$

The annual loss = $365 \times 8.583 \times 10^5 R$

$$= \frac{5.3254 \times 10^7}{a} \text{ kWh}$$

Cost of energy waste = $\dfrac{5.3254 \times 10^7}{a} \times 0.50$

$$= \text{Rs } \frac{2.6627 \times 10^7}{a}$$

and interest and depreciation on the capital, that is

$$\text{Annual fixed cost} = (3000 + 16000a) \times 0.10 = \text{Rs } (300 + 1600a)$$

Therefore, from Kelvin's Law

$$1600a = \frac{2.6627 \times 10^7}{a} \quad \text{or} \quad a = 129 \text{ cm}^2$$

17.6 Influence of Voltage on the Size of a Feeder and a Distributor

The electric energy is supplied to consumers through a distribution system. A distribution system can be subdivided into three distinct parts: *feeders, distributor* and *service mains*. Feeders and distributors are explained in the previous sections. The service mains are small conductors, which deliver power to the consumer's premises up to the metering point. Figure 17.14 shows the feeders, distributors and mains. *SA* and *SB* are the feeders, *AB*, *BC*, *CD* and *DA* are the distributors, and power coming out of distributors is the service mains.

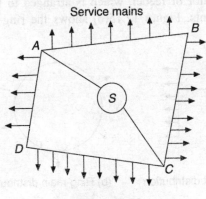

Figure 17.14

To see the effect of voltage on the cross-section of the feeder and distributor, let us assume that the system voltage is increased n times. Take power factor at unity in the case of ac.

(a) *Feeders:* Since the feeders are designed based on the current density, it is assumed to be the same for normal voltage and with increased voltage. If power delivered is P at voltage V, the current I will be P/V. If the voltage increases to n times, then $I' = P/(nV) = I/n$. For the same current density, the cross-section can be made $1/n$ times the original value.

(b) *Distributor:* Since the distributors are designed based on the voltage drop, it is assumed to be the same for normal voltage and with increased voltage. If I is the current which causes a voltage drop v volts in it, its resistance R is v/I. If the voltage is increased to n times its original value, then voltage drop is nv. The current flowing in the second case is I/n, therefore, the drop = $IR'/n = nv = nRI$, where R' is the resistance in the second case. Therefore, $R' = n^2R$. Thus for the same percentage of the voltage drop, the cross-section can be made $1/n^2$ times the original value.

17.7 Radial and Ring-main Distributors

If a distributor is connected to the supply system from one end only, it is called *radial system* of distribution. This is also true for the feeders i.e. if a feeder is connected to the supply system from one end only that feeder is called *radial feeder*. Figure 17.15(a) shows a radial distribution system. The main drawbacks of this system are:

1. Distributor nearest to the substation is highly loaded.
2. Severe voltage variation to the consumers far away from the substation due to load variations.
3. Consumers are dependent on a single feeder and a single distributor and a fault on either of them causes interruption of supply to all the consumers away from the fault.

The difficulties of a radial system can be overcome by using a ring-main system. A *ring main* is the name given to a distributor or feeder, which is arranged to form a closed loop. It may have one or more feeding points. Figure 17.15(b) shows the ring-main distributing system.

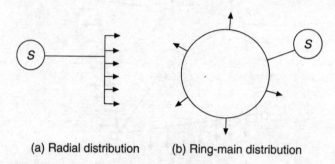

(a) Radial distribution   (b) Ring-main distribution

FIGURE 17.15   Radial and ring-main distribution systems.

17.8   INTERCONNECTORS

Sometimes between the two points of a ring main, the potential difference becomes very high which can be reduced by increasing the cross-section of the feeder ring or by joining those points which have high potential difference by an interconnector. Since increasing the cross-section requires the replacement of older ring main and also more volume of conductor, inter-connectors provide economy and are frequently used. Interconnected distribution system and system with interconnectors are different. In the interconnected distribution system, different feeding stations (more than one) are connected by interconnected feeders. However interconnectors are used in distributors to reduce the potential difference between any two points. Figure 17.16 shows the interconnected distribution system and interconnectors.

17.9   METHODS OF FEEDING DISTRIBUTORS

A distributor may be fed at one end or at both ends. If it is fed at both ends, it may have either equal voltages or unequal voltages at both the ends. The loads may be either (a) concentrated loads or (b) uniformly distributed loads or (c) concentrated and uniformly distributed loads. Concentrated loads are the loads which act at a particular point, whereas distributed loads are those loads which act on all points of a distributor. In practice, there are no ideally distributed loads but densely concentrated loads can be treated as distributed loads for analysis purpose. Since the voltage drop is the main criteria for designing the distributors, the procedures for evaluating voltage drop at various points are discussed in the following sections.

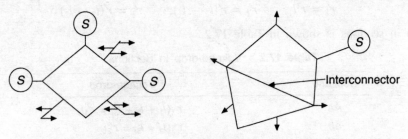

(a) Interconnected system   (b) Ring main system with interconnector

FIGURE 17.16   Interconnected distribution system.

17.9.1   DC Distributors with Concentrated Loads Fed at One End

Consider a dc distributor is fed from the one end (AA') only, as shown in Figure 17.17(a). Three concentrated loads I_1, I_2 and I_3 are connected at points a, b and c at distance l_1, l_2

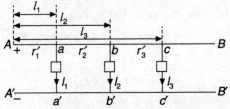

(a) DC distributor fed from one end

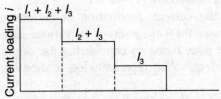

(b) Current distribution at various points

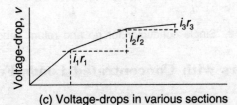

(c) Voltage-drops in various sections

FIGURE 17.17   DC distributor with concentrated loads.

and l_3, respectively. Wire AB is go-conductor, whereas $A'B'$ is the return-conductor. If the resistance per unit length of conductors is r', resistance of sections Aa, ab and bc are

$$r'_1 = r'l_1, \qquad r'_2 = r'(l_2 - l_1), \qquad r'_3 = r'(l_3 - l_2)$$

Voltage-drop in sections is shown in Table 17.2.

Table 17.2   Voltage-drop in Sections

Sections	Voltage-drop
Aa	$r'_1(l_1 + l_2 + l_3) = r'_1 i_1$
ab	$r'_2(l_2 + l_3) = r'_2 i_2$
bc	$r'_3 l_3 = r'_3 i_3$
$A'a'$	$r'_1(l_1 + l_2 + l_3) = r'_1 i_1$
$a'b'$	$r'_2(l_2 + l_3) = r'_2 i_2$
$b'c'$	$r'_3 l_3 = r'_3 i_3$

where i_1, i_2 and i_3 are the currents in sections Aa, ab and bc respectively.

Now, we get voltage at the load point bb'

$$
\begin{aligned}
V_b &= V_{AA'} - V_{Ab} - V_{b'A'} \\
&= V - (i_1 r'_1 + i_2 r'_2 + i_1 r'_1 + i_2 r'_2) \\
&= V - 2r'_1 i_1 - 2r'_2 i_2 \\
&= V - (i_1 r_1 + i_2 r_2) \\
&= V - \Sigma\, ir
\end{aligned}
\tag{17.36}
$$

where $r\ (=2r')$ is the resistance per unit length of both go and return conductors. In general, voltage at any point can be calculated by $(V - \Sigma\, ir)$.

Figure 17.17(b) shows the current distribution at various points in the distributor, whereas Figure 17.17(c) indicates the voltage-drops in various sections of the distributor.

This analysis can also be done based on considering the single equivalent conductor for return and go conductors. The equivalent representation is shown in Figure 17.18.

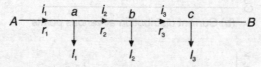

FIGURE 17.18   Single conductor for go and return conductors.

17.9.2   DC Distributors with Concentrated Loads Fed from Both the Ends

Ends maintained at equal voltages

Figure 17.19 shows a distributor with three concentrated loads which is fed from both the ends with equal voltages. Only equivalent representation of both return and go conductors is

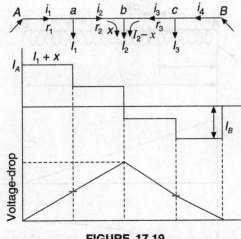

FIGURE 17.19

shown here. Let us assume that current I_2 consists of current x from end A and remaining current $(I_2 - x)$ flows from end B as shown in Figure 17.19. Currents in each section can be represented in terms of load currents and x. Potential at b calculated from both ends is the same. Therefore

$$V_A - i_1r_1 - i_2r_2 = V_B - i_3r_3 - i_4r_4$$

Since $V_A = V_B$, we have

$$i_1r_1 + i_2r_2 = i_3r_3 + i_4r_4$$

or

$$(I_1 + x)r_1 + xr_2 = (I_2 - x)r_3 + r_4(I_2 + I_3 - x)$$

Current in each section is also given in Figure 17.19. Simplifying above equation, we get the value of x. Therefore, the value of current from both the ends can be calculated as

$$I_A = I_1 + x \qquad \text{and} \qquad I_B = I_2 + I_3 - x$$

It should be noted that the value of x might be negative. The minimum potential point will have the currents from both the ends. In Figure 17.19, the current at b is from both the ends and thus it is the minimum potential point.

Ends maintained at unequal voltages

When V_A and V_B are not equal but known, x can be determined with the following equation:

$$V_A - i_1r_1 - i_2r_2 = V_B - i_3r_3 - i_4r_4$$

or

$$V_A - (I_1 + x)r_1 + xr_2 = V_B - (I_2 - x)r_3 + r_4(I_2 + I_3 - x)$$

17.9.3 DC Distributed Load Fed at One End

Figure 17.20 shows the uniformly distributed load of i amp/unit length. If r is the resistance per unit length of loop of the distributor, the total current fed from end A will be il ampere, where l is the length of loading. Let us consider an element of length dx at distance x from

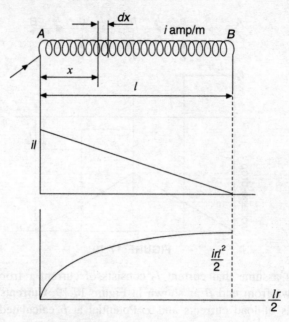

FIGURE 17.20 Uniformly distributed load.

end A. The tapped current in this element will be $i\,dx$ but it is not the current carried by this section. The current carried by small section will be $(l - x)i$. The resistance of the section will be $r\,dx$. Thus the voltage-drop at distance x from A is $i(l - x)\,r\,dx$. Total drop over length x will be

$$v = \int_0^x i(l - x)\,r\,dx = ilrx - \frac{ix^2 r}{2} \qquad (17.37)$$

Equation (17.37) represents a parabola. The voltage-drop is shown in Figure 17.20. Total drop over length l is

$$irl^2 - \frac{il^2 r}{2} = \frac{irl^2}{2} = \frac{(il)(lr)}{2} = \frac{IR}{2} \qquad (17.38)$$

where I is the total current fed from end A and R is the total loop resistance of the distributor. It is noted that total drop in the case of uniformly distributed load fed at one end is equal to that produced by the total load assumed concentrated at the middle point.

17.9.4 DC Distributed Load Fed from Both the Ends

Figure 17.21 represents the uniformly loaded distributor fed from both the ends. If the voltage at both the ends is same, the minimum potential point is at $l/2$. Therefore, the distributor could be imagined to have two equal lengths of $l/2$ for the voltage-drop calculation. The current supplied from each end is $il/2$ and voltage drop at mid-point of distributor is

$$\frac{I}{2}\frac{rl}{2} = \frac{il/2}{2}\frac{rl}{2} = \frac{irl^2}{8}$$

Figure 17.21 illustrates the advantage of feeding the distributor at both the ends as the drop is (1/4)th the drop when the distributor is fed from one end only. The figure also shows the current distribution in the distributor and the voltage-drop along the distributor.

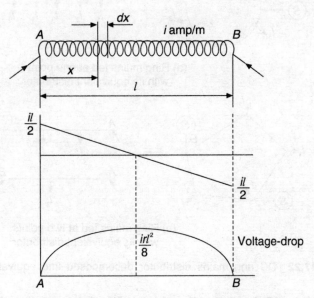

FIGURE 17.21 Current distribution in the distributor and voltage-drop along the distributor.

In the concentrated load case, the power loss in distributors can be easily calculated after knowing the currents in each section because the resistance of each section is known. Power loss in the case of distributed load fed from one end is calculated now. Since the power flow in elemental dx is $(l - x)i$, whereas the loss in this section is $((l - x)i)^2 \, r \, dx$,

$$\text{Loss over the complete distributor} = \int_0^l (l - x)^2 \, i^2 r \, dx = \frac{i^2 r l^3}{3} \text{ watt} \qquad (17.39)$$

The power loss in the distributor fed from both the ends can be calculated firstly for half of the line and then can be doubled it. The current in any small element in the half of the section is $i[(l/2) - x]$. Thus

$$\text{Loss} = 2 \int_0^{l/2} \left(\frac{l}{2} - x \right)^2 i^2 r \, dx = \frac{i^2 r l^3}{12} \qquad (17.40)$$

This can also be concluded that in the case of feeding from both the ends (at equal voltage), the loss is reduced by (1/4)th that of the fed from one end only.

17.9.5 DC Ring Mains Distributor

In the ring main distribution, the supply is either fed from one point or from more points but the distributors get the supply from both the ends. For the calculation of voltage drop, the ring main distributors are decomposed into the equivalent distributor fed from both the ends, as shown in Figure 17.22, and the same analysis can be done as done in the earlier sections.

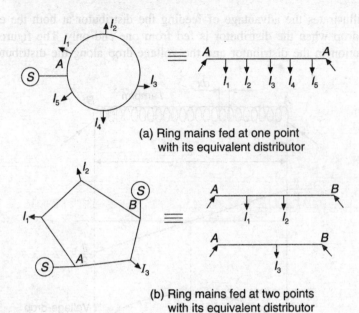

(a) Ring mains fed at one point
with its equivalent distributor

(b) Ring mains fed at two points
with its equivalent distributor

FIGURE 17.22   DC ring mains distributor decomposed into equivalent distributor.

17.9.6 DC Ring Main Distribution with Interconnector

Double ring distributors or ring distributor with interconnector is used to reduce the voltage-drop between some points. The voltage-drop is calculated using the Kirchhoff's law, Thevenin equivalent, etc. Figure 17.23 shows the ring main distributor with an inter-connector. In the figure, it is assumed that the current in section AB is x and the interconnector is y. Thus the current in each section can be calculated using Kirchhoff's current law (KCL). Using Kirchhoff's voltage law, two equations can be obtained for two loops. Therefore the unknowns x, y and the current fed from a source can be calculated.

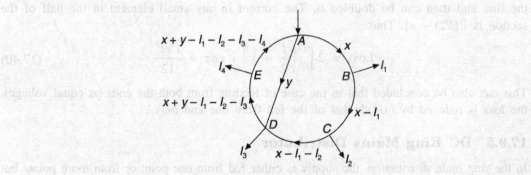

FIGURE 17.23

17.10 DC Three-wire Distributors

Fed at one end

Figure 17.24 shows the dc 3-wire distributors with five loads. To calculate the voltage drop and voltages at different points, currents in each section must be calculated using KCL. Using KCL, currents in different sections are shown in Table 17.3. In some sections it can be known by looking at the network, such as in section BA and $A'D$ the current is I_1, in section BD it is I_2.

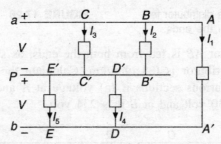

FIGURE 17.24 DC 3-wire distributors with five loads.

Table 17.3 Sections and the Currents Passing through Them

Section	Current
BA and $A'D$	I_1
CB	$I_1 + I_2$
DE	$I_1 + I_4$
Ca	$I_1 + I_2 + I_3$
Eb	$I_1 + I_4 + I_5$
$E'P$	$(I_2 + I_3) - (I_4 + I_5)$
$C'E'$	$I_2 + I_3 - I_4$
$D'C'$	$I_2 - I_4$
$D'B'$	I_2

Knowing current in each section, we can easily calculate the voltage drop because the resistance of each section is known. Thus the total loss can also be evaluated. It should be noted that the current direction is very important for the voltage-drop whether it is positive or negative.

Fed from both the ends

Figure 17.25 shows the dc 3-wire distributor fed from both the ends with voltages V and V_1 which may be equal or unequal. Such distributors are best dealt with by first considering the positive outer alone, as shown in Figure 17.26(a) (as a 2-wire distributor) and finding the point of minimum potential and current distribution and thereafter the negative outer is considered separately, as shown in Figure 17.26(b). The current in various sections of neutral wire are obtained using KCL. The voltage across various load points can also be obtained in similar manner.

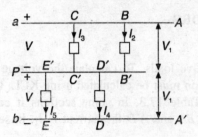

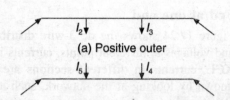

(a) Positive outer

FIGURE 17.25   DC 3-wire distributor fed from both the ends.

FIGURE 17.26   Two-wire distributor as in Figure 17.25.

Example 17.3   A distributor *AB* is fed from both the ends, as shown in Figure 17.27. The loop resistance of the distributor is 0.5 ohm/km. Calculate the minimum voltage and its location, and currents in various sections if (a) voltage at *A* and *B* are equal to 230 volt, (b) voltage at point *A* is 230 volt and at *B* it is 234 volt.

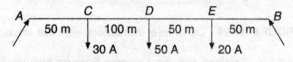

FIGURE 17.27   Example 17.3.

Solution   Let current from the end *A* is I_A and from the end *B* it is I_B. The total current is

$$I_A + I_B = 30 + 50 + 20 = 100 \text{ A}$$

Let the *x* amp current at load point *D* is fed from the end *A* and remaining current of load point *D*, $(50 - x)$ is fed from end *B*. Currents in sections *AC*, *CD*, *DE*, *EB* are $(30 + x)$, *x*, $(50 - x)$ and $(50 - x + 20)$ amp, respectively. The voltage at point *D* can be written as

$$V_A - (30 + x) \times 0.5 \times \frac{50}{1000} - x \times 0.5 \times \frac{100}{1000}$$

$$= V_B - (70 - x) \times 0.5 \times \frac{50}{1000} - (50 - x) \times 0.5 \times \frac{50}{1000}$$

or

$$V_A - V_B = 0.125x - 2.25$$

(a) If $V_A = V_B = 230$ volt, $x = 18$ A. The current at load *D* from the end *B* is 32 $(=50 - 18)$ A. This shows that the current of load *D* is met from both the ends and thus point *D* will be the minimum potential point. The potential at *D* is

$$V_A - (30 + x) \times 0.5 \times \frac{50}{1000} - x \times 0.5 \times \frac{100}{1000} = 230 - 1.2 - 0.9$$

$$= 227.9 \text{ volt}$$

(b) If V_A = 230 volt and V_B = 234 volt, x = –14 A, this shows that the current in section *CD* is 14 A from *C* to *B*. Load point *C* is the minimum potential point because the load is met from both the end-currents. The potential at *C* is

$$V_A - (30 + x) \times 0.5 \times \frac{50}{1000} = 230 - 0.4 = 229.6 \text{ volt}$$

When $V_A = V_B = 230$ volt		When $V_A = 230$ volt and $V_B = 234$ volts	
Section	Current	Section	Current
AC	48 (from *A* to *C*)	AC	16 (from *A* to *C*)
CD	18 (from *C* to *D*)	CD	14 (from *D* to *C*)
DE	32 (from *E* to *D*)	DE	64 (from *E* to *D*)
EB	52 (from *B* to *E*)	EB	84 (from *B* to *E*)

Example 17.4 If the resistance of a distributor (both return and go) is 0.005 ohm/m and the distributed load in section *DE* is 1 A/m, find the current distribution and minimum voltage in the distributor, as shown in Figure 17.28, when (a) both the ends are at same potential and (b) potential difference between the ends *A* and *B* is 4 volt.

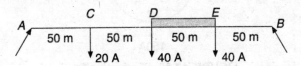

FIGURE 17.28 Example 17.4.

Solution Total load = 20 + 40 + 1 × 50 + 40 = 150 A. Let I is the current flowing from the end *A*. The current in sections *AC*, *CD* and *EB* are I, $(I - 20)$ and $(I - 150)$, respectively. The current in section *DE* at any distance x from *D* is $(I - 60 - x)$. The voltage drop between *A* and *B* is

$$V_A - V_B = I \times 0.005 \times 50 + (I - 20) \times 0.005 \times 50$$

$$+ 0.005 \int_0^{50} 1 \times (I - 60 - x) \, dx + (I - 150) \times 0.005 \times 50$$

$$= 0.25I + 0.25I - 5 + 0.005 \left[(I - 60)x - \frac{x^2}{2} \right]_0^{50} + 0.25I - 37.5$$

$$= I - 63.75$$

(a) When both the ends are at equal potential, i.e. $V_A - V_B = 0$, we have $I = 63.75$ A and the current from the end *B* is 86.25 (=150 – 63.75) A.

Currents in sections *AC*, *CD* and *EB* are 63.75 A, 43.75 A and –86.25 A, respectively. At point *D*, 3.75-A current is flowing into section *DE*. This is completely taped in a length of 3.75 m because the current distribution in section *DE* is 1 A/m. Hence the minimum point voltage is 3.75 m from *D* toward *E*, i.e. 103.75 m from the end *A*.

(b) When the potential difference is 4 volt, i.e. $V_A - V_B = 4$, we have $I = 67.75$ A and the current from the end B is 82.25 ($=150 - 67.75$) A. Currents in sections AC, CD and EB are 67.75 A, 47.75 A and -82.25 A, respectively. At point D, 7.75-A current is flowing into section DE. This is completely taped in a length of 7.75 m because the current distribution in section DE is 1 A/m. Hence the minimum point voltage is 7.75 m from D toward E, i.e. 107.75 m from the end A.

Example 17.5 A 2-wire dc ring main, having the loading at points C, D and E, is fed at point B from a feeder AB, as shown in Figure 17.29. If the cross-section area of the feeder is a cm^2 and that of the distributor is b cm^2, find the values of a and b for minimum volume of copper in the system. Given that the maximum drop from A does not to exceed 10 volt. The length of the feeder AB is 500 m and the length of distributors BC, CD, DE and EB are 200, 150, 120 and 70 m, respectively. Take resistivity of copper = 1.7 μΩ-cm.

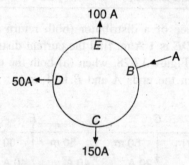

FIGURE 17.29 Example 17.5.

Solution For solving such problems, one current should be assumed in one section of the distributor near to the feeding point. The total current which flows from A to B is 300 A ($=150 + 50 + 100$). Let the current I flows in section BE from B to E. Therefore, the currents in other sections ED, DC and CB are $(I - 100)$, $(I - 150)$ and $(I - 300)$, respectively. If r is the resistance per unit length, the voltage equation using KVL in loop $BEDCB$ can be written as:

$$I \times 70r + (I - 100) \times 120r + (I - 150) \times 150r + (I - 300) \times 200r = 0$$

Solving this, we get $I = 175$ A.

Since the current at the point comes from both the sides, it will be the point of minimum voltage. The maximum voltage drop should not exceed 10 volt (given). The resistance of feeder AB (r_F) (both go and return) will be

$$r_F = \frac{1.7 \times 10^{-6} \times 500 \times 100}{a} \times 2 = \frac{0.17}{a} \text{ ohm}$$

The voltage drop in the feeder will be

$$300 \times \frac{0.17}{a} = \frac{51}{a} = V_F$$

Similarly drop in distributor BC will be

$$V_{BC} = (300 - 175) \times \frac{1.7 \times 10^{-6} \times 200 \times 100}{b} \times 2 = \frac{8.5}{b}$$

Since $V_F + V_{BC} = 10,$ $V_F = 10 - V_{BC}.$ Then

Volume of copper in feeder $AB = 500 \times 100 \times 2 \times a$

$$= 500 \times 100 \times 2 \times \frac{51}{V_F} \text{ cm}^3$$

$$= \frac{5.1}{V_F} \text{ m}^3$$

and

Volume of copper in distributor $= 540 \times 100 \times 2 \times b$

$$= 540 \times 100 \times 2 \times \frac{8.5}{V_{BC}} \text{ cm}^3$$

$$= \frac{0.918}{V_{BC}} \text{ m}^3$$

Therefore,

$$\text{Total volume of copper} = \frac{5.1}{V_F} + \frac{0.918}{V_{BC}} = \frac{5.1}{10 - V_{BC}} + \frac{0.918}{V_{BC}}$$

For the minimum volume of the copper,

$$\frac{d(\text{volume})}{dV_{BC}} = 0$$

Therefore,

$$\frac{5.1}{(10 - V_{BC})^2} - \frac{0.918}{V_{BC}^2} = 0$$

Solving this and ignoring the negative value, we get $V_{BC} = 2.985$ volt. Therefore,

$$\text{Area of the feeder} = \frac{51}{10 - 2.985} = 7.29 \text{ cm}^2 = a$$

and

$$b = \frac{8.5}{2.985} = 2.83 \text{ cm}^2$$

Example 17.6 Find the percentage change in the volume of copper required with and without interconnector AB for the same voltage drop between points A and B of the distributor, as shown in Figure 17.30. Assume, all the conductors have the same cross-section area and same resistivity. The length of sections AC, CB, BD, DE, EA and AB are 100, 150, 100, 200, 50 and 200 m, respectively.

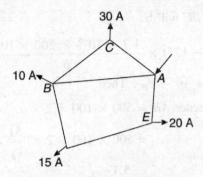

FIGURE 17.30   Example 17.6.

Solution   (a) *When there is no interconnector:* Let current x in the section AC is flowing from A to C. Thus, the currents in other sections are:

Section	Current
CB	$x - 30$
BD	$x - 40$
DE	$x - 55$
EA	$x - 75$

If r is the resistance per unit length, using KVL in loop $ACBDEA$, we have

$$100 \times xr + (x - 30) \times 150r + (x - 40) \times 100r + (x - 55) \times 200r + (x - 75) \times 50r = 0$$

Solving, we get, $x = 38.75$ A. This shows that the current in sections AC and CB are respectively 38.75 and 8.75 A. Now, the voltage drop from A to B is

$$\frac{\rho}{a_1} (38.75 \times 100 + 8.75 \times 150) = \frac{5187.5\rho}{a_1} \tag{1}$$

where a_1 is the cross-section of distributors and ρ is the resistivity of conductors.

(b) *When there is an interconnector AB:* Let current x flows from A to C and current y from A to B. Currents in various section are:

Section	Current
AC	x
AB	y
CB	$x - 30$
BD	$x + y - 40$
DE	$x + y - 55$
EA	$x + y - 75$

Using KVL for loop $ACBA$, we have

$$100 \times xr + (x - 30) \times 150r - y \times 200r = 0$$

or

$$2.5x - 2y = 45 \tag{2}$$

Using KVL for loop *AEDBA*, we have

$$(x + y - 40) \times 100r + (x + y - 55) \times 200r + (x + y - 75) \times 50r + y \times 200r = 0$$

or

$$3.5x + 5.5y = 187.5 \tag{3}$$

Solving equations (2) and (3), we get $x = 30$ A and $y = 15$ A. Now,

$$\text{Voltage-drop between interconnector } AB = \frac{\rho}{a_2} (15 \times 200) = \frac{3000\rho}{a_2} \tag{4}$$

where a_2 is the cross-section of all the sections when the interconnector is present. For the same voltage drop between A and B, using equations (1) and (4), we have the following relation

$$\frac{5187.5\rho}{a_1} = \frac{3000\rho}{a_2}$$

or

$$\frac{a_1}{a_2} = 1.729 \tag{5}$$

When there is no interconnector, the volume of copper

$$v_1 = (100 + 150 + 100 + 200 + 50)a_1 = 600a_1$$

When the interconnector AB is present, the volume of copper

$$v_2 = (100 + 150 + 100 + 200 + 50 + 200)a_2 = 800a_2$$

Therefore,

$$\text{Change in volume} = \frac{v_2 - v_1}{v_1} = \frac{800a_2 - 600a_1}{600a_1} = \frac{8a_2}{6a_1} - 1$$

From equation (5), we get

$$\text{Change in volume} = \frac{8a_2}{6a_1} - 1 = \frac{8}{6}\frac{1}{1.729} - 1 = -0.229$$

Therefore, the percentage change is 22.9% (saving).

Example 17.7 A 3-wire distributor is shown in Figure 17.31 having five loads. If the supply voltage is 220 volt, find the voltage across load points. The resistance of outers is 1 ohm/km and the neutral has 1/2 cross-sectional area of the outers. The section lengths aC, CB, BA, $B'D'$, $D'C'$, $C'E'$, $E'P$, $A'D$, DE and Eb are respectively 100, 100, 150, 50, 50, 50, 50, 200, 100, 50 m.

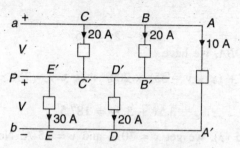

FIGURE 17.31   Example 17.7.

Solution   Since the neutral cross-section area is half that of the outers, the resistance will be double that of the outers, i.e. 2 ohm/km. The current distribution in the section and the drops are:

Section	Resistance (ohm)	Current (A)	Voltage-drop (volt)
BA	0.15	10	1.5
A'D	0.20	10	2.0
CB	0.10	30	3.0
DE	0.10	30	3.0
aC	0.10	50	5.0
Eb	0.05	60	3.0
C'E'	0.05	20	1.0
D'C'	0.05	0	0.0
B'D'	0.05	20	1.0
PE'	0.05	10	0.5

It should be noted that the direction of current is very important while calculating the voltage drop. Therefore,

Voltage across CC' = 220 – Drop in aC – Drop in $C'E'$ + Drop in PE'
$$= 220 - 5.0 - 1.0 + 0.5$$
$$= 214.5 \text{ volt}$$

Voltage across BB' = voltage CC' – Drop in CB – Drop in $B'D'$ – Drop in $D'C'$
$$= 214.5 - 3.0 - 1.0 - 0.0$$
$$= 210.5 \text{ volt}$$

Voltage across $E'E$ = 220 – Drop in PE' – Drop in Eb
$$= 220 - 0.5 - 3.0$$
$$= 216.5 \text{ volt}$$

Voltage across $D'D$ = Voltage across $E'E$ + Drop in $E'C'$ + Drop in $C'D'$ – Drop in DE
$$= 216.5 + 1.0 + 0.0 - 3.0$$
$$= 214.5 \text{ volt}$$

Voltage across AA' = 440 – Drop in aC – Drop in CB – Drop in BA – Drop in $A'D$ – Drop in DE – Drop in Eb

$$= 440 - 5.0 - 3.0 - 1.5 - 2.0 - 3.0 - 3.0$$

$$= 422.5 \text{ volt}$$

Example 17.8 A train is running from station A and is crossing another train standing at 2 km from station B. The loading due to running train is 500 A, while at standing it takes 50 A (Figure 17.32). What will be the position of running train for having minimum potential at a point in the section having distance 10 km between stations A and B, if both the ends are maintained at equal dc potentials?

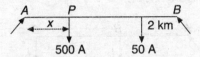

FIGURE 17.32 Example 17.8.

Solution Let when moving train A is at point P (x km from station A), be the minimum potential point. If the resistance of the section is r ohm/km, the potential at point P is

$$V_P = V - Irx = V + 2r(I - 550) + (8 - x)(I - 500)r$$

where V is the potential of both the stations, I is the current assumed to flow from station A. The current that flows from station B is $(I - 550)$. Simplifying, we get

$$I = \frac{2900 - 500x}{6} \text{ A}$$

Therefore, the potential at point P is

$$V_P = V - \frac{rx}{6}(2900 - 500x)$$

The potential to be minimum, when dV_P/dx. Thus

$$-\frac{r}{6} \times 2900 + \frac{500 \times 2x}{6} = 0$$

Hence $x = 2.9$ km.

17.11 AC DISTRIBUTION

In ac distribution, the effect of power factor of load and the reactance of line are to be considered. The voltage drop is due to the combined effects of resistance and reactance. In Chapter 10, the calculation of voltage drop for transmission lines has been discussed for calculating the regulation. The main difference in voltage-drop calculation in distribution system compared to transmission system neglects the capacitive effect of line. In the case of distributors, it is very less. One specialty in ac voltage-drop calculation is to use all impedances, currents and voltages in phasor rotation taking voltage (or current) as reference and the same methods as were used in dc distribution are applicable to ac distribution, too.

It should be noted that all the calculations are normally carried out on single-phase basis and the power factors of the loads may either referred to supply (or some other points such as receiving end) voltage or referred to the respective load points.

17.12   AC Distributor with Concentrated Loads

Power factor with respect to receiving end

Consider a distributor with two loads I_1 and I_2 at power factors $\cos\phi_1$ and $\cos\phi_2$ respectively, as shown in Figure 17.33. Taking voltage at point C (V_C) as reference, the phasor diagram is shown in Figure 17.34.

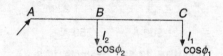

FIGURE 17.33   A distributor with two loads.

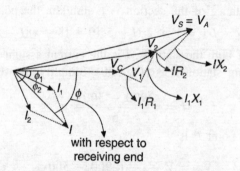

FIGURE 17.34   Phasor diagram.

If the resistance of section BC is $R_1 + jX_1$ and of section AB is $(R_2 + jX_2)$, the voltage drop in section BC will be $\overline{I}_1(R_1 + jX_1)$ and in section AB it will be $(\overline{I}_1 + \overline{I}_2)(R_2 + jX_2)$, where

$$\overline{I}_1 = I_1(\cos\phi_1 - j\sin\phi_1)$$

$$\overline{I}_2 = I_2(\cos\phi_2 - j\sin\phi_2)$$

$$\overline{V}_A = V_C + \overline{v}_1 + \overline{v}_2$$

$$\overline{I} = \overline{I}_1 + \overline{I}_2$$

where $\overline{v}_1$ and $\overline{v}_2$ are complex voltage drops in sections BC and AB, respectively.

Power factor with respective load points

If the power factors are with respective load point voltage, the power factor angle ϕ_2 is with respect to voltage V_B, whereas power factor angle ϕ_1 is with respect to voltage at point C, i.e. receiving-end voltage. For calculating the voltage drop, in this case, first the voltage at the respective load is to be determined. Then the actual power factor angle with respect to the reference point is determined to calculate the voltage at other points.

Example 17.9 Figure 17.35 shows a 1-phase line having resistance and reactance (go and return) as 0.06 and 0.1 ohm/km. The lengths of section *AB* and *BC* are 1.0 km each. The voltage at the farther end is 220 volt. Find the voltage at the sending end and the phase angle difference between the voltages of two ends (load angle), if

(a) power factors of the loads are with reference to farther-end voltage

(b) power factors of the loads are with reference to the voltages at the load points.

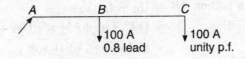

FIGURE 17.35 Example 17.9.

Solution (a) *Taking voltage at the receiving end as reference:* The current at points *B* and *C* are:

$$\bar{I}_B = 100 \,(0.8 + j0.6) \text{ A} \quad \text{and} \quad \bar{I}_C = 100(1.0 + j0.0) \text{ A}$$

Resistance of section *BC* and *AB* are

$$\bar{Z}_{BC} = (0.06 + j0.10) \text{ ohm} \quad \text{and} \quad \bar{Z}_{AB} = (0.06 + j0.10) \text{ ohm}$$

Then

$$\text{Drop in section } BC = I_C Z_{BC} = 100 \times (0.06 + j0.10) = (6 + j10) \text{ volt}$$

The potential at point *B* is

$$\bar{V}_B = 220 + (6 + j10) = 226 + j10 = 226.22 \angle 2.53° \text{ volt} \qquad \text{(i)}$$

$$\text{Current in section } AB = I_B + I_C = (180.0 + j60.0) \text{ A}$$

and

Voltage drop in section *AB* = $(I_B + I_C)\, Z_{AB}$

$$= (180 + j60) \times (0.06 + j0.10)$$

$$= 4.8 + j21.6$$

Therefore, voltage at point *A* is

$$\bar{V}_A = \bar{V}_B + 4.8 + j21.6$$

$$= (226 + j10) + (4.8 + j21.6)$$

$$= 230.8 + j31.6$$

$$= 232.95 \angle 7.80° \text{ volt}$$

Thus the voltage at the sending-end 232.95 volt and the angle difference is 7.80° with receiving-end voltage.

(b) *When the power factors are with respect to respective load point voltages:* Taking the receiving-end voltage as reference in this case, too, the voltage at point *B* is the same as equation (i), we have

$$\overline{V}_B = 220 + (6 + j10) = 226 + j10 = 226.22\angle 2.53°$$

Power factor angle of the load at point B is $\cos^{-1}(0.8) = 36.87°$ (lead) with respect to the voltage V_B. Thus the power factor angle with reference to common reference V_C is $-36.87 - 2.53 = 39.40°$. Therefore,

$$\overline{I}_B = 100 \ [\cos (39.40) + j \sin (39.40)] = 100 \ (0.773 + j0.635)$$

and

$$\text{Current in section } AB = \overline{I}_B + \overline{I}_C = 177.3 + j63.5 \text{ A}$$

Therefore,

$$\text{Voltage drop in section } AB = (I_B + I_C) \ Z_{AB}$$
$$= (177.3 + j63.5) \times (0.06 + j0.10)$$
$$= (4.284 + j21.54) \text{ volt}$$

Now, voltage at point A is

$$\overline{V}_A = V_B + 4.284 + j21.54$$
$$= (226 + j10) + (4.284 + j21.54)$$
$$= 230.284 + j31.54$$
$$= 232.43\angle 7.80°$$

Thus the voltage at the sending end will be 232.43 volt and the angle difference is 7.80° with the receiving-end voltage.

17.13   THREE-PHASE, FOUR-WIRE DISTRIBUTION SYSTEM

Some loads are single phased and some are 3-phased. AC distribution system normally is a 3-phase, 4-wire system. Fourth wire is used as the return conductor for all the three phases, which is connected to the star point of the load and neutral of the supply system. The current through it is zero under balance condition but practically it is not possible however utilities try to balance the load on each phase. Moreover, it is necessary to balance the loads otherwise it will result in unbalance voltages which is dangerous to the induction motors.

Three-phase, 4-wire system can be analyzed based on the single-phase. The neutral current is the phasor sum of all the phase currents. The potential e of the load star point can be obtained using Miliman's theorem as,

$$e = \frac{\overline{E}_1 \overline{Y}_1 + \overline{E}_2 \overline{Y}_2 + \overline{E}_3 \overline{Y}_3}{\overline{Y}_1 + \overline{Y}_2 + \overline{Y}_3} \tag{17.41}$$

17.14   SUB-MAINS

Figure 17.36 shows a sub-mains arrangement. *Service mains* are conductors between a distributor and the metering point of the consumers' premises. There are possibilities of several connections of consumers from one service mains; it is called *sub-mains*. The diameter of conductors of sub-mains is more than the normal service mains.

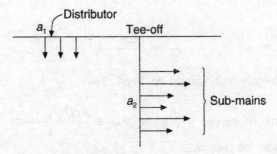

FIGURE 17.36 Sub-mains.

17.15 STEPPED AND TAPERED MAINS

When a series of loads are tapped off from the mains, it is obvious that the current along the length will vary, as shown in Figure 17.37(a). If the area of cross-section is same throughout a distributor in view of its current carrying capacity, much copper will be required. It is seen that the cross-section area should not be according to the fixed current density but criterion is a fixed voltage drop. Let us consider a distributor, as shown in Figure 17.37(b) with two loads I_1 and I_2 tapped off at points A and B respectively. Let the lengths and cross-section area be l_1, a_1 for FA and l_2, a_2 for AB. Then

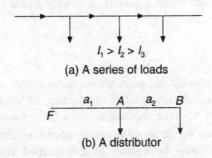

$$l_1 > l_2 > l_3$$

(a) A series of loads

(b) A distributor

FIGURE 17.37 Stepped and tapered mains.

$$\text{Resistance for section } FA \text{ (go and return)} = \frac{2\rho l_1}{a_1}$$

Therefore,

$$\text{Voltage drop in section } FA = \frac{2\rho l_1}{a_1}(I_1 + I_2) = v$$

or

$$a_1 = \frac{2\rho l_1}{v}(I_1 + I_2) \qquad (17.42)$$

and

$$\text{Voltage drop in section } AB = \frac{2\rho l_2}{a_2}I_2 = v' = v_t - v$$

or

$$a_2 = \frac{2\rho l_2}{v_t - v} I_2 \qquad (17.43)$$

where v_t is the total drop, which should be fixed. Thus

$$\text{Total volume of copper} = 2l_1 a_1 + 2l_2 a_2 = \frac{4\rho l_1^2 (I_1 + I_2)}{v} + \frac{4\rho l_2^2 I_2}{v_t - v}$$

For the minimum volume of copper,

$$\frac{d(\text{volume})}{dv} = 0$$

Therefore,

$$0 = -\frac{4\rho l_1^2 (I_1 + I_2)}{v^2} + \frac{4\rho l_2^2 I_2}{(v_t - v)^2}$$

Simplifying with help of Equations (17.42) and (17.43), we get

$$\frac{a_1}{a_2} = \sqrt{\frac{I_1 + I_2}{I_2}} \qquad (17.44)$$

Equation (17.43) shows that the current density is not the same in the sections. For the same current density,

$$\frac{a_1}{a_2} = \frac{I_1 + I_2}{I_2} \qquad (17.45)$$

Practically, it is economically not possible to manufacture conductors of varying cross-section. However, more joints are involved if conductors of different cross-section are used. But it is technically desirable to have minimum joints. The most important objection of this method is that future additions to the system may completely alter the distribution of current in sections, and sometimes it may be useless to use stepped conductors.

PROBLEMS

17.1 One train is running from station *A* and is crossing another train standing at 3 km from station *B*. The loading due to the running train is 600 A, while at standing it is 50 A. What will be the position of the running train for having minimum potential at a point in the section having distance 8 km between stations *A* and *B*, if both the ends are maintained at equal dc potentials?

17.2 An electric train taking a constant current of 500 A moves on a section of line between two substations 10-km apart and maintained at 600 and 590 volt, dc respectively. The track resistance is 0.05 ohm/km both go and return. Find the point of minimum potential along the track and current supplied by two substations at that instant.

17.3 In a 2-core dc distributor cable 400-m long supplies there are concentrated loads of 120, 80, 50 and 120 A at 50, 150, 200 and 300 m, respectively from the end *A*.

Determine the position of the lowest voltage when the cable is fed at 250 volt from both the ends.

17.4   In a dc 3-wire network, as shown in Figure 17.38, calculate (i) the potential difference between D and D' (ii) the power dissipated in the conductor and (iii) the total power supplied to the loads. The conductor resistances of sections aC, CB, BA, PE', $E'C'$, $C'D'$, $D'B'$, bE, ED, are 0.2, 0.4, 0.6, 0.4, 0.4, 0.4, 0.6, 0.4 and 0.5 ohm, respectively. Take supply voltage = 250 V.

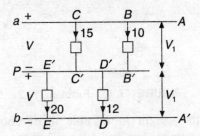

FIGURE 17.38   Problem 17.4.

17.5   In a dc network, as shown in Fig. 17.39, power fed at point A which is kept at 240 volt and loads of 50 A, each are tapped at points B, C and D. Resistances marked are for both go and return. Find the voltages at various load points.

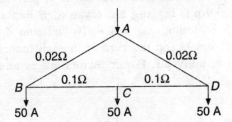

FIGURE 17.39   Problem 17.5.

17.6   A 1-phase distributor has a total resistance of 0.2 ohm and a reactance of 0.3 ohm. At the mid-point A, a current of 100 A at 0.8-p.f. leading and at the far-end B, a current of 100 A at 0.8-p.f. lagging is tapped. If the voltage at the midpoint is 200 volt find the voltage at the supply-end and also its phase angle with respect to voltage at the far-end when (i) the power factors are with respect to respective voltages at the load points (ii) the power factors are with respect to voltages at the midpoint.

17.7   Compare the ratio of weights of copper with and without interconnector CE for the same voltage drop between the points A and D of the network, as shown in Figure 17.40. The length of sections AB, BC, CD, DE and AE are 100, 150, 200, 250 and 200 m, respectively. The length of the interconnector is 350 m. All conductors have common cross-section in both the cases.

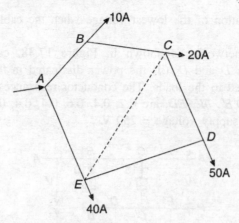

FIGURE 17.40   Problem 17.7.

17.8   Compare the conductor weight in a cable distribution system for a low-voltage network with (i) dc 3-wire system and (ii) ac 3-phase, 4-wire system. Neglect losses in the middle conductors (which are half the cross-section of respective outers) and assume the same voltage (to neutral) at the consumer's terminals, same percentage loss, unity power factor and balance loads in both the cases.

17.9   A 3-phase distribution system is shown in Figure 17.41. Power is supplied at A at a line voltage of 11 kV and balanced loads of 25 A per phase at 0.8-p.f. lagging and 35 A per phase at 0.9-p.f. lagging are taken at B and C. The impedances of the feeders are: $Z_{AB} = 5 + j9$ ohm, $Z_{BC} = 6 + j10$ ohm and $Z_{CA} = 4 + j8$ ohm. Calculate the voltages at B, C and D and the current in each branch. Load at mid-point D of section BC is 10 A at unity p.f. Power factors are assumed with respect to voltage at A.

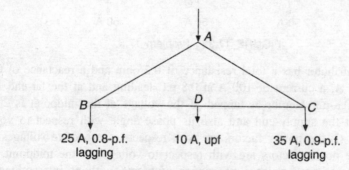

25 A, 0.8-p.f.   10 A, upf   35 A, 0.9-p.f.
lagging   lagging

FIGURE 17.41   Problem 17.9.

18

Power Substations

18.1 Introduction

Normally large power-generating stations are built far away from load centres. There are a number of transformations and switching stations built between generating stations and the ultimate consumers. These are generally known as *substations*. A typical substation may include the following equipments: transformers, circuit breakers, disconnecting switches, station buses and insulators, reactors, capacitors, current and potential transformers, grounding system, lightning arrestors and spark gaps, wave traps, protective relays, station batteries, etc.

18.2 Types of Substations

A substation or switching station functions as a connection and switching points for transmission lines, subtransmission feeders, generating units, and transformers. Depending upon the purpose, the substations may be classified into five categories:

1. *Generating substations or step-up substations:* Normally the generating voltages are limited and need to be stepped up to the transmission voltage so that large amount of power can be transmitted economically over long. Each generating unit is connected to generating transformers to increase the secondary voltage up to transmission voltage levels.

2. *Grid substations:* These substations are located in the intermediate points between the generating stations and load centres. The main purposes of these substations are to provide connections of low-voltage lines, some compensating devices, etc.

3. *Secondary substations:* These substations are connected with the main grid substation with the help of secondary transmission lines. The voltage at these substations is stepped down to the subtransmission voltage (primary distribution voltage). Some large power consumers are also connected to these substations.

4. *Distribution substations:* These are made where the subtransmission voltage (primary distribution voltage) is to be stepped down to the supply voltage. These substations feed power to the actual consumers through distributors and service lines.

5. *Special purpose substations:* Some special substation for bulk power and some industrial loads are set up. Traction substations and mining substations are the examples of these. Special design considerations are required in these substations such as load distribution in phases in traction substation and safety precautions in the mining substations. Some mobile substations are also used for construction purposes, which are temporary as mobile.

Depending upon the physical features, the substations can also be of four types:

1. *Outdoor type:* Normally outdoor substations are used for 33-kV voltage and above for cost and safety reasons. The air clearances required are large. All equipments lie open in the air however control and monitoring is performed inside the control rooms.

2. *Indoor type:* The equipments of these substations lie in a room. The operating voltages are normally 400 V and 11 kV. These substations are located in big cities.

3. *Pole mounted or open or kiosk type:* As its name, these substations are mounted on the poles. These substations are very simple and cheap as no building for housing the equipments are required. However, these substations are of low capacity usually having up to 500-kVA transformer.

4. *Underground type:* These are used when the space is not available. Whole substation is made underground. The size of the substation can be high or low depending upon the capacity.

In a substation, there may be several transformers and several incoming and outgoing lines. The highest voltage rating of transformer and transmission lines are the rating of a substation. If a substation is of 220 kV, it means there is a transformer of high-voltage side of 220 kV or a line of 220 kV or both. The substation design aims to achieve a high degree of continuity, maximum reliability and flexibility, to meet these objectives with the highest possible economy.

18.3 Bus-Bar Arrangements

Substation bus-bars are the most important part of the substation structure since they carry high amount of energy in a confined space and their failure would have very drastic repercussions on the power supply continuity. Therefore the bus system must be built to be electrically flexible and reliable enough to give continuous service. It must have adequate capacity to carry all loads and robust construction to withstand foreseeable abnormal electro-mechanical forces.

Bus-bars may be either of rigid or of strain type. Low voltage and medium voltage bus bars are usually of the rigid bus type using copper or aluminium bars or tubing as the phase conductors with pedestal type insulator supports. Higher voltage bus-bars use strain type that is an overhead system of stranded aluminium (ACSR) or copper conductors strung between supporting structures and supported by strain insulators. This arrangement is more economical than the rigid type arrangement. Substations of the EHV class (voltage levels of 345 kV, 400 kV, 500 kV, 765 kV) and UHV class (voltage levels of 1100 kV, 1500 kV) are usually of strain bus design. The advantages of rigid type bus compared to strain type bus design are presented as follows:

- The rigid bus design employs less steel and simple low-level structures.
- The rigid conductors are not under constant strain.
- The pedestal type bus supports are usually easier in maintenance and cleaning.
- The rigid bus has low profiles, which provides good visibility of the conductors and apparatus.
- Due to larger diameter of pipes, corona loss is extremely less.

The disadvantages of rigid bus bars are:

- It is comparatively expensive due to higher cost of tubing and the connections.
- It usually needs more supports and insulators.
- It is more sensitive to structural deflections which may lead to possible damage.
- It requires usually more ground space than strain type.

Combination of rigid and strain bus constructions are sometimes used in conventional arrangements, up to 765 kV, to benefit from both types. The comparisons of materials used in bus-bars at different voltages are given in Table 18.1.

Table 18.1 Bus-bar Materials

Voltage levels (in kV)	Rigid type (aluminium pipe diameters in mm)	Strain type overhead wires
33	40	
66	65	37/2.79 mm ACSR
132	80	37/4.27 mm ACSR
220	80	61/3.99 mm ACSR
400	100	61/4.27 mm ACSR duplex

18.4 SUBSTATION BUS SCHEMES

The choice of the bus schemes or arrangements depends on the relative importance assigned to such items as safety, reliability, voltage level, simplicity of relaying, flexibility of operation, least cost, ease of maintenance, available ground area, location of connecting lines, ease of rearrangement, and provision of expansion.

18.4.1 Single Bus Scheme

Figure 18.1 shows a typical single bus scheme. It is commonly used scheme for a voltage of 33 kV or lower and has a simple design. It is used in small outdoor substations having relatively a few outgoing or incoming feeders and lines. The main advantage of single bus scheme is its low cost. However, it has several disadvantages, such as:

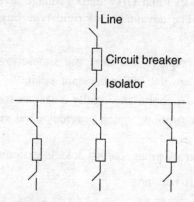

FIGURE 18.1 Single bus scheme.

(a) Dependence on a single bus can cause a serious outage in the event of bus failure.

(b) Difficult to do any maintenance.

(c) Bus cannot be extended without completely de-energizing the substation.

(d) It can be used only where loads can be interrupted or other supply arrangements.

With single bus arrangement there are a lot of arrangements possible. If it is a terminating substation, the arrangement can be seen in Figure 18.2.

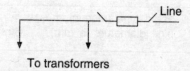

FIGURE 18.2 Terminal station scheme.

In single bus-bar with bus sectionalizer scheme, the bus bar is normally divided in two sections with help of a breaker and isolators as shown in Figure 18.3. The incoming or outgoing circuits are distributed evenly on the sections. When double feed is provided to any single load, it is preferred to have one circuit from each section where each section behaves as a separate bus bar. Differential protection can be used for tripping the faulty section.

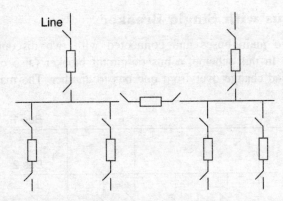

Line

FIGURE 18.3 Single bus scheme with bus sectionalizer.

18.4.2 Double Bus with Double Breaker

This scheme, as shown in Figure 18.4, is useful for most of the purposes where the loads and continuity of supply justify additional costs. The main advantages of this scheme are:

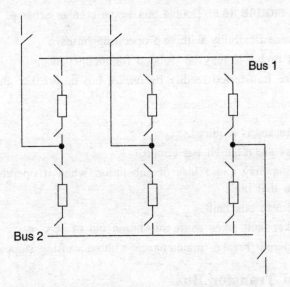

Bus 1

Bus 2

FIGURE 18.4 Double bus double breaker scheme.

(a) Each circuit has two dedicated breakers.

(b) It has flexibility in permitting feeder circuits to be connected to either bus.

(c) Any breaker can be taken out for maintenance.

(d) It is more reliable than single bus scheme.

The main drawbacks of this scheme are that it is most expensive; and it may lose half the circuits for breaker failure if circuits are not connected to both buses.

18.4.3   Double Bus with Single Breaker

This scheme uses two main buses and connected with two disconnecting switches, as shown in Figure 18.5. In this scheme, a bus tie-circuit breaker (also called *bus coupler*) is used as it enables a load change over from one bus to another. The main advantages of this scheme are:

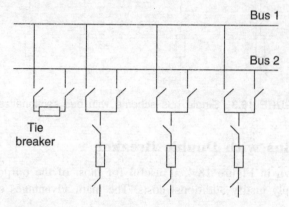

FIGURE 18.5   Double bus single breaker scheme.

(a) It permits some flexibility with two operating buses.

(b) Either bus 1 or bus 2 may be isolated for maintenance.

(c) Circuit can be transferred readily by use of bus-tie breaker and the isolators.

However main drawbacks of this scheme are:

(a) One extra breaker is required.

(b) Four isolators are required per circuit.

(c) Bus protection may cause loss of substation when it operates if all circuits are connected to that bus.

(d) High exposure to bus fault.

(e) Bus-tie breaker fault takes entire substation out of service.

(e) It does not permit breaker maintenance without causing stoppage of supply.

18.4.4   Main and Transfer Bus

The main and transfer bus, as shown in Figure 18.6, is used for mostly in distribution substations. The transfer bus is a standby for emergency use. In this scheme several circuit breakers are saved, however one extra breaker is provided to tie the main and transfer bus together when the need arises. The main advantages of this scheme are its low initial and ultimate cost. Any breaker can be taken out of service for maintenance and potential devices may be used on the main bus for relaying. The main drawbacks of this scheme are: switching is somewhat complicated when maintaining a breaker, failure of a bus or any circuit breaker results in shut down of entire substation, and requires an extra breaker.

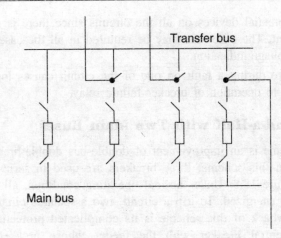

FIGURE 18.6 Main and transfer bus.

18.4.5 Ring Bus

This scheme is also known as *mesh scheme*. Figure 18.7 shows a ring bus scheme. It requires only one circuit breaker per circuit. Moreover, each outgoing circuit has two sources of supply. The main advantages of this scheme are:

(a) low initial cost,

(b) flexible operation for breaker maintenance,

(c) any breaker can be taken out for maintenance without interrupting load,

(d) it requires only one breaker per circuit,

(e) it does not use main bus,

(f) each circuit is fed by two breakers,

(g) all switching is done through breakers.

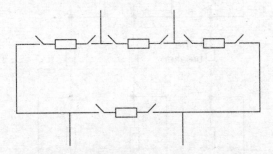

FIGURE 18.7 Ring bus or mesh scheme.

The main disadvantages are:

(a) If fault occurs during a breaker maintenance period, the ring will be divided into two sections.

(b) Automatic reclosing and protective relaying circuitry is complex.

(c) It requires potential devices on all the circuits since there is no definite potential reference point. These devices may be required in all the cases for synchronizing, live line or voltage indication.

(d) Breaker failure during a fault on one of the circuit causes loss of one additional circuit owing to operation of breaker failure relay.

18.4.6   Breaker-and-a-Half with Two Main Buses

Breaker-and-a-half scheme is an improvement of double-bus double-breaker scheme to save the cost of breakers. In this scheme, three breakers are used in series between the main buses, as shown in Figure 18.8. Under normal operating condition, all breakers are closed and the main buses are energized. To trip a circuit, two associated circuit breakers must be opened. The main drawback of this scheme is its complicated protection since it must be associated with the central breaker with the feeder whose breaker is taken out for maintenance. The advantages of this scheme are:

(a) Most flexible operation

(b) High reliability

(c) Breaker failure of bus side breakers removes only one circuit from service

(d) All switching is done with breakers

(e) Simple operation and no disconnect switching required for normal operation

(f) Either main bus can be taken out of service with supply interruption

(g) Bus failure does not remove any feeder circuit from service.

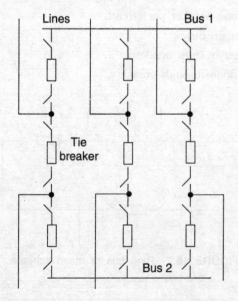

FIGURE 18.8   Breaker-and-a-half scheme.

18.4.7 Double Bus-bar with Bypass Isolators

This is a scheme similar to main and transfer bus, where transfer bus is also a main bus. The transfer from bus 1 to bus 2 is done through the isolators. With this scheme as shown in Figure 18.9 any bus can act as main bus and second bus as transfer bus. The main advantage of this scheme is that any breaker can be taken out of service without interrupting the supply of any feeder. This scheme is very simple and economical.

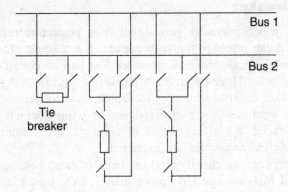

FIGURE 18.9 Double bus with bypass isolators.

18.5 SUBSTATION LOCATION

Location of distribution substation depends on the several technical factors such as voltage levels, voltage regulation considerations, subtransmission costs, substation costs, and the cost of primary feeders, mains and distribution transformers. Some non-technical factors such as availability of land, public safeties, etc., are also important. The most economical position of the substation is at the centre of gravity of the loads to be supplied. As far as the industrial and commercial substations are concerned, they are normally located near to or within the premises of the consumer.

To select an ideal location for a distribution substation, following rules should be observed:

1. Locate the substation as much as close to the load centre of its service area so that the sum of the load times distance of the substation is minimum.

2. Locate the substation such that proper voltage regulation can be obtained without taking extensive measures.

3. Select the substation location such that it provides proper access for incoming subtransmission lines and outgoing primary feeders and also capable to handle the future expansion.

4. Selected location should be in accordance with the electricity rule and land use regulation.

5. The selected substation should help minimize the number of customers affected by any service discontinuity.

18.6   SUBSTATION EQUIPMENTS

A substation has several equipments: transformers, circuit breakers, disconnecting switches and fuses, station buses and insulators, reactors, capacitors, current and potential transformers, grounding system, lightning arrestors and gaps, line traps, protective relays, station batteries, etc. The main substation equipments are briefly discussed below:

18.6.1   Circuit Breaker

Circuit breaker (CB), which normally gets signal from protective relays to operate, is an automatic switch which can interrupt the fault current. For a single-phase operation, such as traction etc., 'single pole' circuit breakers are used. The part of circuit breaker connected to one phase is called the *pole*. Three-pole circuit breaker is used for a 3-phase operation. Each pole of the circuit breaker consists of one or more interrupter or arc extinguishing chambers. An interrupter, which encloses a set of fixed and moving contacts, is mounted on the insulators. Arc is produced due to separation of contacts and is interrupted by a suitable medium and by suitable techniques for arc extinction.

The circuit breakers can be classified on the basis of rated voltages such as low-voltage CB (up to 1 kV) and high-voltage CB (more than 1 kV). Based on the medium of arc extinction, the circuit breakers are classified as follows:

(a) Air breaks circuit breaker (used up to 12 kV) and miniature circuit breaker (up to 600 V) where air at atmospheric pressure is used.

(b) Oil circuit breaker (bulk oil or tank type)(used for 3.6 kV to 12 kV), where dielectric oil is used.

(c) Minimum oil circuit breaker (for 3.6–245 kV), where dielectric oil is used.

(d) Air blast circuit breaker (for 245–1100 kV), where compressed air is used.

(e) SF_6 circuit breaker (for 36–420 kV), where SF_6 gas is used.

(f) Vacuum circuit breaker (up to 36 kV), where vacuum is used.

Based on the mode of arc extinction, circuit breakers can be classified as high-resistance interruption or low-resistance (or zero point) interruption. The circuit breakers are decided based on the voltage and fault current of the place where it should be installed. The voltage rating of CB is normally from 1.05 to 1.10 times more than normal operating voltage. For example, the rating of CB for 400 kV line would be 420 kV.

Most of the EHV circuit breakers are provided with auto reclosure. It has been verified that 90% faults (arcing faults) are transient in nature and the arcs in the fault can be extinguished by de-energizing the line by simultaneous opening of circuit breakers of either both the ends or single end of the line. Since transient faults disappear after a short duration, the circuit breaker can be closed and continuity of supply can be restored. Normally, only one reclosing attempts are allowed. If fault persists, the circuit breaker will be in open position.

18.6.2   Isolators and Fuses

An isolator (disconnecting switch) operates under no-load condition and does not have any current breaking and making capacity and used for disconnecting the circuit breaker from live part of the maintenance. Isolators are used in addition to circuit breakers which can make and break circuit under normal- and short-circuit conditions. The position of isolators is shown in Figure 18.10. For opening a circuit, the circuit breaker is opened first and then isolator is operated. In addition to isolators and circuit breakers, another device called *load break switch* (or *load interrupting switch*) combines the functions of an isolator and switch. These are used for breaking the load current.

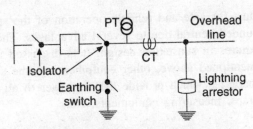

FIGURE 18.10 Isolator positions.

A fuse is the simplest current-interrupting device for protection of excessive currents due to overload or fault. They are normally used up to 600-V installations. High rupturing capacity cartridge (HRC) fuses are more reliable and give better discrimination and accurate characteristics. Sometimes these are superior to the circuit breakers.

18.6.3 Lightning Arrester

It is also known as *surge arrestor* which is normally connected between phase and ground at the substation, as shown in Figure 18.10, to protect the substation equipments from lightning and switching surges. Surge arrestors offer low resistance to the high voltage surge for diverting to the ground. After discharging the surge energy to ground, it blocks the normal current flowing to ground by offering a high-resistance path.

18.6.4 Reactors and Capacitors

To limit the line charging current, long-distance EHV lines are connected with line reactors at both the ends. These reactors are permanently connected to the line. Besides these, there are bus reactors and tertiary reactors which are connected with switches. These are used during light-loading conditions and at the line charging. Bus reactors are connected at the substation bus whereas tertiary reactors are connected in the tertiary winding of the transformers. By using these reactors the Ferranti effect is reduced.

Capacitors are normally connected in low-voltage systems. During the peak-load conditions, the system voltage falls and therefore capacitive reactive power is required. In EHV system, it is preferable to use the static VAr system because it takes care of reactive power which can supply both leading and lagging reactive powers. In distribution system or in sub-transmission system, capacitors are connected to improve the power factor of the system.

18.6.5 Current and Potential Transformers

Current transformers (CTs) and potential transformers (PTs) are very common in the substation. They are used for either measuring purpose or for giving the input to the relays. The connection of CT and PT is shown in Figure 18.10.

18.6.6 Grounding

A proper grounding is must for safe and reliable operation of the substation. All the power systems operate with grounded neutral due to several advantages. The neutral earthing is one of the most important features in substation design. It is discussed in next chapter.

Apart from those mentioned above, other equipments in the substation are substation transformers, substation batteries which provide the dc power to all the control equipments, protective relays, wave traps, measuring equipments, etc.

varies with seasons, reduces its resistivity. Therefore, the grounding system should be installed deeper to the optimum water level, if possible, to minimize the effect of seasonal variation on the soil resistivity.

The soil resistivity increases as the temperature decreases. When conductivity is by the conduction, ions also depends on the amount of salt dissolved in its moisture which affects the resistivity considerably. Different salts have different effects on the soil resistivity. Distribution of grain size has an effect on the manner in which moisture is held. The smaller the grain size, the lower will be the resistivity. Higher pressure usually will result in lower resistivity.

19.2.1   Resistance of Driven Rods

For the driven rods resistance formula can be derived.

It could be assumed that if its geometry approximates to that of an ellipsoid of revolution having a major axis a that is twice the rod's length (l) and a minor axis equal to its diameter d, then

$$R = \frac{\rho}{2\pi l} \ln\left(\frac{4l}{d}\right) \qquad (19.1)$$

If the rod is assumed carries the current uniformly along its length, then

$$R = \frac{\rho}{2\pi l} \ln\left(\frac{4l}{d}\right) \qquad (19.2)$$

If that is valid two electrodes in parallel is derived as

$$R_2 = \frac{\rho}{4\pi l}\left[\ln\left(\frac{4l}{d}\right) + \ln\left(\frac{4l}{s}\right)\right] \qquad (19.3)$$

varies with seasons, reduces its resistivity. Therefore, the grounding system should be installed nearest to the permanent water level, if possible, to minimize the effect of season variation on the soil resistivity.

The soil resistivity increases as the temperature decreases with a discontinuity at the freezing point. It also depends on the amount of salt dissolved in its moisture which reduces the resistivity remarkably. Different salts have different effects on the soil resistivity. Distribution of grain size has an effect on the manner in which the moisture is held. The finer the graining, the lower will be the resistivity. High pressure results in lower value of resistivity.

19.2.1 Resistance of Driven Rods

One of the simplest and cheapest forms of electrodes is the driven rod. Its ground resistance (R) could be calculated if its space is approximated to that of an ellipsoid of revolution having a major axis equal to twice the rod's length (l) and a minor axis equal to its diameter d; then

$$R = \frac{\rho}{2\pi l} \ln \frac{4l}{d} \tag{19.1}$$

where ρ is the earth resistivity. For the cylindrical rod with hemisphere end, the equation for R becomes

$$R = \frac{\rho}{2\pi l} \ln \frac{2l}{d} \tag{19.2}$$

If the rod is assumed carrying current uniformly along its length, we have

$$R = \frac{\rho}{2\pi l} \left(\ln \frac{8l}{d} - 1 \right) \tag{19.3}$$

The resistance of a single rod is in general not sufficiently low and therefore it is required to use a number of rods connected in parallel. The distance between the rods should be as large as possible to minimize the overlap among their areas of influence. In practice, it is very difficult. One of the approximate methods is to replace a rod by a hemispheric electrode having the same resistance. The resistance of n rods in parallel is thus found to exceed (1/n) of that of a single rod because of their mutual screening. The screening coefficient η for n electrodes in parallel is defined as

$$\eta = \frac{\text{Resistance of one elecrode}}{(\text{Resistance of } n \text{ elecrodes in parallel}) \times n} \tag{19.4}$$

19.2.2 Resistance of Grounding Point Electrode

The simplest possible electrode is a hemisphere, as shown in Figure 19.1. The ground resistance can be calculated as considering an infinite number of thin hemispherical shells of soil. Consider each shell with radius x and thickness dx, the total resistance up to a large radius r_1 is

$$R = \int_r^{r_1} \frac{\rho dx}{2\pi x^2} = \frac{\rho}{2\pi} \left(\frac{1}{r} - \frac{1}{r_1} \right) \tag{19.5}$$

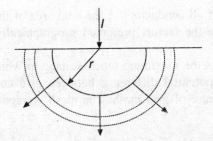

FIGURE 19.1 A hemisphere electrode.

As $r_1 = \infty$, Equation (19.5) becomes

$$R = \frac{\rho}{2\pi r} \qquad (19.6)$$

The general equation for electrode resistance is

$$R = \frac{\rho}{2\pi c} \qquad (19.7)$$

where c is the electrostatic capacitance of the electrode combined with its image above the earth's surface. This relation is applicable to any shape of electrode.

19.2.3 Grounding Grids

In high-voltage substations, a common method for obtaining a low-ground resistance is to use interconnected ground grids. A typical grid system is comprised of bare solid copper conductors buried at a depth of 30–60 cm, spaced in a grid pattern. At each junction, the conductors are securely bonded together. The size of grid conductors required to avoid fusing under the fault current I is estimated as

$$a = I\sqrt{\frac{76t}{\ln\left[(234 + T_m)/(234 + T_a)\right]}} \qquad (19.8)$$

where a is copper cross-section (circular mils), t is the fault duration (seconds), T_m is the maximum allowable temperature and T_a is the ambient temperature.

A grid not only effectively grounds the equipment but also has the added advantage of controlling the voltage gradient at the surface of the earth to the values safe for human contacts. Ground rods may be connected to the grid for further reduction in the ground resistance when upper layer of soil resistivity is higher than the soil underneath.

Resistance to ground and mesh voltages of grounding grids

The resistance to ground determines the maximum potential rise of the grounding system during a ground fault. The following equation for grid resistance can be used:

$$R = \frac{\rho}{L}\left(\ln\frac{2L}{\sqrt{dh}} + K_1\frac{L}{\sqrt{A}} - K_2\right) \qquad (19.9)$$

where L is the total length of all conductors, A the total area of the grid, d the grid conductor diameter, and K_1 and K_2 are the factors presented geographically as functions of length-to-width ratio of the area.

Mesh voltage represents the maximum touch voltage to which a person can be exposed at the substation. It is the potential difference between grid conductor and a point at the ground surface above the centre of grid mesh. The mesh voltages of ground-grounding grids can be calculated as

$$E_m = K_m K_i \rho \frac{I}{L} \tag{19.10}$$

where I is the current flowing into the ground and K_m is a coefficient that takes into account the effect of n number of grid conductors and their spacing S, diameter d and depth of burial h which is defined as,

$$K_m = \frac{1}{2\pi} \ln \frac{S^2}{16hd} + \frac{1}{\pi} \ln \left(\prod_{j=3}^{j=n} \frac{2j-3}{2j-2} \right) \tag{19.11}$$

K_i is an irregularity correction factor, to allow for ground non-uniformity current flow from different part of grid and can be calculated as

$$K_i = 0.65 + 0.172n \tag{19.12}$$

Conductor length required for gradient control

The step voltage E_{step} can be calculated as

$$E_{\text{step}} = K_s K_i \rho \frac{I}{L} \tag{19.13}$$

where K_s is a coefficient that takes account of the effect of number, spacing S and depth of burial h of conductors and calculated as

$$K_s = \frac{1}{\pi} \left(\frac{1}{2h} + \frac{1}{S+h} + \frac{1}{2S} + \frac{1}{3S} + \cdots \right) \tag{19.14}$$

The tolerable step voltage with duration t, E_{step}, which is the voltage between any two points on the ground surface that can be touched simultaneously by the feet, is

$$E_{\text{step}} = \frac{165 + \rho_s}{\sqrt{t}} \tag{19.15}$$

where ρ_s is the resistivity of ground beneath the feet, in ohm-metre, taking its surface treatment into account.

The tolerable touch voltage, E_{touch}, which is the voltage between any point on the ground, where a person may stand and any point that can be touched simultaneously by either hand, is

$$E_{\text{touch}} = \frac{165 + 0.25\rho_s}{\sqrt{t}} \tag{19.16}$$

The graphical representation of step, touch and transferred voltages are given in Figure 19.2.

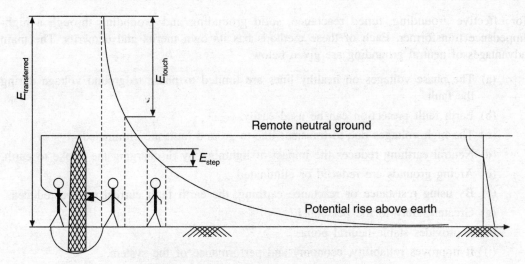

FIGURE 19.2 Step, touch and transferred voltages.

19.3 DESIGN PRINCIPLES OF SUBSTATION GROUNDING SYSTEM

The grounding of a substation is very important as it provides the ground connection for the system neutral, the discharge path for surge arrestors and ensures safety to operating personnels. It also provides low-resistance path to ground to minimize the rise in ground potential which depends on the fault current magnitude and grounding system resistance. It is very difficult to achieve low-resistance substation ground in deserts and rocky areas. The grids are the most convenient means of obtaining a suitable ground connection. Sometimes ground rods are also used to further reduce the resistance. The size of grid and number and length of driven rods depend on the substation size, nature of soil and the ground resistance required.

The grid system usually extends over the entire substation yard and sometimes several metres beyond. The grounding conductors should have low impedance and carry prospective fault current without fusing or getting damaged, taking account of future expansion of connected power system.

19.4 NEUTRAL GROUNDING

In the design of power system, the grounding of generators, transformers and transmission schemes is very important as it has a considerable bearing on the levels of transient and dynamic over-voltages stressing the equipment insulations. Ground affects the short circuit current of power system and thus the rating of switchgear needed to cope with them. The words 'earthing', which is used in UK and 'grounding', which is used in USA, have the same meaning. It should be noted that the equipment 'earthing' (connecting the body of equipment to the earth for safety precautions) is different from the neutral-point earthing. There are several methods of neutral grounding such as resistance grounding, low reactance for effective grounding, tuned reactance, solid grounding and grounding through a high-impedance transformer. Each of these methods has its own merits and demerits. The main advantages of neutral grounding are given below:

(a) The phase voltages on healthy lines are limited to phase to ground voltage during the fault.

(b) Earth fault protection can be used easily.

(c) The high voltages due to transient line-to-ground fault are eliminated.

(d) Neutral earthing reduces the impact of lightning by discharging the stroke to earth.

(e) Arcing grounds are reduced or eliminated.

(f) By using resistance or reactance earthing, the earth fault current can be reduced.

(g) Greater safety to the personnel.

(h) It provides stable neutral point.

(i) It improves reliability, economy and performance of the system.

There are some advantages to operate the system with isolated neutral such as

(a) With single line to ground fault, it is possible to operate the system.

(b) Due to absence of zero sequence currents, the radio interference is minimized.

19.5 UNGROUNDED SYSTEM (ISOLATED SYSTEM)

A temporary fault creates an arc between an overhead line and ground. This arc extinguishes and restrikes in repeated and regular manner. This phenomenon is known as *arcing ground* which is very common in ungrounded system. A simple explanation is given as follows.

Figure 19.3 shows a 3-phase system with isolated neutral. When there is no fault, the inherent distributed capacitances of the line get charged to the respective phase voltages. The charged capacitances of phase c get discharged through the fault F between phase c and ground. These capacitances again get charges in opposite direction and again discharged. Such repeated charging and discharging of line to ground is called *arcing grounds*. This produces severe voltage oscillations reaching three to four times normal voltage. The problem of arcing ground can be solved by earthing the neutral through Peterson coil or arc suppression coil connected between neutral and earth.

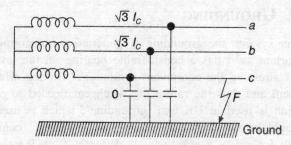

FIGURE 19.3 A 3-phase isolated neutral system.

When a fault occurs in a phase of line, the voltage of healthy phases of line is increased to √3 times of the phase voltages. This causes severe stress on the insulation of the equipments connected to the system. To understand this phenomenon, let us consider a fault in line c (Figure 19.3). Before the fault, the phase voltage are V_a, V_b, V_c and the charging currents will be leading to the respective voltages, as shown in Figure 19.4.

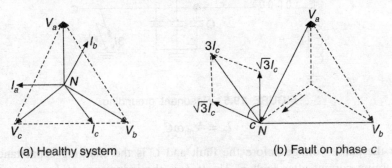

| (a) Healthy system | (b) Fault on phase c |

FIGURE 19.4 Phasor diagram.

Due to fault on phase c, the voltage of phase c with respect to earth becomes zero (assuming zero-fault impedance). The voltage of phases a and b becomes √3 times the normal phase voltages which can be seen from Figure 19.4(b), where point N is moved to c. The line-to-line voltages V_{ac} and V_{cb} remain unchanged. The value of fault current (vector sum of I_{ac} and I_{bc}) becomes three times the normal phase charging current. The charging current from healthy phases is

$$I_{ac} = \frac{V_{ac}}{x_c} = \frac{\sqrt{3}V_{ph}}{x_c} = \sqrt{3}I_c$$

Similarly

$$I_{bc} = \frac{V_{bc}}{x_c} = \frac{\sqrt{3}V_{ph}}{x_c} = \sqrt{3}I_c$$

where x_c is the capacitive reactance of line to the ground and I_c is the phase-charging current during the normal condition.

The increase in the voltage can be eliminated by using a reactor of suitable size between the neutral and the ground. If the value of inductance is such that the fault current I_f balances exactly the charging current, this type of grounding is known as *resonant grounding* or *Peterson coil* or *ground fault neutralizer*.

19.6 RESONANT GROUNDING

Figure 19.5 shows a resonant grounded 3-phase system. If the fault current I_f is equal to $3I_c$, there is no current. Theoretically, in the fault it is very small and therefore no arc is maintained and the fault is extinguished.

The per phase charging current (I_c) is

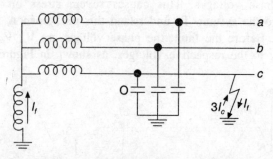

FIGURE 19.5 Resonant grounding.

$$I_c = V_{\text{ph}}\omega C \tag{19.17}$$

where V_{ph} is the phase voltage before the fault and C is the charging capacitance.
The total charging current after fault is $3I_c$. If L is the inductance to be connected between
the neutral point and the earth, then

$$I_f = \frac{V_{\text{ph}}}{\omega L} \tag{19.18}$$

At resonant condition, following condition will hold

$$I_f = 3I_c \quad \text{or} \quad \frac{V_{\text{ph}}}{\omega L} = 3\omega C V_{\text{ph}} \tag{19.19}$$

or

$$L = \frac{1}{3\omega^2 C} \tag{19.20}$$

Arc suppression coil

Although resonant grounding reduces the line interruption due to transient line-to-ground (LG)
fault and thus reduces the possibility of developing a 2-phase or 3-phase fault. The location
of fault in the line is not fixed and therefore a variable inductor is required. Arc suppression
coil, which is an iron-cored reactor provided with tappings, is used. This provides the
selection of reactance depending upon the length of line and the capacitance to be neutralized.
The continuous rating of the coil is equal to the maximum earth fault current but due to the
double line to ground fault, the fault current may be higher. To avoid this condition, a circuit
breaker is connected, as shown in Figure 19.6.

Circuit breaker is normally opened and it is closed after a time lag when the fault
current exceeds the rating of coil which is sensed by relay through CT. Due to closing of CB
the current flows through the parallel path.

19.7 SOLID GROUNDING OR EFFECTIVE GROUNDING

In this case neutral is directly connected to ground without any intentional impedance
between neutral and ground. Due to line to ground fault on any phase, the potential of that

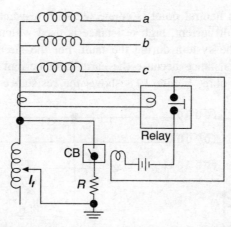

FIGURE 19.6 Arc suppression coil connection.

phase becomes the neutral potential whereas the potential of healthy phases remains approximately unchanged. From phasor diagram, it is evident that the total charging current is equal to the charging current of healthy phases. The fault current in phase *c* will be totally inductive and will completely cancel the charging current. Hence the arcing grounds are substantially reduced. The coefficient for earthing is less than 80%. For circuits above 22 kV, the solid grounding is used as there are enough charging current. Figure 19.7 shows the solid grounding and is phasor diagram during fault in phase *c*.

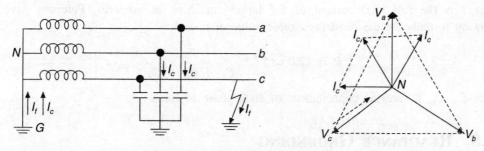

FIGURE 19.7 Solid grounding.

Nowadays the term 'effectively grounded' is most widely used instead of the term 'solidly grounded'. IEEE definition of effective grounding is as "A system or portion of system can be said to be *effectively grounded* when for all points on the system or specified portion thereof the ratio of zero-sequence reactance to positive sequence reactance is not greater than 3 and the ratio of zero-sequence resistance to positive sequence reactance is not greater than 1 for any condition of operation and for any amount of generator capacity".

19.8 RESISTANCE GROUNDING

For the voltage level between 3.3 kV and 22 kV, the ground current is not large to use the reactance grounding. And also, the ground fault current, for solid grounding become very high. Hence in practice the neutral point is connected with resistance and is called *resistance grounding*. To limit the fault current, high resistance is used which saves the power loss and improves the stability of the system during the fault. For the circuit below 3.3 kV, there is no need to use external resistance because the earth fault current is limited due to inherent ground resistance, i.e. 1.5 ohm. Figure 19.8 shows the resistance grounding.

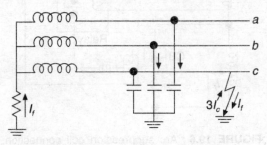

FIGURE 19.8 Resistance grounding.

In resistance grounded systems, the power loss during the line to ground faults is the main consideration. In practice it is common to set the value of resistor such that the fault current is limited to the full rating of the largest generator or transformer. Normally, resistor value (in ohm) is given by

$$R = \frac{V_{LL}}{\sqrt{3}I}$$

where I is the full load current of the largest machine in amperes. Peterson gave the following formula for the most favourable value of resistor:

$$R = (2.0 \text{ to } 1.25)\, \frac{1}{C_a + C_b + C_c}$$

where C_a, C_b, C_c are the capacitances of each phase to earth.

19.9 REACTANCE GROUNDING

Between the voltage 3.3 kV and 22 kV, the solid grounding is not used due to excessive fault current and therefore resistance or reactance grounding must be used. To limit the fault current, 'resistance' is popular in UK, whereas 'reactance' is popular in Europe. The reactance connected between neutral and ground provides the lagging current which neutralize the capacitive current. There is no set rule for using either resistance or reactance in the neutral. Whenever the charging current is high such as for cables, EHV transmission lines, capacitors, etc., the reactance grounding is used. Otherwise, resistance grounding is preferred. The reactance grounding lies between the solid grounding and resonant grounding. The grounding of solid and reactance is decided by the following relations:

For solid grounded system, $\dfrac{X_0}{X_1} < 3.0$

For reactance grounded system, $\dfrac{X_0}{X_1} > 3.0$

where X_0 and X_1 are the zero and positive sequence reactance, respectively. If a solidly grounded system has $X_0/X_1 > 3.0$, the system is presumed to be reactance rather than solidly grounded.

19.10 EARTHING TRANSFORMER

Normally neutral point of generator or transformer is available. In some cases, it is not available such as delta connection, bus-bar points, etc. The most common method is to use a zig-zag transformer. This transformer does not have a secondary winding. Two identical windings are wounded differentially on each limb of the transformer so that total flux in normal condition is negligible. Therefore, the transformer draws very little magnetizing current. Since the grounding transformers are of short time rating (10 seconds to 1 minute), the sizes of such transformers are small compared to power transformers. Figure 19.9 shows a zig-zag transformer connection.

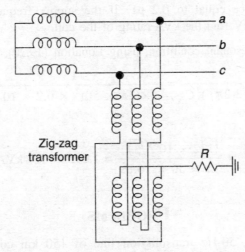

FIGURE 19.9 Zig-zag transformer for neutral grounding.

19.11 NEUTRAL GROUNDING PRACTICE

The main grounding practices are enumerated below:

(a) Normally one neutral ground is provided at each voltage level between generator voltage level and distribution voltage level. It is desirable to have one ground at each level.

(b) The grounding is provided at the source end rather than load end.

(c) When several generators at a generating station are operating in parallel, only one generator neutral is grounded. If more generators are grounded, the zero sequences current will cause more interference. Normally two grounds are available in a generating station but only one is used at a time.

(d) If several generators are connected to a common neutral bus which is connected to ground directly or through reactance, the neutral point of one generator is connected with neutral bus through a circuit breaker.

(e) When there are one or two power sources, no switching equipment is used in the grounding system.

(f) The main station earthing should be separate from the earthing for lightning protection.

(g) The resistance of earth and the current path should be low enough so as to prevent voltage rise between neutral and earth.

(h) For low voltage up to 3.3 kV and for high voltage above 22 kV solid grounding is used, whereas for voltage between 3.3 kV and 22 kV, a resistance or reactance grounding is used.

Example 19.1   Determine the value of inductance of arc suppressor coil to be connected between the neutral and ground to neutralize the charging current of overhead line having the line to ground capacitance equal to 0.2 µF. If the supply frequency is 50 Hz and the operating voltage is 132 kV find the kVA rating of the coil.

Solution   For the resonant condition, using Equation (19.20), we have

$$L = \frac{1}{3\omega^2 C} = \frac{1}{3(2\pi f)^2 C} = \frac{1}{3\times(2\pi \times 50)^2 \times 0.2 \times 10^{-6}} = 16.89 \text{ H}$$

The kVA rating of coil is

$$\frac{V_{ph}^2}{\omega L} = \frac{\left(132 \times 10^3/\sqrt{3}\right)^2}{2\pi \times 50 \times 16.89} = 1.095 \times 10^3 \text{ kVA}$$

PROBLEMS

19.1 A 220-kV, 3-phase, 50-Hz transmission line of 150 km consists three conductors equilaterally spaced with 7 m and having effective diameter of 3 cm. Find the inductance and MVA rating of the Peterson coil in the system.

19.2 Line-to-ground capacitance of an overhead transmission line operating at 50 Hz is 1 µF. Find the reactance to neutralize the capacitance of:

(a) 100% of the line length
(b) 95% of the line length
(c) 90% of the line length.

Chapter 20

Power System Restructuring

20.1 INTRODUCTION

There is growing dissatisfaction with limited incentives for efficient operation faced by a cost-of-service regulated or government-owned electric utility. According to this view, even if scale of economies in the production of electricity exists, the mode of production chosen by the firm does not allow them to be realized because of the incentives for input choice provided by the regulatory process or by state-ownership. In addition, the regulated utility and regulatory body joint decision-making process and the state owned-enterprise decision-making process have historically had difficulty in making economically efficient new generation capacity investment decisions, both in terms of the size and fuel type of the generating facility.

Although privatization is often part of the restructuring process, in all of the developed countries where it has taken place, there are state and privately-owned companies competing in the electricity generation market. Some of these countries only have municipally-owned distribution companies, and others have only privately-owned distribution companies. There are even some countries where the distribution sector is composed of a combination of privately-owned and government-owned companies. The market structure and the rules governing the operation of the electricity industry in these countries are not the direct result of independent actions by market participants—generators, retailers and customers. Consequently, it is perhaps a misnomer to call these markets competitive. Instead, they are

407

the outcome of a deliberate government policy to restructure (and often privatize) the industry. The final form of the electricity industry in US is the result of joint decisions by the state regulatory commissions and legislatures, as well as the market participants. In addition, the Federal Energy Regulatory Commission (FERC) must also approve all state restructuring plans.

All of these restructurings are consistent with the view that competition should be introduced into the electricity supply industry wherever it is technologically feasible. Only those portions of the production process most efficiently supplied by a single firm remain regulated. The prevailing view is that the technologies for electricity generation and retailing are both such that competition is feasible. As discussed above, economies of scale in generation are exhausted at levels of production significantly below the current levels of industry output. It is also difficult to imagine that there are increasing returns to scale in electricity retailing, assuming that all retailers have equal access to the distribution network and electricity from the wholesale generation market. On the other hand, because competition in the transmission and distribution of electricity would require duplication of the current network, these two portions of the electricity supply industry are thought to be the only portions that possess the features of a natural monopoly. Therefore, the transmission and distribution sectors of the electricity supply industries in most of the countries are regulated.

Restructuring of electric supply industries (ESI) is taking place all over the world in different rates and shapes. Different terms are also appearing in the literatures which confuse the readers. Restructuring includes both privatization and deregulation (competition). Deregulated power market is also known by different names, viz. re-regulated market, open power market, competitive power market, vertically unbundled power system, open access etc. Commonly used terms in power system are as follows

- *Competition*: In competition two or more entities are vying for the same business or opportunity. In power system, competition can be introduced in generation and distribution businesses.
- *Deregulation*: The better word is re-regulation which creates changes to encourage competition wherever it is possible. In power system, deregulation is more frequently used; however re-regulation is very common in economics and regulatory aspects. Deregulation is a restructuring of the rules and economic incentives that the government sets up to control and drive the ESI.
- *Restructuring*: In ESI, it is disassembly of the original structure and re-assembly into another form or cooperatives are created for better efficiency and performance.
- *Open access*: A common way for a government to encourage competition in ESI is an open access of wire business (transmission and distribution), which provides a way for competing generators to reach the customers.

These deregulation processes have been developed after debate, with opposition by private and state monopolies that have defended the vertically integrated model. The most discussed deregulation has been the British one, with growing interest in the Norway model and much attention has been paid to actions in the United States, especially California State. There is greater experience in South America, especially Chile, where pioneer deregulation has been in place for several years.

20.2 NEED FOR REGULATION OF EARLY ELECTRIC POWER UTILITIES

When utilities operate, develop and manage their functions under the rules and laws laid down by the government, then these are called *regulated utilities*. Nearly all the industries in all nations are regulated up to some extent. Airlines and auto-manufacturing businesses are very competitive whereas nuclear related industries are highly regulated. There were several reasons for regulated power utilities.

Standardization of electric business. Early power system development witnessed the different operating voltages and frequencies due to which interconnections were not possible. Loads were localized and generators were built near load centres. Due to scale of economies of larger generators, the importance of interconnections was realized along with other benefits. The power developments were mostly in the hands of private investors. With proper regulation, the government had to control the power development in one standard all over the country.

Huge Investment with high risk. The investment in the power sector was huge due to rapid growth in electricity consumption. It was very difficult for the private investor to invest where the future was uncertain. The establishment of electric utilities required huge capital for infrastructure. At the same time, it was realized that there should be some assured rate of return on the investment. In turn, the government guaranteed them a fair return on their investment through regulated rates. The government authorities overseeing the utility define a rate schedule of prices the utility must charge. The concept behind these prices, cost recovery and a regulated rate of return, means that prices will be fixed by the government so that the utility is certain to recover all its costs and its permitted profit.

Simple buying process. The cost of generation of electricity is different for different generation. It also involves the transmission and distribution of power to reach the final consumers. The location of the consumer may be different, and therefore the actual cost to deliver power to different consumers is different due to involvement of long transmission and distribution lines and power loss. The cost of delivery of power also changes with time as system losses change during the day. By regulating the electric utilities, the government could manage the same tariffs in a region which is very simple to understand.

Least cost operations. Loads on the generators are varied throughout the day due to change in the demand of electricity. It is very much desired to operate the power system in the least cost manner. It is only possible when electricity is regulated and belongs to the same utility. Least cost operation could only be achieved if there is sufficient generation with the utility. The government defines how the utility computes costs and sets its prices.

Meeting social obligations. Electricity is one of the basic needs for the social and economic development of a nation. The cost of supplying electricity to the rural consumers is very high, which may not be affordable. On the other hand, supplying electricity to the rural people at even urban rates would not be non-profitable to utility. For the social uplift of the people, it is must that the Government takes steps to ensure that electricity reaches to all. It is obligatory for the utilities to serve the people for two reasons.

- To guarantee that all consumers are offered service in a non-discriminatory way.
- To assure that the grid is eventually extended to all places where it is needed.

Reduction in acquiring land and right-of-way. Acquiring land for making generating station was not so easy without government intervention. The right-of-way for erecting transmission and distribution lines was another hurdle. The regulation gave utilities recognition and limited support from the local government in approving the ROW and easements.

The main characteristics of the traditional electricity utilities are the following.

1. *Monopoly franchise*:   Only the national or regional electric utility was permitted to produce, transmit, distribute and sell commercial electric power within its service territory.
2. *Obligation to serve*:   The utility had to provide electricity for the needs of all consumers in its service area, not just to those that were profitable.
3. *Regulatory oversight*:   The utility's business and operating practices had to conform to the guidelines and rules laid down by government regulators.
4. *Regulated rates*:   The electric utility's rates were either set or regulated in accordance with government regulatory rules and guidelines.
5. *Assured rate of return*:   The government guaranteed that regulated rates would provide the electric utility with a "reasonable" or "fair" profit margin above its cost.
6. *Least cost operation*:   The electric utility was required to operate in a manner that minimized overall revenue requirements.

20.3   MOTIVATION FOR POWER SYSTEM RESTRUCTURING

The electricity supply industry, since the 1980s, has been undergoing rapid and irreversible changes, reshaping the industry that for a long time has been remarkably stable and had served the public well. A significant feature of these changes is to allow for competition among generators and to create market conditions in the industry which are seen as necessary to reduce costs of energy production and distribution, eliminate certain inefficiencies, shed manpower, and increase customer choice. The reasons for deregulation are different in different countries. Many countries made the changes due to the failure of the state to adequately manage electricity companies. In other countries, the force behind this has been the lack of public resources to finance the required investment for the development. The World Bank took initiative to give loans to the utilities with a condition to start deregulation processes. Hence, a great variety of organizational forms is emerging.

The main reasons behind the restructuring are given below:

High tariffs. The electricity price in several countries/states is much more and it was expected that the price will drop after deregulation. Service may improve as a result of the restructuring, but there is also a serious concern in many countries about falling maintenance standards. Competition breeds innovation, efficiency, and lowers costs but also leads to short-termism. For example, the electricity in the state of California was more than 50% above the national average before deregulation. It was also the case with several Latin American countries.

Encourage innovations. A competitive power industry will provide rewards to risk takers and encourage the use of new technologies and business approaches. The regulated monopoly scheme was unable to provide incentives for innovation since the utility had little motivation to use new ideas and technologies to lower costs under a regulated rate of return framework. The lack of competition also gave electric utilities little incentive to improve service, and in countries such as India and China, the standards of service were generally very low. A more commercial ethos could be helpful in improving standards of service to customers.

Better customer choice. The main drive for electric industry restructuring in the classic case of the UK came from the government's belief that the advantages of competition among energy suppliers, and wide choice for electricity consumers, outweighed the benefits of the long established arrangement. Although restructuring of the power industry inevitably results in some new problems, governments and consumers in many countries believed that the benefits of the restructuring would outweigh potential problems.

Change in generation economies of scale. The change in generation economies of scale that occurred throughout the 1980s was an important stimulus to industry restructuring. The advances in gas turbine technology led to more efficient small turbines and generators. As a result, smaller generators could nearly match the efficiency of very large units, particularly if run on natural gas rather than coal. The price of natural gas declined and the prohibition on gas burning for electricity generation was removed in this period.

Improve in managerial efficiencies. Restructuring of the government-owned electricity industry encouraged privatization, although privatization does not have to be part of a restructuring effort. In the 1980s and early 1990s, several Western governments were of the view that private organizations could do a better job of running the power industry and that higher operating efficiencies and reduction of manpower could be achieved by privatization. Private utilities also refuse to subsidize rates and have a greater interest in eliminating power thefts and managerial or workplace inefficiencies. In other countries either ownership or responsibility for various functions was transferred to co-operative, or to private organizations, or to new types of public corporations, or quasi-governmental entities that could act like market sensitive economic agents. Ownership and functional restructuring have therefore taken many different forms. Incremental involvement of private capital, which has played an important role in Asia, can be considered as private sector participation rather than privatization.

Better experience of other deregulated market. The industries like oil and gas, airlines, banking, auto-manufacturing etc. had already showed very good performance. Although electricity is a different type of commodity which cannot be stored in bulk quantity and also related to the interconnected grid management, it is expected the electric supply industries will also show the good results as other deregulated industries. In UK, oil and gas industry was deregulated before the electric supply industry. After looking at the performance of other sectors, the ESI was deregulated. The other problem experienced was that the market participants were less and there was some market power which is not good for any deregulated market. Due to this, the volatility of the price was much more during the early days of deregulation.

Pressure from financial institutions. The electricity supply industries in the developing countries are in the red and require huge financial assistance/loan from foreign financial institutions like the World Bank, the Asian Development Bank etc. Knowing the situation of ESI that it is difficult to get the loans back from these industries, financial institutions are providing the loans/assistance with condition. These conditions are nothing but to restructure their operational and managerial structure.

Lack of public resources for future development. As the economic development of developing countries is faster than the other developed countries, the resource required is also enormous. The governments are unable to concentrate much on electric sectors as there are several other sectors where much attention is required. Due to limited resource, the electricity sector is now open to private investors which required some regulation to be changed. Restructuring of ESI gave an opportunity to the private investors to build, own and operate in the electricity business.

Need for regulation changed. The basic need of regulation was to provide risk-free investment to build infrastructure, which is no more important. Now, a power system grid, which comprises generation, transmission and distribution, is in a mature state. The network is expanded to reach each customer. The revenue obtained from the existing set-up can be used for future extension and development of the systems. Now, technology is almost matured and there is only incremental addition in the system. Therefore, there is little risk in the investment.

Some other forces behind the restructuring are:

- Global economic crises
- Overstaffing in the regulated electric industry
- Political and ideological changes
- Rise in environmentalism

20.4 WHAT IS TRANSFORMING?

Vertically integrated system as shown in Figure 20.1 is broken into three distinct businesses (generation, transmission and distribution) by separating vertically (cutting horizontally) to provide competition in generation and distribution businesses. For effective competition, there should be a large number of market participants and therefore generation and distribution businesses are separated horizontally (cutting vertically) as shown in Figure 20.2. After unbundling and creating competition, the regulated cost based generation becomes unregulated price-based generation. The monopolistic behaviour of the electricity industry will become competitive. In monopoly system, electricity was assumed as service where end-users are known as consumers, but in competitive electricity market, electricity is now a commodity which is used by customers. The main difference is that consumers get privilege whereas customers get choice. It is also seen that in several countries, engineers are becoming lawyers or managers. Figure 20.3 shows competitive market structure.

As the electric utility industry progresses from a cost-based regulated structure to a price-based unregulated system, suitable measures will be needed to successfully make this transformation.

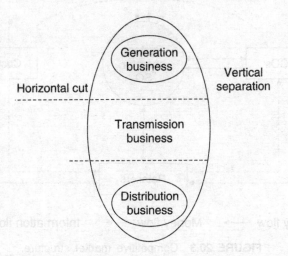

FIGURE 20.1 Vertically integrated electricity market.

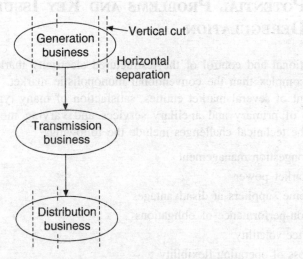

FIGURE 20.2 Vertically unbundled power system.

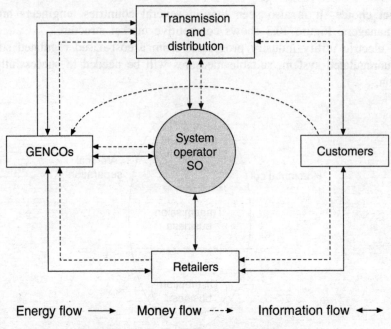

Energy flow ⟶   Money flow ┄┄►   Information flow ⟷

FIGURE 20.3   Competitive market structure.

20.5   POTENTIAL PROBLEMS AND KEY ISSUES IN DEREGULATION

The operational and control of the restructured electricity market poses technical challenges far more complex than the conventional monopolistic market. The complexity arises due to involvement of several market entities, satisfaction of many types of contractual obligations, separation of primary and ancillary services and varying models of market management. Some of the technical challenges include the following.

- Congestion management
- Market power
- Some suppliers at disadvantages
- Non-performance of obligations
- Price volatility
- Loss of operating flexibility
- Pricing of energy and transmission services
- Available transfer capability calculations
- Ancillary services management

Congestion management.   The power flow pattern in the deregulated environment is different from that in existing regulated ones. All parties will try to get the benefits of cheaper source and greater profit margins, leading to overloading and congestion of certain transmission corridors. This may well exceed the thermal, voltage and stability limits, thereby undermining the system security and reliability. A condition when operating limits of any apparatus in the system is violated, the system is called *congested system*. More often, it is related to exceeding the power flow of the lines. Congestion in a transmission system, whether vertically organized or unbundled, cannot be permitted except for very short duration, for fear of cascade outages with uncontrolled loss of load. Some corrective measures such as outage of congested branches (lines or transformers), using FACTS devices, operation of transformer taps, re-dispatch of generation and curtailment of pool loads and/or bilateral contracts can relieve congestion.

Market power.   Market power is the ability to profit by moving the market price away from the competitive level. Most of the firms have some market power and this causes no significant problems if the amount is small. Market power raises the price and thereby transfers wealth from consumers to all the suppliers in the market. It also creates inefficiency in the market. A supplier may have an unfair, nearly monopolistic, competitive advantage (i.e. excessive market power) for having major share or locational advantage. Electricity is different from other commodity. It cannot be stored in bulk quantity, power generated must be consumed at that time and also related to the grid operation. In competitive power market, marginal generator can exercise the market power. The main causes of market power are:

- Large generator capacity
- Network constraints
- Additional opportunity to create intentional congestion

The factors that determine the market power are:

- Market concentration
- Demand elasticity
- Style of competition
- Forward contract
- Geographical extent of market

Different approaches to study the market power are:

- Ex-post analysis of recently restructured market
- Market concentration analysis (ex-ante studies)
- Market simulation (ex-ante studies)
- Equilibrium modelling (ex-ante studies)

Monopsony power is a market power exercised on the demand side with the intention of lowering the market price. An independent system operator can exercise by interrupting loads or by curtailments. Monopsony power can be an effective and beneficial method for combating market power but can also be abused.

Some suppliers at disadvantages.   Some suppliers may be at a competitive disadvantage due to operating or economic constraints such as significant start-up times and costs; minimum output levels, run times and down times; and restrictive fuel constraints. To the extent that these suppliers can be accommodated so they have a more realistic opportunity to compete (i.e. by awarding some contracts two days ahead as well as one day and one-hour ahead), a lower cost outcome may be attained. Non-conventional energy producers may also suffer due to cost and other constraints.

Non-performance of obligations.   In order to run a fair electricity market, all suppliers that submit bids in response to solicitations should be obligated to accept a contract if awarded. Thus, submitted bids should be considered executed contracts if they are accepted and awarded. In some cases, the system operator may award a day-ahead forward contract in which the supplier receives the higher of its own bid price or the day ahead forecast market clearing price for its scheduled output; deviations from its schedule would be priced at the actual market clearing price. The failure of the supplier to perform some contracted services could result in serious consequences for the power system. For example, the failure of a supplier that was awarded a contract for operating capacity, to provide reserve energy during a system disturbance could sacrifice system security. In these cases, a non-performance penalty may need to be imposed on the supplier for not meeting the contractual obligations.

Price volatility.   Due to several reasons, the price of electricity is not the same thoughout the day. It is very volatile, especially during the peak hours. The main reasons for this volatility are system constraints, market model, market power, imperfect competition, unavailability of cheaper resources etc. The number of suppliers in an electricity market is limited, therefore they can intentionally increase the price. There should be some mechanism to reduce the volatility of price. There may be future contracts, option contracts, contract for differences etc.

Loss of operating flexibility.   Regulated electric utilities have reasonable degree of flexibility in scheduling supply to serve customer load reliably and economically. In deregulated market environment, the number of participants is more and their intention is to get maximum profit from the market. During any disturbance, reduction or increase in their power supply/demand may not be possible and may raise several disputes. A rigid bidding system could conceivably reduce this flexibility and compromise either reliability or economics or both. System operator should have very accurate load forecast, clear rules and regulation etc. to meet these challenges.

Pricing of energy and transmission services.   For the proper management of any electricity utility, it is important to have a source of income to meet its expenses. It is also important that the electricity industry should have some income for future expansion work. In regulated electricity industries, there are two different types of charges: Fix charges and running charges, which are fixed for a few months, are same in a geographical area. However, in the deregulated market, there is only one charge based on the market clearing price, which varies throughout the day and may be different at different nodes of the system. Energy pricing and transmission wheeling charges are the centre of debate for quite some time and there is no clear cut way to impose these. The main aim of framing these pricing is given below.

(i) The users must readily understand.

(ii) It must be equitable as between different users.

(iii) It should also be such as to encourage users to improve the power factor.

(iv) It should also be such as to encourage users to improve load factor or to transfer their demand from peak to off-peak hours.

(v) It can be modified from time to time.

(vi) Use of electricity is encouraged so that the economy of utilities is improved.

Available transfer capability calculations.   NERC (North American Reliability Council) has defined '*Available Transfer Capability (ATC) as a measure of power transfer capability remaining in the physical transmission network for further commercial activity over and above the already committed uses*'. In other words, it is the additional amount of power that can be transferred over the network with margins for a range of uncertainties and contingencies when power is injected and extracted at the specified seller and buyer buses, respectively. Power transactions between a specific seller bus/area and a buyer bus/area can be committed only when sufficient ATC is available for that interface, and then the power companies may reserve the transfer rights as per their need. Thus, any commercial transaction is restricted by the ATC so as to ensure the system security. Hence information about the ATC is to be continuously updated and made available to the market entities through internet based open access same time information system (OASIS). The methods required for computation of ATC must be fast and accurate. This computation becomes much more complex during the system disturbances.

Ancillary services management.   Ancillary services (AS) are defined as all those activities on the interconnected grid that are necessary to support the transmission of power while maintaining reliable operation and ensuring the required degree of quality and safety. This includes the following.

- Reserve capacity
- Ten minute start-up reserve capacity
- Ten minute non-spinning quick start reserve capacity
- Ten minute response spinning reserve capacity
- Regulation of frequency and tie-line power flows
- Voltage and reactive power control
- Ensuring system stability
- Transmission reserves
- Black start capability

As per NERC definition, an ancillary service is an interconnected operation service that is necessary to affect a transfer of electricity between purchasing and selling entities and which a transmission provider must include in an open access transmission tariff. In regulated system, AS is an integral part of electricity supply whereas in deregulated market, it varies with market structure. In several countries, there is a parallel for AS. Since it is directly related to the system security and stability, a proper ancillary services management is required.

20.6   Question to be Answered before Moving towards Deregulation

Given the competitive market forces, initiatives towards deregulation by countries, the electric supply industry, all over the world, is poised for deregulation and restructuring. In the debate of competitive power market, two questions have consistently arisen. How can system reliability and security be maintained; and how can economic efficiency be assured? From this debate, the concept of independent system operators as an unbiased coordinator to balance reliability with economics has emerged. There are several other questions to be answered before moving for deregulation which include the following.

- What are the key issues in moving towards deregulation?
- Is deregulation good for our society?
- What are the implications for the current industry participants?
- What type of new participants will be seen and why?
- What should be the structure of market and operation?
- How might an electricity transaction of future look like?

20.7   Milestones of Deregulation

From 1980 onwards, a major transformation took place throughout the electric power industry in South America. The first was Chile which made efforts in 1980 to restructure its electricity sector. The year-wise milestones of restructuring are given below.

- 1982: Chile
- 1990: UK
- 1992: Argentina, Sweden and Norway
- 1993: Bolivia and Colombia
- 1994: Australia
- 1996: New Zeeland
- 1997: Panama, El Salvador, Guatemala, Nicaragua, Costa Rica and Honduras
- 1998: California, USA and several others.

Bibliography

Arogyaswamy, J., *Power Station Practice,* Oxford and IBH Publishing, New Delhi, 1976.

Arrillaga, J., *High Voltage Direct Current Transmission,* IEEE, 1998.

Bergen, A.R., *Power Systems Analysis,* Prentice Hall, New Jersey, 1986.

Bhattacharya, K., Bollen, M.H.J. and Daalder, J.E., *Operation of Restructured Power Systems,* Kluwer Academic Publishers, USA, 2001.

Cotton, H. and H. Barber, *The Transmission and Distribution of Electrical Energy,* B.I. Publication, New Delhi, 1985.

Danekar, M.M. and Sharma K.N., *Water Power Engineering,* Vikas Publishing House, New Delhi, 1979.

Deshpande, M.V., *Electrical Power System Design,* Tata McGraw-Hill, New Delhi, 1984.

Diamant, R.M.E., *Total Energy,* Pergamon Press, Oxford, 1970.

Drbal, L., Westra, K. and Boston, P., *Electric Power Plant Design*, Springer, 1995.

Elgard, O.I., *Electric Energy Systems Theory: An Introduction*, McGraw-Hill, New York, 1982.

Goncharov, A.N., *Hydropower Station*: *Generating Equipment and Its Installation,* Keter Publishing House, Jerusalem, 1975.

Gonen, T., *Electric Power Distribution System Engineering,* McGraw-Hill, New York, 1986.

Gonen, T., *Electric Power Transmission System Engineering: Analysis and Design,* John Wiley & Sons, New York, 1988.

Healy, T.J., *Energy, Electric Power and Man,* Boyd & Fraser Publishing, California, 1974.

Ilic, M., Galiana, F. and Fink, L., *Power System Restructuring: Engineering and Economics,* Kluwer Academic Publishers, 1998.

Jog, M.G., *Hydro-Electric and Pump Storage Plants,* Wiley Eastern, New Delhi, 1982.

Khalifa, M., *High Voltage Engineering: Theory and Practice,* Marcel Dekker, New York, 1990.

Lie, L.L., *Power System Restructuring and Deregulation,* John Wiley & Sons, UK, 2002.

Kundur, P., *Power System Stability and Control,* McGraw-Hill, New York, 1994.

Mathur, B.L. and C.S. Sangha, *Electric Power,* New Asian Publishers, New Delhi, 1970.

Padiyar, K.R., *HVDC Power Transmission Systems,* Wiley Eastern, New Delhi, 1993.

Philipson, L. and Willis, H.L., *Understanding Electric Utilities and Deregulation,* Marcel Dekker Inc. 1999.

Severn, W.H., H.E. Degler and J.C. Miles, *Steam, Air and Gas Power,* Modern Asian Edition, John Wiley & Sons, New York, 1954.

Shahidehpour, M. and Alomoush, M., *Restructured Electrical Power Systems: Operation, Trading and Volatility,* Marcel Dekker Inc. 2001.

Soni, M.L., P.V. Gupta and U.S. Bhatnagar, *A Course in Electrical Power,* Dhanpat Rai & Sons, New Delhi, 1984.

Srisastra, P., Economic and environmental implications of distributed generation: A case study of Thailand, *M. Eng. Thesis,* Asian Institute of Technology, Thailand, 2001.

Wadhawa, C.L., *Electrical Power Systems,* New Age International, New Delhi, 2000.

———, *Generation, Distribution and Utilization of Electrical Energy,* Wiley Eastern, New Delhi, 1989.

Willis, H.L. and W.G. Scott, *Distributed Power Generation: Planning and Evaluation,* Marcel Dekker, New York, 2000.

Yahya, S.M., *Turbines, Compressors and Fans,* Tata McGraw-Hill, New Delhi, 1987.

Answers to Problems

Chapter 3

3.1 3266.12 W in 4-Ω resistor
1070.92 W in 5-Ω resistor
2141.83 VAr in 10-Ω inductor
6693.30 VAr in 4-Ω capactor

3.2 $S_2 = S_1 - j \dfrac{V^2}{\omega L - \dfrac{1}{\omega C}}$

3.4 $S_1 = 1 + j0.5$; $S_2 = 2 + j0.4$ Power base is 100 MVA for all elements

3.5 New Voltage base for transformers = 33 kV
Base voltage for line = 113.44 kV
New Base voltage for motors = 33 kV
pu impedance of transformers = 0.0684
$X_{m_1} = 0.55$, $X_{m_2} = 0.826$, $X_{m_3} = 0.3305$
pu impedance of line = 0.388

3.6 $X_{g_1} = 0.686$, $X_{g_2} = 0.457$, $X_{m_1} = 1.026$, $X_{m2} = 0.684$

3.7 $j0.002066$ pu

3.8

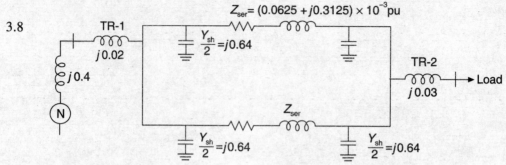

$$Z_{ser} = (0.0625 + j0.3125) \times 10^{-3} \text{pu}$$

3.9 (a) pu values of reactances

Generator G = $j0.2$ pu

TR–1 = $j0.2$ pu; TR–2 = $j0.15$ pu; TR–3 = $j0.16$ pu

TR–4 = $j0.2$ pu.

Line–1 = $j0.1$ pu, Line–2 = $j0.5407$ pu

Motor = $j2.5$ pu

Total load in pu = $0.0874 + j5.7 \times 10^{-3}$ pu

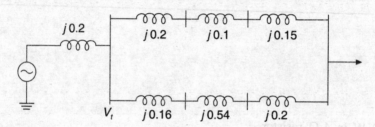

(b) $V_t = 20.94$ kV

$E_g = 20.98$ kV

Chapter 4

4.1 (a) 1248 MWh   (b) 50 MW   (c) 3120 MWh   (d) 1468.24 MWh

4.2 758.59 kVA

4.3 (b) 3.6 kWh   (c) 0.81; 150 W; 680 W; 0.22

4.4 (a) Rs 281.25 × 10⁵   (b) Rs 298.58 × 10⁵   (c) Rs 19.50 × 10⁵

4.5 (a) 2100 kW; 1602.08 kW; 0.7629

(b) 1.0, 1.0, 0.385

(c) 1.381   (d) 0.724   (e) (i) 100 kW (ii) 5110 kWh (iii) 0.84

4.6 (a) 80 MW   (b) 50%   (c) 1920 MWh   (d) 40 MW   (e) 4800 MWh

(f) 2560 MWh   (g) 80%

4.7 (a) 0.73   (b) 64747 kW

(c) One unit for 8760 hrs, Two units for 7135.2 hrs, Three units for 2637.34 hrs.

(d) 4747.2 kW

Chapter 6

6.1 (a) 1920.83 m^3/s

6.2 Maximum power = 1709.97 MW
Average power = 801.11 MW
Load factor = 0.468

Chapter 10

10.1 1.46R;   1.723R;   1.248R;   1.704R

10.2 L_A = 0.623 mH/km, L_B = 0.770 mH/km

10.3 $L = 2 \times 10^{-7} \ln \left[2^{1/6} \left(\dfrac{d}{R'} \right)^{1/2} \left(\dfrac{g}{f} \right)^{1/3} \right]$ H/m/phase

$$c_n = \frac{2\pi\varepsilon_0}{\ln \left[2^{1/6} \left(\dfrac{d}{R} \right)^{1/2} \left(\dfrac{g}{f} \right)^{1/3} \right]} \text{ F/m/phase}$$

10.4 1.353 mH/km

10.5 L_A = 1.902 − j0.179 mH/km = L_C
L_B = 1.85 mH/km

10.6 0.617 mH/km

10.7 1.46R;   1.723R;   1.248R;   1.704R

10.8 C_n = 16.3 pF/m/phase
L = 0.694 mH/km

10.9 (a) 10.04 pF/m/phase
(b) 19.94 pF/m/phase

10.10 9.652 pF/m

10.11 31.027 × 10^{-6} coulomb/km

10.12 C_{AN} = 18.3 pF/m
C_{BN} = 13.64 pF/m
49.1 mA/km

10.13 C_{AN} = C_{BN} = 12.56 pF/m
0.0217 A/km

10.14 C_n = 11.71 pF/m/phase;
0.467 A/km/phase

10.15 0.018 μF/km/phase;   1.361 A/km/phase

10.16 L = 1.402 mH/km/ph
L = 1.055 mH/km/ph
(Bundle conductor)

10.17 C = 8.23 pF/m/phase
C = 10.8 pF/m/phase
(Bundle conductor)

10.18 (a) 0.614 mH/km
0.192 Ω/km
(b) 18.87 nF/km
0.236 A/conductor/km

Chapter 11

11.1 Regulation = 1.78%; Efficiency = 98.46%

11.2 3335.41 volt; 0.8095 (lag)

11.3 614.25 kW

11.4 150.32 kV;   0.835;   88.67%;   14.54% for nominal-T.
150.38 kV;   0.837;   88.35%;   14.57% for nominal-π
146.62 kV;   0.792;   95.96%;   11.71% for exact

11.5 (a) (i) Nominal-π Nominal-T
A = 0.6906 $\angle 4.98°$ = D A = D = 0.6906 $\angle 4.98°$
B = 268.29 $\angle 81.15°$ Ω B = 317.7 $\angle 79.11°$ Ω
C = $j20 \times 10^{-4}$ mho C = $j16.88 \times 10^{-4}$ mho
(ii) A = D = 0.7057 $\angle 4.38°$
B = 285.14 $\angle 80.3°$ Ω
C = $j18.0 \times 10^{-4}$ mho

(b) Z = 285.11 $\angle 80.3°$ Ω; $\dfrac{Y}{2}$ = $j10.55 \times 10^{-4}$ mho (Equivalent-π)

Z = 167.59 $\angle 78.6$ Ω, Y = $j17.9 \times 10^{-4}$ mho (Equivalent-T)

(c) 353.01 A;   375 kV;   0.588 (lead); 15.9°

(d) 415.46 A

11.6 228.2 kV; 114.77A; 41.45 MW; 0.865; 10.83%

11.7 141.14 kV; 135.60 kV

11.8 50.81 µF

11.9 1493.1 A

11.10 11.07 µF

11.11 137.3 kV; 4.64%

11.12 (a) 151.97 kV $\angle 7.39$ (c) 39.59 MW
(b) 179.66 $\angle -25.17$ A   (d) 90.93%

11.13 (a) $e^{-\alpha l}$ (b) $e^{-\alpha l}$ (c) $e^{-2\alpha l}$ (d) $e^{-2\alpha l}$
when lossless (a) 1 (b) 1 (c) 1 (d) 1

11.14 (a) $\bar{V}_s = 359.19 \angle 19.56°$ kV, $\bar{I}_s = 794.75 \angle -1.32°$, Reg = 44.68%

(b) $A = D = 0.96$, $B = j39.2$ $C = j0.002$

(c) $\bar{V}_s = 306.441.2 \angle 6.786°$, $\bar{I}_s = 891.14 \angle -5.65°$ A, Reg = 10.576%

11.15 614.25 kW

Chapter 12

12.1 (a) 0.1385 V; .1524 V; 0.1815 V; 0.2287 V; 0.2988 V (Top to bottom)

(b) 66.92%

12.2 6

12.3 $11C$; $13C$; $16C$; $20C$, $25C$

12.4 19.29%, 17.19%, 27.66%, 35.86%, 69.71%

12.5 36.81 kV (phase to neutral)

Chapter 13

13.1 (a) 0.557 m   (b) 3.86 m   to 42.38° from vertical plane

(c) 2.85 m

13.2 4.5 m;   300.18 m

13.3 141.66 m from lowest end

13.4 237.81 m from lowest support

13.5 20.76 m,   541.9 kg

13.6 4.802 m

Chapter 14

14.1 100.23 kV to neutral; 110.98 kV to neutral; no corona loss at 132 kV coronal loss at 220 kV 1039.34 W (fair weather); 3177.19 (bad weather)

14.2 1.492 cm

14.3 30.475 kV/cm, corona present

14.4 65.99 kV to neutral

14.5 36.32 volt; $V_d = 6.315 \angle -171.16°$ kV above earth.

14.6 5.011 V/km

Chapter 15

15.1 4.18 cm

15.2 101.03 kV

15.3 (i) 0.085 μF (ii) 0.39 μF (iii) 1.17 A

(c) 0.33 μF

15.4 $V = E_{\max} \, r \ln \dfrac{R}{r}$

Chapter 16

16.1 $q = 3,$ $s = 4,$ $r = 1$

16.2 (a) 297.1 kV   (b) 286.98 kV   (c) 0

16.3 395.51 kV (line-to-line)

16.4 21.78 ohm

16.5 388.58 kV (line-to-line)

Chapter 17

17.1 4.125 km from station A

17.2 5.2 km from station A; 260 A from end A −240 A from end B

17.3 Point E

17.4 (i) 232.8 V   (ii) 795.4 W   (iii) 13454.6 W

17.5 $V_B = V_D = 238.5$ volt; $V_e = 236.0$ volt

17.6 (a) 217.44 $\angle 7.92°$ (b) 217.33 $\angle 6.34°$

17.7 $W_1 : W_2 :: 0.715 : 1$

17.8 (a) : (b) :: 1 : 0.933

17.9 $V_B = 10.55 \angle{-1.66°}$ kV $V_D = 10.52 \angle{-2.04°}$ kV
      $V_C = 10.54 \angle{-1.94°}$ kV (line-to-line)
      $I_{AB} = 27.42 - j14.04$
      $I_{BD} = 7.42 + j0.96$
      $I_{CD} = 3.58 - j0.96$
      $I_{AC} = 34.08 - j16.52$

Chapter 19

19.1 2.49 H;   20.62 MVA

19.2 (a) 1061.03 ohm   (b) 1116.88 ohm   (c) 1178.9 Ω

Index